SHADOW
OF
PERIL

BY ALEKSANDR I. ZHDANOV

CURTIS
BOOKS

MODERN LITERARY EDITIONS PUBLISHING COMPANY
NEW YORK, N.Y.

Publisher's Note

☐ A pseudonym has been used to veil the authorship of this story, which has been written as if it were indeed the account of a "defected Russian submarine commander."

Some of the incidents in the Zhdanov story are known to have taken place. Many of the persons named in the book are well known, either internationally or in the U. S. or Communist worlds. A U. S. sailor *was* wounded by a mysterious bullet while on his ship in the harbor at Beirut; Russian trawlers *have* brought "sick" crewmen into American ports; the presence of Russian submarines and trawlers in sensitive areas *has* been authenticated. Russian activities on and under the sea are reported in news dispatches almost daily.

Additionally, the presence and the activities of U. S. Navy ships seem to be accurately reported, whether in the Mediterranean in 1958 or in the Atlantic and Caribbean four years later. The mechanics of submarine operation and details of life aboard are authentically portrayed.

From this launching pad of fact, however, *Shadow of Peril* takes off into the unlimited space of fiction. The cold war patrols of the *W-7* and the *F-689* are doubtless products of the author's imagination. Whether they could happen or could have happened is left entirely to the reader's own imagination.

Introduction

☐ My name is Aleksandr Ivanovich Zhdanov.

Until just a few months ago, I was the most celebrated young naval hero in the Soviet Navy. Today, largely through the vindictiveness of one man and the workings of the Communist system, I am a refugee from my beloved homeland—disgraced, and in constant danger of assassination. The story I am about to unfold has until now been one of the most closely guarded secrets of Soviet Russia. It is the story of espionage against the United States of America, from under the seas. By disclosing this information, I acknowledge that I am guilty of treason in the eyes of the government of the Soviet Union. But these disclosures, however unbelievable, may serve to awaken others who may someday, somehow, find a way to world peace and human understanding.

In preparing this detailed account, I have not relied upon memory alone. Memory dims with the passage of time, no matter how short. In support of all major operational events, all tactical exercises and several until now unanswerable incidents (quite probably enigmas to the United States Navy) I have referred to not only my personal diary, but to copies of my own official submarine patrol reports. For example, a most perfunctory type of check by an American or Allied reader would corroborate the stage settings in time and place, with all actors present —be they people, or ships and units of war, except for one unseen entity: that of the Soviet.

The now famous American astronaut, Marine Lieutenant Colonel John H. Glenn, Jr., owes his life today not only to the skill of American scientists and technical workers, but in part also to the impact upon me of the words of a soul-searching Christian hymn I had heard three years before in a Washington, D.C. cathedral.

On February 20, 1962, at 2:38 P.M. Eastern Standard Time, on board the Soviet submarine *F-689,* which I commanded, I looked through the cross hairs of the periscope and watched Colonel Glenn's space capsule drift slowly down into the sea a few thousand yards away. In obedience to MOST SECRET instructions from Moscow, I had maneuvered the submarine into the expected orbital recovery area. Our mission was surveillance. But the bobbing space capsule very narrowly missed being destroyed at this time. In truth, the violent obliteration of *Friendship 7* would have occurred had I yielded to the submarine's political commissar, who urgently and almost hysterically demanded the firing of a specially built electric homing torpedo at the capsule. Had that torpedo from the V. I. Lenin Plant in Pilsen, Czechoslovakia ever been triggered, the result would have been an explosion heard round the world—a bolt of yellow flame, a cloud of white smoke, and no Wall Street ticker-tape parade for a brave man, a new American hero. He would have been oxidized in burning white phosphurus.

But this disclosure is only a small part of my story. You must know the full accounting, incredible as it may seem. Therefore, I will take you back to the years 1959 and 1958.

PART I

MARE NOSTRUM:

Behind the Dim Unknown

1

For the Good or Evil Side

☐ During the 1959 visit of Premier Khrushchev to the
United States, I was hustled into Washington in civilian
clothes as an extra interpreter for the special military-
economic staff accompanying the Number One World
Communist. As an unpublicized Russian guest of an intermediary staffer at the British Embassy, I was one Sunday
invited to attend divine worship services at Washington's
Anglican Cathedral. To have declined at that time would
not have been to the advantage of the Soviet Union. This
was a period when strong voices in England were calling
for more understanding with Russia and world Communism. It was the hour when peace lovers in the West were
groping blindly for some signs that the Communist way was
not wholly reprehensible. It was the day when hope still
sprang from the idealists' breasts that co-existence between capitalist and Communist worlds was possible. So,
I went to church.

Could it have been a coincidence, the hymn that was
sung as the recessional that Sunday, when I and a mere
handful of others from the Soviet Embassy were a captive
audience? As the majestic organ notes swelled and receded
with the congregation's chant, the words became etched
in my memory:

> "Once to every man and nation
>   Comes the moment to decide
> In the strife of truth with falsehood
>   For the good or evil side;
> Some great cause, God's new Messiah,

11

> Offering each the bloom or blight,
> And the choice goes on forever
> 'Twixt that darkness and the light."

Unaccountably and with no explanation or logic, I, Aleksandr Ivanovich Zhdanov, a Soviet Navy officer, have often had occasion to remember those meaningful words. As the sun irregularly and fleetingly shines, now and again, in an otherwise cloud-patched sky, so also have I thought of that Sunday morning when the Cathedral choir marched behind the Cross under the Gothic arches, with the vibrant voices singing:

> "Then to side with truth is noble,
> When we share her wretched crust,
> Ere her cause bring fame and profit,
> And 'tis prosperous to be just;
> Then it is the brave man chooses,
> While the coward stands aside
> Till the multitude make virtue
> Of the faith they had denied."

In lonely hours since that day, I have often reflected on my early boyhood days in Aleksandrov, near Moscow, when my mother and father still went to church in the tradition of our ancestors—before it became expedient for us all to deny that faith of the patriarchs.

If you look at this Anglican-American hymn of Christians, you will come, finally, to those last lines which must have applied to the American astronaut John H. Glenn, Jr:

> And, behind the dim unknown,
> Standeth God within the shadow
> Keeping watch above His own.

And so begins my story. It is a story of darkness and light, of a quest for fame and profit, of my own moment to decide—*in the strife of truth with falsehood, for the good or evil side.*

2

Saturday Night at the Movies

☐ AUTUMN 1958

On the evening of September 15, 1958, Captain Fedor F. Presnakov, the Russian naval attaché in Washington, walked hurriedly into the Soviet Embassy on Sixteenth Street. In the absence of the Ambassador, who was attending another of the endless diplomatic functions on Embassy Row, the attaché made a direct report via coded short-wave wireless to Soviet Admiral Sergey Gorshkov, the First Deputy Minister of Defense, in Moscow. Simultaneously, via diplomatic pouch, he submitted an intelligence report to that same officer. Both reports concerned two American press accounts which he had dutifully clipped from leading Atlantic seaboard newspapers in the United States.

As a direct result of this collection of information, I was later to undergo an intensive investigation to determine my fitness for command of a Soviet submarine assigned to a sensitive mission. I was required to report personally to Admiral Gorshkov and also to the Commander in Chief of the Black Sea Fleet, Admiral Vladimir Kasatonov. Only by fervent appeals to them, during which I preferred court-martial charges against my Third Officer, Lieutenant Commander Igor Sverdlov, was I able to avoid administrative discipline depriving me of command of a newly built submarine.

Of the pertinent American news articles one was noted by Captain Presnakov as he glanced through the Washington *Post* while relaxing late in the afternoon on the terrace of the Army and Navy Country Club in Arlington;

13

the other was read a half hour later in his study back in Washington, as he quickly scanned the other American newspapers subscribed to by the diplomatic staff. It appeared in the New York *Herald Tribune*.

Not very much later, Presnakov took the two clippings over to the Embassy.

In Washington during the week of August 24, 1958, Captain Presnakov and the Soviet Ambassador had been briefed by MOST SECRET code that a "W" class submarine, Commander Aleksandr Ivanovich Zhdanov commanding, had secretly and successfully transited the Bosporus, passed without harm through the Dardanelles, and was heading for a secret point in the eastern Mediterranean. It had been decided to alert the Russian diplomatic representatives in the American capital to the fact that a surprise action by a Soviet submarine was pending. However, no further details were provided these emissaries until September 10, when a cryptic intelligence message was passed to the naval attaché in his Washington office on Belmont Road. It merely said, "Molten coffin imminent. Note periodical cover August 4."

On receipt of this encoded message, which reflected an oft-made declaration by Premier Khrushchev that the U. S. Sixth Fleet could easily be turned into molten coffins, Presnakov and his assistant, Captain Dmitri K. Ryazantsev, examined the major American magazines published on August 4, to see which one had a cover that might seem applicable to the message, "Molten coffin imminent. Note periodical cover August 4." They found it—the cover of *Time* magazine, for August 4, 1958. Splashed across the cover was a portrait of United States Navy Admiral James L. Holloway, Jr., the commander in chief of the thirteen thousand American troops which had landed in Beirut, Lebanon. To Presnakov this meant only one thing: The Soviet Union was planning on making a molten coffin of the flagship of the American admiral, and the action was imminent. If we were lucky, the admiral himself would be on board!

Armed with this exciting news of an international incident about to take place, Presnakov nearly broke his neck rushing to get the word to Ambassador Mikhail A. Menshikov. But as it developed, they both waited in vain for the explosion. In its place, five days later (September 15) Presnakov found the American press articles revealing a mere pistol shot at the scene of the "molten coffin." He sensed the submarine mission might have aborted. He was correct, as I well know, for I commanded the submarine.

Without doubt, I, Aleksandr Zhdanov, had fleetingly filled a role of great power and awesome responsibility. Fulfillment of my mission could have triggered a third world war. I was frustratingly thwarted from achieving my goal—and perhaps a memorable niche in naval history —by an infuriatingly incorrigible and uncontrollable political commissar attached to my submarine. Assigned to my command as Third Officer (but in no sense answerable to me even though I was the captain), Lieutenant Commander Igor Vladimirovich Sverdlov barred my role as a Man of Destiny. Capricious, unpredictable, and wholly undisciplined, this man proved to be the unexpected foil to one of the most daring Russian operations since World War II. My shipmates will verify the story.

In an effort to visibly unnerve the United States and to create suspicion that perhaps the Egyptians or Israelis might be involved, the main political administrator of the Soviet Navy, Vice Admiral Vasily Grishanov, had managed to persuade both Admiral Gorshkov and Premier Khrushchev that the Soviet Navy should covertly move against the American forces in Lebanon. Without being detected we could sink the U.S.S. *Taconic,* the flagship and headquarters of the commander of the American force. This ship was known to be tied up at a pier in the inner harbor of Beirut. From it, the American Navy's Admiral Holloway was able to maintain good communications with higher Allied commands and with the United States. What greater depredation than to sink him in his soft bunk one night! How American prestige would sink also! And on whom would the finger of blame be pointed? According to Grishanov world opinion would have immediately, and vehemently, blamed either Egypt or Israel —and they would have blamed each other. Then the USSR could demand UN sanctions upon Israel for the "dastardly deed." Furthermore, a third likely blame at the time would possibly be Iraq, or even Jordanian or Lebanese "subversive elements."

The blame would never be placed seriously or directly on the USSR. Why not? First, because of the inherent difficulty in classifying the predator as the submarine of any specific nation; in fact, the detonation might even be considered as having been set off internally, by accident. It could be another case reminiscent of the sinking of the battleship *Maine* in Havana Harbor in 1898. Furthermore, the proud American Navy claimed that its Mediterranean Fleet ruled that area of the globe—so who would believe that an unaccounted-for Russian submarine was loose in a Mediterranean harbor full of American ships? After all, the British and Turks at each end keep the tightest of tabs on what ships enter the Mediterranean. The amusing part, then, would be the failure of the Americans to believe it possible for a Soviet submarine to move undetected from the Black Sea to the Mediterranean.

Yet this is precisely what occurred, and it is no less fantastic than the exploit of Nazi U-boat commander Gunther Prien in World War II when he slipped undetected and undeterred through the "impenetrable" waters of Scapa Flow to sink the English battleship *Royal Oak*.

In any event, on the night of September 13, 1958, following the earlier, unparalleled clandestine voyage from the Black Sea, the Soviet submarine *W-7*, myself commanding, crept silently into the outer harbor of Beirut, Lebanon. Our approach was from the northwest at periscope depth—from out of the blackness to seaward. On the shore, thousands of lights glittered, many of them reaching up into the mountains and hills which form this ancient Near East traders' haven. Two miles offshore, I brought the submarine up with decks awash, and standing on the small open bridge, painstakingly brought the boat closer to our target.

That we were tensely approaching our quarry on a most sensitive and extraordinary mission did not interfere with the routine administration of the *W-7*. The quartermaster petty officer of the watch made it his business to make whatever notations he could in the log. On the open bridge, he made quick calculations, checked various instruments, and at 9 P.M., also noting sea conditions and current, logged the true wind as coming from the north at 2.6 meters per second (5.2 knots); barometer 1016.6 millibars (thirty inches); atmospheric temperature 19.5 Raeumurs (76°F.).

The myriad electric lights on the shore were dazzling. They reminded me of thousands of sparkling diamonds, rubies, and emeralds. Here, it seemed, was "business as usual," except that as we crept closer, certain shapes in the harbor began forming into identifiable naval craft. At about a mile from the inner harbor breakwater, I discerned the configuration of a destroyer, lying anchored, some 750 yards to the west of the entrance to the inner harbor. Within that mole, moored to a pier, was the United States flagship. That the Americans would plant a destroyer so close to the shore was something we had not counted upon. Rather, I had anticipated that the enemy would have his supporting ships cruising offshore, in maneuverable waters. Thus, it was no little shock to suddenly note an anchored destroyer practically blocking our penetration of the breakwater.

Nonetheless, we were not thwarted at this point. I looked at the destroyer through my binoculars, and then swept around with them in a nearly complete circular arc. To port I could see what appeared to be a naval cargo-type ship, also anchored. But the destroyer, three points on our starboard bow at a range of about a thousand yards, claimed my major interest at the moment. The evening tide had begun to swing the ship at her anchorage, and she presented an aspect of about forty-five degrees at this time. It appeared that the Americans had made no provision for a surprise attack. Through my binoculars, I could see a large number of the destroyer crew congregated on the forecastle. They were watching a movie. I peered then at the ship's radar antennas, silhouetted against the sparkling white lights of the city beyond. The larger air-search antenna was rotating; the smaller surface-search radar antenna was not—it was aligned fore and aft as for a Saturday in-port inspection! That explained why no radarscope operator on the destroyer had detected our approach. Probably in the other naval ships in the harbor, auxiliaries and noncombatant types, radar crews were only giving perfunctory attention to their equipment, preferring to believe that the destroyer would, as a combatant ship, assume such guard responsibilities. Of course, for several hours we had known, merely through electronics listening, that there was an air-search-type radar operating in the vicinity. But until now we had not been able to link it with any specific ship.

Through the voice tube to the control room, I passed the word (through cupped hands) to "make minimum slow speed turns" in order to hold present depth and heading.

The commissar and my Second Officer, Lieutenant Commander Vladimir Rurik, came up beside me. The former, uniquely stupid, began to talk too loud. I told him to keep quiet. He stated that the capitalist pigs couldn't hear him—they were too busy watching their decadent movie. He raised his binoculars in an attempt to see what we were up against.

Looking through my own glasses, I could see the red truck lights and white accommodation ladder lights of the *Taconic* in the inner harbor. My pulse quickened. Excitement surged within me. The grip of my fingers on the binoculars was vicelike. Steady, calm, detached thinking was required . . .

Under the circumstances, the trick would be to maneuver slowly and attempt to drift down to the entrance of the inner harbor. We would be taking advantage of the current, and would use motor speeds as necessary to quietly penetrate the opening in the breakwater. Then, with our bow pointing at the target, we would let go with four torpedoes. With continued luck, I could then extricate myself from the inner harbor and, if necessary, bring the stern torpedo tubes into line with the destroyer, fire the after torpedoes, and then head for the open sea. Or, I could gamble on the destroyer crew being unprepared for action, and make good a fast escape in the excitement. At this point in plotting my possible courses of action, I was aware that my unwanted political commissar was still at my side.

Suddenly, this political spy who had been foisted upon me, this blundering, ersatz "naval officer," Lieutenant Commander Sverdlov, drew his .35-caliber revolver and, quickly aiming it in the direction of the open-deck cinema watchers on the bow of the destroyer, fired two shots in rapid succession. The second bullet was deflected almost straight up in the air, as I, rushing to stop him, grabbed his arm. With my left hand, I slapped his thick, pale, flabby face. I would have liked to have picked him up and thrown him overboard, but he was much too heavy for that. He was, in fact, so grossly lardlike that he reminded me of his boss, Vice Admiral Grishanov. Possibly it was thinking of Grishanov that made me try to control myself. So I merely hit Sverdlov again with the back of

my hand, this time across his bulbous Ukrainian nose.
Rurik, a reliable submariner who at one time had been a
junior staff assistant to Commodore Tripolsky of World
War II fame, came to my assistance. Disarming Sverdlov, he forced him from the bridge down the manhole.

I raised my binoculars in trepidation. My pounding
fear was that the shots had been heard and that we would
be discovered. Through the glasses, I saw that the showing
of the film had been stopped. The audience of sailors
was clustered around what appeared to be one man. Just
below the level of the main deck, on the destroyer's bow,
and lit up by electric light bulbs, I could now make out
the huge white and black numerals 629. Above, I saw
three white-clad sailors run down the main deck toward
the amidships section. Here, I surmised, would be
the officer of the watch, standing his duty. Rurik, also
peering through his binoculars, confirmed my own opinion.

"Son of a Japanese mongrel! They're going to sound an
alarm! That stupid oaf Sverdlov has shot one of them.
We'll never get it done tonight. Let's get out of here while
we can!"

I concurred with Rurik. Sending him down the hatch,
I twisted the W-7 around quickly and pointed her bow to
the open sea and deep water, which beckoned from due
north counterclockwise to the west. With nothing but increasingly deep water now before us, I jumped down
from the open bridge with the order, "DIVE, DIVE,
DEPTH ONE HUNDRED FEET," shouted even as my
hands were slamming the watertight hatch cover into
place.

On passing beyond the one hundred-fathom curve, I
ordered speed increased to twelve knots and told Rurik
to take us down to three hundred feet. At that depth, the
sudden change of water temperature was such that our
detection by surface ship sonar echo-ranging devices
would have been most difficult.

Half an hour later, at 10:30 P.M. I directed that we slow to three knots and rig for silent running, in order for the sonar operator to listen better for any telltale sounds generated by American warships' propellers. There were none.

It was apparent that we had not been detected. But in view of the increased degree of alert to which I believed the Americans would now resort, I decided to remain unobtrusive for a few days before again attempting to sink the United States Headquarters flagship. Accordingly, I planned to spend the next few days in random submerged cruising in waters from ten to twenty miles north of Beirut, no further removed in that direction than due west of Ras esh Shigá.

Every night we recharged our batteries by snorkeling, and during the day remained deep enough to be unidentifiable visually from an aircraft passing overhead. Occasionally, we would come up to periscope depth for observation of the area.

On Monday morning, September 15, shortly after the forenoon watch had relieved, we were suddenly alerted to possible danger by the sonarmen reporting that our listening gear was receiving propeller noises likely to be those of a distant warship. The range was estimated to be several miles to the southward, bearing 185 degrees true. Rurik put on a pair of headphones and listened attentively to the echoes. I again rigged the boat for silent running. Sonar reported the contact probably a destroyer type, and estimated its speed to be about fifteen knots.

"Contact heading westward," Rurik announced. My next move was to order the submarine to periscope depth, and maneuver the boat to present a minimum target to the contact. In doing this, I was conforming to standard submarine patrol doctrine. Sonar now reported a sudden decrease in propeller turns, indicating the contact was slowing to about five knots. Calling, "UP PERISCOPE," I quickly sighted along the given bearing to the sonar contact, then swiftly trained around to cover all directions, checking for any other possible ships or aircraft in the immediate proximity. There were none. The periscope was lowered.

What a beautiful day it was up there—bright and sunny, with unlimited visibility, and small wavelets blanketing the sea surface . . . so excellent for hiding the periscope!

Rurik, who had been standing at my elbow to be of assistance with the periscope, broke the silence:

"Shall I make the torpedo tubes fully ready for firing, sir?"

I did not want to alarm the crew. "No, wait."

"Captain!—"

It was the navigator, Vasili Petrovich Yukhnov, and he was perfunctorily going ahead with his standard routine morning position report.

"Captain," he continued in his distinct Kiev accent, "this is our eight o'clock position report, Monday, September fifteenth."

The figures designating latitude and longitude meant little to me by themselves. Turning to the right, over my shoulder, I glanced down at the navigator's chart desk.

"Show me where we are now, Vasili Petrovich," I said, with ill-concealed iritation. "Hmmmmm."

Navigator Yukhnov bit his lip. He was a conscientious fellow, had been caught once in error by me, and was overly nervous about making a similar mistake in his navigational calculations. He now decided, I thought, to divert my attention away from the chart.

"We have a full battery, Captain," he offered. Noting my smile in answer to his revelation, he continued.

"Yes, Captain, we completed recharging the battery just before daybreak."

He appeared obviously relieved when the sonar operator interrupted, changing the whole conversation.

"Contact appears to be increasing speed, bearing 190 degrees true."

It was time for another look. Nothing had been visually detected on the original bearing some minutes before.

"Up periscope!"

I peered through the cross hairs on a true bearing of 190 degrees. At an estimated ten-mile distance, I could now barely make out two puffs of black smoke in the air. This confirmed my opinion that the contact was an American destroyer. According to the indoctrinational information disseminated at the Voroshilov Naval Academy, one or more puffs of dense black smoke are the trademarks of American destroyer types as they suddenly accelerate their movement through the water.

Rurik removed the headphones, signaled for the watch to raise a directional antenna, and spoke up again:

"It will be interesting to see what radars they have in use."

Reaching into his hip pocket, Rurik produced his huge red and white polka-dot handkerchief, with which he then proceeded to mop his perspiration-beaded brow. He had two such handkerchiefs, one alternating each day with the other as his "duty brow wiper." The other one was *blue* and white polka dot. Before the cruise was over, he was to become enraged to learn that the crew had begun circulating a rumor that on a previous cruise when the submarine in which he was serving had run out of toilet paper, he had used both of these handkerchiefs as substitutes. (He finally suspected Sverdlov of having "planted" the rumor to discredit him after the Beirut harbor incident.)

Presently, the radar intercept operator reported receiving U. S. Navy air and surface-search radar emissions on the same bearing as our destroyer contact. That they were destroyer radars was calculated from our intelligence book showing the various frequencies and types of radars installed in U. S. warships.

Then, at about 9 A.M., it was apparent that the American ship was returning—eastward—to port, in Beirut harbor. At 9:20 A.M., all propeller noises from this source ceased.

My first thoughts were that the American destroyer had picked up a possible contact in the immediate vicinity of the harbor, and had moved over quickly to investigate it. But then very possibly, it was just an "alert" training exercise in getting underway quickly.

These possibilities didn't fully answer the question which began plaguing me: Why had the propellers suddenly slowed and then returned to increased revolutions? I sought answers from my several officers. Various explanations were forthcoming. One, I thought, might have some solid foundation in fact. It was that the destroyer had gone out to get a bathythermograph reading of the water temperatures outside the harbor. This would be important in case of an action against a submarine, since the destroyer would want to know what the sonar detection possibilities would be.

My own reasoning was that he probably did take a reading of the water temperatures at various levels, and I also suspect he may have used the opportunity to dump a mounting accumulation of garbage. Not all small ships can dispose of their garbage, except by throwing it overboard. This is almost always done in open sea beyond any territorial limits.

In any event, this sortie of the destroyer caused me to extend our period of inactivity. I decided to wait for another three days before attempting the attack.

But events were to overtake us. I was later to learn that Captain Fedor Presnakov's transmittal to Moscow of the American press reports (concerning our abortive "Saturday night at the movies" in Beirut harbor) had caused a re-evaluation of the basic plan. A high-level decision was made to cancel the operation on the basis of feeling that we might have been detected, or that we might *again* fail to accomplish the goal. Very possibly, too, it was reasoned, we might get caught in the act. And that was to be avoided at all costs. Consequently, within twenty-four hours of Supreme Soviet Headquarters getting the news of the shooting of the American sailor, Russian Navy wireless broadcasts began sending out coded supplementary instructions to me.

On the night of the eighteenth of September, while snorkeling, the message was received. Without explanation at the time, we were directed to abandon the attack on the *Taconic;* I could not help suspecting that Russian intelligence had learned of our ill-starred and abortive venture of the previous Saturday night—and I was correct.

At several minutes past midnight, the wireless operator on watch had received the coded message addressed to *W-7;* he had called it to the attention of the watch officer, who in turn had ordered the commissary officer, Lieutenant Yuri Andreevich Koslov, out of his bunk where he spent so much of his time. Traditionally, the commissary officer—not being a regular watch-stander—is utilized on board Soviet men-of-war in whatever ways the commanding officers feel appropriate. My instructions to the watch had been that whenever a late-hour message was received, commissary Lieutenant Koslov would decipher it.

When the drapes to my small but nonetheless private sleeping space were swooshed forcefully aside by Yuri, unveiling a flood of light from the passageway electric light bulbs, I sat upright in my bunk and looked, blinking, at the luminous-dialed bulkhead clock. It was nearly 2 A.M. Yuri, never one to give possible offense if it could be avoided, pleaded forgiveness for arousing me, but would the captain be pleased to look at his latest triumph —a message marked "EXTRAORDINARILY IMPORTANT"— which he had finally succeeded in decoding, without the help of the watch or signals officer. I reached out for the message, which Koslov had had typed up from his penciled decoding. I had really not expected this message, at least so soon. My eyes moved over the wording . . .

CANCEL MY OPERATIONAL MESSAGE OF AUGUST 15. CEASE PRESENT OPERATION. CONDUCT AREA SURVEILLANCE OBSERVING GENERAL FLEET OPERATIONS IN BEIRUT PROXIMITY UNTIL NO LATER THAN SEPTEMBER 22. THENCE PROCEED OBSERVE MAJOR UNITS SIXTH FLEET IN MIDDLE/WESTERN MEDITERRANEAN. REPORT NO LATER THAN OCTOBER 18 TO VLONE ALBANIA.

(SIGNED) KASATONOV

I remembered Vlone had an airfield nearby. I wondered whether upon my arrival there would be a plane there, with a large red star emblazoned on the fuselage, waiting to fly me back to the Soviet Union.

3

Stalking the Prey

☐ (SEPTEMBER 22-OCTOBER 5, 1958)

Beautiful! Invigorating! That, on Monday, September 22, 1958, would have been a good description of the azure eastern Mediterranean Sea. The warm, golden sun shone down brightly from a fleckless blue sky overhead. The water was swept by a mild sea breeze which produced small wavelets and occasional whitecaps. Unfortunately, I could only see this delightful weather when I raised the periscope occasionally to look around for any telltale signs of shipping or of transiting aircraft.

This was the day that we departed the Beirut area, westward-bound for surveillance of the major Sixth Fleet units under command of the American Vice Admiral Charles R. Brown, of whom my superiors subsequently talked so disparagingly.

We were well on our way by 8 A.M. At a depth of one hundred feet, moving out at four knots on a course of 275 degrees true, I intended to come upon the American fleet units somewhere in the central Mediterranean, and sometime within the next two weeks. Word-of-mouth intelligence passed on to us some weeks earlier had revealed that the Americans usually spent a week or ten days in operations at sea. Then, the ships would depart for various liberty ports for about the same period of time. At the conclusion of each period, the various units of the American fleet would rendezvous at sea and proceed with their pre-planned exercises. I hoped to trail one such fleet unit from its in-port merrymaking to the rendezvous with other units.

27

By midnight of September 23, while snorkeling and re-charging the batteries, I ordered a course change to approach closer to the southern coast of Cyprus. I wanted to take advantage of the numerous known fishing vessels operating ten to fifteen miles off the coast. Such action is often taken at night to cover a snorkeling submarine during its transit. In a calm sea, such as it was on this night, unfriendly naval search radars can pick up a snorkeler. My action would reduce such a possibility, since the numerous small radar contacts (or "pips," as the Americans call them) reflected by fishing vessels would be almost impossible to distinguish from those of a submarine.

Shortly after we had completed recharging the batteries, in the early morning hours of Wednesday, September 24, an alert sonarman electrified the watch officer and me with a critical contact report. Ears glued to his listening equipment, he relayed the word that he had picked up the distant but definite fast, light propeller noises of a possible warship astern of us. The oncoming vessel was closing on us from the east. He was making an unchanging moderate speed, such as would be employed in a routine transit. My Second Officer, Rurik, determined that the ship was heading on a course of 280 degrees true, at a speed of about five meters per second (ten knots).

"Range closing, Captain."

This was Rurik's matter-of-fact, repeated observation. He applied himself to a maneuvering board solution of our respective positions, and presently came up with his report: At our present respective courses and speeds, the ship would overtake us, close aboard, in two hours and ten minutes.

Since it was still before morning twilight, and would be sufficiently dark for the next hour and forty-five minutes, I decided to resume snorkeling at maximum speed to delay intercept until daylight hours. My plan was to enable me to choose the time and place of intercept, in order to insure positive identification and, if possible, again take advantage of the fishing fleet as cover.

It was my hope that the contact, if indeed a warship, would be en route to a possible rendezvous to the westward with other fleet units. This, then, would present the wonderful opportunity for which I was looking—tagging along behind just such an independently cruising ship.

At length, as darkness began lifting and vision through the early morning mists began to improve, I gave the order to terminate snorkeling, and reduced speed to three knots. I purposely delayed any course change until our contact was in sight. The officer of the watch, in the conning station, was detailed to take observations at intervals of every three to five minutes, and to inform me immediately upon sighting the contact. He was also to advise me upon any change noted in the contact's maneuvers. Sonar still held the distant ship on the same bearing and estimated range as closing. By our electronic listening equipment, there was no indication that the stranger's radar had picked up our snorkel. This was good. Our tactics were beginning to pay off.

At 7:02 A.M., the conning officer of the watch reported to me that sonar now classified our stranger as a small warship, by nature of sound. Also, range was still closing. A few minutes later I received another report that sonar had just detected similar distant propeller noises to the westward. As I evaluated this intelligence, a third report was passed to me. Sonar had gained contact on the light, fluttery propeller noises of small fishing craft dead ahead. How fortunate!

Rodion Trubetovski, commissary-porter who attended to the eating requirements of the officers, had just supplied me with a morning tonic of vodka and canned Italian tomato juice. With a half-filled glass in one hand, I moved quickly from the wardroom to the conning station. Nikolai Volkonski, officer-artilleryman on board, was the watch officer. His steely gray, round little eyes seemed to dominate his countenance even though they formed but a small fraction of the larger expanse of his massive, jowled face. His high cheekbone features were typically Cossack. From his thin, almost imperceptible lips came a "Good morning, Captain," followed by his further rendering of a situation report to me. According to the navigator's best calculations, he announced, we were now in sight of the ancient gods of Mount Olympus, and ought to watch our step! I turned to check the navigator's chart. Taking a pair of Soviet Navy nautical dividers, I measured our dead-reckoned distance from the last known fix, and put a mark on the chart track. Taking the rest of my morning tonic, I quickly formulated my plan for immediate action.

"Lieutenant Volkonski," I said, unexpectedly fighting to suppress a sudden hiccup, "let me take a look through the periscope."

Volkonski needed no prodding.

"Up periscope!" he shouted.

I grabbed the handles as they rose up from the deckplates, set to take full advantage of the limited time practicable for scanning the immediate area.

To the east, there was still nothing in sight. Just the propeller noises reported by sonar. To the west, dead ahead, I could see several fishing trawlers. The nearest one appeared to be moving very slowly in our own direction, and was about forty-five hundred yards away. The day was now sunny and the morning mists were being burned off by the increasingly warmer temperature of the air mass over the water. To the north, looming large and stark against the sky, were the mountainous ranges of Cyprus.

"Down periscope!"

Backing away, my voice continued to crackle orders to the watch.

"Get the navigator, the engineer, and the Second Officer," I said firmly. Then, to Volkonski, who had not yet been relieved from his duties of the watch, which he had assumed nearly three and a half hours earlier, I said, "You may go get yourself some breakfast. When you get to the pantry, tell your relief to awaken Lieutenant Commander Sverdlov and inform him that we will soon be maneuvering to intercept what we believe to be one or more small warships."

The jowls of Nikolai Volkonski flapped as his massive head shook violently.

"Captain," he intoned, "after what that politico did at Beirut, do you still want him around the control or conning areas when we get into delicate situations?"

Under the system, and additionally in order to restore some semblance of discipline, it would not have been appropriate for me to discuss Sverdlov with another officer, especially an officer of inferior rank.

"Get going and do as I say!" was my answer to that impertinence.

Volkonski immediately saluted and made for the pantry. Perhaps he would gorge himself on more potato salad and caviar, which I knew he dearly loved. As he disappeared from sight, I momentarily envisioned him at the wardroom table, acting the part of the glutton—a natural role to him, and one which had not endeared him to some of the other officers. But I agreed with his judgment about Sverdlov and braced myself to deal with that psychotic officer upon his arrival. I knew he would come. He did, but not before the others.

Second Officer Rurik was the first to respond. Rushing up swiftly, he reported that he had checked the ship contact information on the way to the conning station, was apprised of the situation from the sonar aspects, and had alerted the sonar technicians to make good tape recordings of the ship's propellers when they were at close range.

Good. Good. We would want to get the actual noises of those propellers so as to be able to identify the same ship at some future time.

"What about the camera party, Captain, any special instructions?" It was Vasili Yukhnov, the navigator.

"Lieutenant Yukhnov," I replied, "I will want the camera rigged to the periscope before using it. Do you have the Laika 35-millimeter? Ah, yes. Good. Oho! Yuri Andreevich! Good morning. We will want to take at least one good picture of the passing warship or warships. There may be two."

Lieutenant Koslov had come from the wardroom, where he had just had his breakfast. But he had forgotten to brush his teeth. He stood there smiling at me in his usual good humor, his prominent teeth now covered with a film of yellow egg yolk. Such residue was not conducive to substantiate his well-known claim among *W*-7 officers that he was the handsomest lieutenant in the Soviet Navy! I looked away from him and concentrated upon Yukhnov.

"You must not leave the periscope raised for more than six seconds. We cannot risk being seen."

The navigator frowned.

"How does the sun look?" he asked.

"It will be good. I will maneuver to a position south of the ship as it goes by. The sun should be no trouble at this hour. It is a bright sun; there is the usual morning haze which you must consider."

"One more thing, Captain," intervened Rurik, who was now flanked by Yukhnov, Koslov, and Makar Rostopchin, the engineer. He looked alternately at all three of them, but addressed his remarks to me.

"How close do you intend to position our ship?"

Koslov now reached into a shirt pocket and produced a wooden toothpick. After studying it a moment, he began to run it delicately through the spaces between his large, egg-stained teeth. Despite this, he was listening attentively.

"If all goes well," I said optimistically, "I intend to close the range to about seven hundred yards. At that distance, either Yukhnov or Koslov will take the picture.

You must take the first picture with the periscope set on low power, to get all of the ship in your field of vision. Following that, if time and tactical situation permit, take a second picture of the bridge and radar antennas with the periscope set on high power. For intelligence reasons, this is important to have."

There was a sudden shuffling and then a silence. The commissar had arrived. He broke the quiet.

"So we will be that close, Captain Zhdanov," he interposed. "Perhaps I should wear my life-vest. You might want to shoot me out the forward torpedo tubes at the enemy as they go by."

I could not afford the luxury of open altercation with Sverdlov. What a misfortune to have such a man assigned to my command. He was incorrigible. A man so potentially powerful . . . a very real danger to any ship of war, in fact. No, I could ill afford to let this situation get further out of hand. I ignored his uncalled-for remarks. Attempting to change the deteriorating atmosphere which he sponsored, I said to him in a detached voice, "Good morning, Lieutenant Commander Sverdlov. Within the next half hour, I anticipate that we will have fine pictures of at least one American warship passing close aboard. I am certain that you and Vice Admiral Grishanov will be much pleased with our stealth."

Sverdlov condescended to nod and then withdrew.

The next quarter of an hour was consumed by listening to sonar reports and taking repeated periscope observations at about three-minute intervals. It became apparent that we could easily maneuver astern of the nearby fishing boat and follow along in its wake, a few hundred yards astern. The swift and unobtrusive appearance of the periscope would go unnoticed on board the fishing boat. And, with luck, American eyes on the passing destroyer-type would be distracted from us to the fisherman close aboard. The situation looked perfect.

Rurik, as the oncoming ship came within five thousand

yards, took a quick look at her and exclaimed, "Ho Ho!
it is the American destroyer from Beirut!"

The announcement chilled everyone in the vicinity.
Although I had suspected that this small oncoming ship
would be a destroyer, I had preferred not to think that he
was tailing us. It seemed too remote. Why would he be
cruising along, over a period of several hours, on the same
westerly course and at the same moderate speed, unless
he were merely in transit from one point to another?

I listened to the amplified propeller echoes as they
came closer. *Swswswswswswswswws* . . . Quite different
from the slow, plodding *plop-plop-plop-plop-plop-plop* of
a merchant ship. The noise was getting much louder.
Range, two thousand yards. *Swswswswswswswws*. Range,
seventeen hundred yards. *Swswswswswws*. Range, fifteen
hundred yards.

"Stand by periscope!" Yukhnov and Koslov moving
over swiftly to their stations.

SwswswswswswsSWSWSWSWS . . .

Range eight hundred, bearing 015 degrees.

"UP PERISCOPE!"

SWSWSWSWSWSWSWS . . .

Contact passing across our bow, from starboard to
port . . .

Bearing rate fast . . .

"DOWN PERISCOPE!"

"Rurik," I said, "any indication that his echo-ranging
equipment is still in operation?"

"Yes, Captain. He appears to be operating a typically
old-type American sonar. I'm sure of this. The frequencies and echo-ranging intervals point to this. He is conducting a normal American search from his port to starboard side, forward of his beam."

SWSWSWSWSWSWSWSisisisisishishishishswswsws.

"Danger area passed, his sonar search missed us,"
Rurik continued.

"Yes," I agreed, "but we must not fail to keep our bow pointed in his direction."

The navigator spoke up now.

"I think we will have a good picture or two, Captain," he said as he and Koslov wrestled momentarily to see who would take the camera and its now important documentary evidence to the makeshift darkroom.

"Good. See to it," I ordered. Then, to Second Officer Rurik, "I will want to follow him at no closer range than three miles. If the waves continue to increase we may be able to snorkel astern of him this evening. We must be very careful. Keep a close eye out for that second possible warship. I'll want a picture or two of it, also."

Yuri could contain himself no longer.

"Captain," he blurted, "that destroyer! it was number 629!"

Aha! so the American fire-support ship in Beirut is now heading to join some of her sisters elsewhere in the blue Mediterranean! Well, well . . . Perhaps this indicates the end of the American occupation of Lebanon. No doubt Premier Khrushchev has gotten tough with the warmonger general in their White House, and the Americans have at last learned that we Russians mean business!

Had the ancient gods of mythology looked down from Mount Olympus at nine o'clock in the morning on this same day, Wednesday, September 24, 1958, they would have been mute witness to the commencement of one of the most interesting and dramatic naval operations of modern times. From the seat of the gods, high on that famous summit, and looking roughly south by west at a distance of approximately forty-three miles, Zeus and his followers could have witnessed the rendezvous of two American destroyers and noted, too, that they were being stalked by an intermittently appearing periscope belonging to a dark green-hulled Soviet submarine . . . that this rendezvous occurred within an hour of the time that one of these destroyers passed close aboard the momentarily exposed periscope of the lurking Soviet underseas craft . . . and that this was the beginning of a period of constant, intense action and observation by the *W-7* submariners.

It had been Rurik who had informed me of the appearance on the scene of the second destroyer. This was the intermittent small-ship propeller noises originally coming from a westerly bearing which we had picked up some time earlier. It had become lost in the excitement of trying to concentrate on the westward-bound destroyer *629* from Beirut. The sonar operators had earlier passed it off as a fishing boat and failed to advise me. In any event, I was both surprised and ashamed to find out from Rurik at a few minutes after nine o'clock that two contacts, one of them the destroyer *629,* which we had been following now for a little time, and another, had formed a column and were now steaming westward together. I felt that we should have been able to better apprise ourselves of this development as it was happening, rather than conclude that such a rendezvous *had occurred*.

By noon, we had dropped back astern of the Americans by some four or five miles. Despite the daylight, the seas were now favorable for snorkeling. I gave the order, therefore, to commence snorkeling and to make ten knots. I also stipulated that in no case were we to approach the destroyers ahead by any closer than four miles. At the same time, I advised the watch officer to be alert for any aircraft in the area. If he were to find himself in doubt as to any action, he was to stop snorkeling. I would, of course, then hear the noise and banging of the head valve shutting, and would consequently—in a matter of seconds—be on my way up to the conning station.

At about one-thirty o'clock in the afternoon, both ships appeared to be maneuvering independently but within a few miles of each other. The leading ship, with the hull number 629, appeared to circle once or twice and at one point came to a complete stop in the water. Perhaps they were conducting a ship-handling drill of some sort; in any event, by midafternoon, both ships were in column again, heading on a base course of roughly west by north, making about twelve knots. It was my conclusion, after looking at the assumed plots of the two ships made up for me by navigator Vasili Yukhnov, that the other destroyer now took the lead in the column formation.

As darkness came, I acted more boldly. Realizing that the Americans were continuing their sonar search arcs from left to right forward of their beams (apparently the custom in the U. S. Navy), I audaciously increased snorkel speed to maximum to stay up with the two destroyers. Their range from us had increased to more than five miles, and they were still heading generally westward in column. I ordered the antennas raised for electronics listening.

At about eight-thirty in the evening, the officer of the watch, while peering ahead through the periscope, noticed bright lights on the sterns of both destroyers. He passed the word to me in the wardroom, where I was sitting talking to Second Officer Rurik, navigator Yukhnov, and engineer Rostopchin. I did not have to inquire further from the watch officer as to what he thought was causing the illumination. At the Voroshilov Naval Academy, one of the more interesting facts brought up concerning the American Navy is that United States naval units when underway at sea customarily show movies on the fantails (or sterns) of ships, in mild weather after the sun has set. Normally, this means that the crews of the American ships are busily watching Marilyn Monroe or presumably a cowboy picture with Tom Mix or Buck Jones every evening from about eight o'clock until about ten o'clock. During this period of time, too, the instructors at the Academy in Moscow pointed out, most American ships of war attempt to (and in most cases do) remain on a steady course proceeding at moderate speed. Since I was the only officer in *W-7* who knew this intelligence, I repeated it for the education of the other officers sitting with me.

Makar Rostopchin, a Ukrainian Jew as was Yukhnov, laughed boisterously. "Maybe they are showing another one of their Mickey Mouse cartoons. Have you ever seen one of those? Once when I was invited to the American Zone at the old German naval base at Wilhelmshaven, I saw an after-dinner cinema show. Everyone was there, including the American admiral and the High Commissioner who was visiting at the time. What do you suppose they showed us? Cartoon after cartoon of Mickey Mouse. Mickey Mouse and some crazy ducks. Don't remember exactly. But you should have seen how that High Commissioner was laughing. I thought he would become hysterical. Frankly, I thought it was just indicative of the intelligence level of the audience. Those Americans are really nothing but big overgrown children."

Yukhnov could hardly wait to jump into the conversation and did so with unrestrained fervor. "Overgrown children! But they are living in a man's world, and it shall not be too much longer before they realize it!"

Rostopchin reached into his shirt pocket and pulled forth his heavily ornamented silver snuff box, a little packet his grandmother had given him as a present marking his nineteenth year. It had once belonged to her father, the Count Nicholas Alexandre Rostopchin, court chamberlain to the Romanovs in the late nineteenth century. He had married Princess Catherine Maria Ourusov upon the death of his first wife, Magda Nataly Trubobetzkoi; her mother, the Princess Catherine Maria, had been killed in the Bolshevik storming of the Winter Palace after World War I. The snuff habit was perhaps the last idiosyncrasy of the old regime's hierarchy that had been passed down intact to the new generation as personified by young engineer Lieutenant Rostopchin.

Yet Rostopchin, for all his noble ancestry in the days of Holy Russia, was a Jew. This, insofar as his religious worship practices were concerned, was a matter largely of his own choice. His mother, from a prominent Ukrainian Jewish family, had only been married to his father a few years when the Bolsheviks' mid-thirties purge liquidated him. Thenceforth his widowed mother lived in Kiev with her mother-in-law, who had managed to escape penury by drawing on the financial reserves that old Count Rostopchin had stashed away in Switzerland prior to World War I.

Unfortunately, when the Germans overran Kiev in World War II, they captured young Rostopchin's mother and grandmother. A special SS battalion whose mission was "the final solution to the Jewish problem" took his Jewish mother and sent her off to a gas chamber. His grandmother, a stolid and defiant communicant of the Russian Orthodox Church, was spared. And, upon the death of this grandmother two years ago, the Soviet State claimed all property rights to the family fortune, leaving Makar Rostopchin wholly dependent upon his naval pay for income. The silver snuff box was one of the few family heirlooms to which young Makar had finally come into ownership.

"Yes. *Da—da*. Overgrown children," said Soviet Navy engineer Lieutenant Rostopchin, as he opened the box, tapped it, and then took a whiff of snuff.

"Ahhhhh-CHEW!"

Unlike Yukhnov, Rostopchin was devoid of any physiological features which might tend to publicize his half-Hebrew blood. In fact, his gently wavy blond hair and blue eyes, set off by a most unusual ruddy complexion, reminded one of the Teutonic or Scandinavian mold.

Yukhnov resumed his part in the conversation. He apparently decided to change the subject. Taking one last large bite into his specially concocted sandwich of garlic cloves, carp eyes, and mayonnaise loosely compressed between thick slices of dark pumpernickel, he offered his evaluation of where we were being led.

"Captain," he began, maneuvering most of the mouthful over to one side of his large, liver-lipped mouth, "this present course of 283 degrees true will take us into the Greek island kingdom. We will pass the northeastern edge of Crete during the night, and should be in well-enough traveled waters to allow us to surface, charge our batteries, and at the same time stay up with the destroyers. There are many fishing boats in and among these islands which I believe we will pass tonight. If this is true, it will present no problem merely to follow in the wake of the Americans, just steering toward their stern lights. I have anticipated our track for the first part of the evening assuming the Americans will not alter course during the showing of their movies. I have also provided the officer of the watch with the characteristics of the lights on the shore that we may encounter tonight—at least, if this course is not changed."

Vasili Yukhnov, I was happy to see, was using his head —and being every bit as conscientious as I would have wanted him to be.

Rodion Trubetovski, the commissary-porter, approached the table with a bottle of port wine and a cake of cheese. Opening a nearby cupboard, he produced several aluminum cups. Pouring a little wine into one, he deftly raised it to his lips and announced, "Good wine for the captain and the officers, certified to be healthful and lacking in harmful ingredients."

He then bowed slightly and made his exit into the pantry, leaving the bottle and several cups on the table. No one had bothered much in listening to his message; he was only repeating what he was supposed to— the standard procedure ordered by Vice Admiral Grishanov for all fleet units. This procedure was set in motion immediately following a mysterious poisoning some years ago of half the wardroom officers on board one of the old-style cruisers. Rumor had indicated that one or two dissatisfied commissary-porters had been culpable; Grishanov, fearing further poisonings, had caused this ridiculous procedure to be introduced whenever wines were served in officers' messes. Somehow, Grishanov had not thought of the possibilities of officers being poisoned by additives in other kinds of foods or beverages besides wine. But no one had taken issue with him. Hence, it had become almost traditional now—certainly routine—for the commissary-porters to act out this ceremony whenever dispensing wines.

The other officers followed my lead in pouring themselves some of the ruby-red beverage. When everyone had provided himself with a full cup, I raised mine and, saying "To the Motherland," drank thirstily.

I had nearly finished my drink when the watch officer sent word that there seemed to be some confusion in one of the destroyers ahead of us. Range was closing; one destroyer had slowed down. Additionally, he observed that two vertical red lights blazed from the masthead of one of the destroyers. It would seem, then, that one of the ships had had a breakdown—if they were adhering to the international "rules of the road" regulations concerning the making of visual signals in the event of a sailing casualty.

This revelation was of sufficient import for me to take a look myself. So, together with Rurik, who was equally anxious to see what was going on, I went up to the conning station and made my own personal investigation. It corroborated the watch officer's information. But strangely enough, I had no sooner seen the two red lights through the periscope than they were both extinguished. Soon after, it was apparent that the ship in question had resumed her normal speed and was moving along now in tandem with the other destroyer. Nothing of further interest transpired during the remainder of the night. Apparently, this had just been an engineering or mechanical

failure, quickly repaired. Not unusual for the Americans
to have such casualties, I thought. After all, if the Voroshilov Naval Academy instruction was correct, most of
the American destroyers had been built during the war
years prior to 1945. Consequently, they had long since
passed through their most efficient years, structurally
and materially, at least. And, of course, most of them
(and *this* was so reassuring) were not even equipped with
up-to-date weapons for antisubmarine use!

All the next day, we shadowed the two American destroyers as they weaved northwestward among the islands
north of Crete. At nine o'clock on the evening of Thursday, the twenty-fifth, we passed Nisoi Khristiana Lighthouse abeam to starboard at a range of about ten miles.
I worked a stopwatch in my hand as I looked at the light
through the periscope—for we were still snorkeling
astern of the destroyers. An hour later, I sighted the lume
of a light which the navigator identified as North Fole-
gandros Lighthouse, bearing almost due north, and at a
range of about twenty-five miles—or possibly more. It
was close to midnight when we passed it directly abeam
to starboard. Finally, well after one o'clock on the morning of the twenty-sixth, I sighted Paximdhi Light ahead
of us at a range of about ten miles.

For some little time now, it had been more or less
obvious where the Americans were leading us. The Soviet submarine *W-7* was trailing unsuspecting Sixth Fleet
destroyers into the nest of Pericles.

And it was quite a nest.

The Americans had entered the ancient harbor of
Piraeus, gateway to Athens, shortly after eight o'clock in
the morning on the twenty-sixth. The Soviet submarine
W-7 brought up the rear and stood off the harbor entrance
at ten-thirty in the morning, with periscope up and the
commanding officer observing the situation. Here indeed

was a good segment of the fleet . . . several large and small ships congregated near that ancient battleground of Salamis, all anchored and, I thought reflectively, waiting magnificently for Russian torpedoes! Alas! That was not my mission. Yet it would be so easy . . .

With the periscope in high power, I could identify the large destroyer tender *AD-28*, which our publications listed as the U.S.S. *Grand Canyon,* one of the U. S. Atlantic Fleet's large auxiliaries. Another large ship, the tanker U.S.S. *Nantahala* (identified after I read off her side identification, *AO-16*), was anchored in the harbor. Tied up alongside the *Grand Canyon* were the two destroyers we had been pursuing.

The confines of Saronikos Kolpos and the adjacent waters in the immediate vicinity of Piraeus are not designed to conceal a submarine for any length of time. Therefore, the *W-7* was maneuvered in those sheltered waters on but one day, and then only for a few hours. Otherwise, I kept the boat to the southward of the island of Nisi Aiyina, which lies about fifteen miles south-southwest of Piraeus. On Sunday night, September 28, we were snorkeling while at the same time conducting a visual and electronics barrier search south of Piraeus. I was hoping to pick up contact with any shipping which might enter or leave the harbor. Our listening for electronic signals from other ships in the vicinity paid good dividends.

At about four o'clock in the morning, September 29, we identified many American radars aproaching the vicinity from the south. Promptly, we terminated snorkeling and recharging of the batteries, in order to move over quickly to a vantage point near the rocks of North Eleousai. Here, there was deep water, and it certainly was a position unlikely for our detection.

From this location immediately adjacent to the rock ledges of North Eleousai, I observed three more American destroyers enter the harbor, all mooring alongside the *Grand Canyon* in a large nest of ships. The hull numbers painted in the typically large, black and white block numerals common to American destroyers, were, in order of entry, the *883, 831,* and *713.* Following them, and anchoring further to the east in Phaleron Bay, was a cruiser flying the two-star flag of an American rear admiral. The large lettering on the cruiser's bow enabled us to check her off by name, using the Soviet list of major U. S. fleet units as a guide. *CA-148,* according to the Soviet publication, was the U.S.S. *Newport News,* presently serving as flagship to the American Atlantic Fleet Cruiser Force Commander. Following the *Newport News* into Phaleron Bay, and about a mile astern, came the large attack aircraft carrier identified as U.S.S. *Randolph* (*CVA-15*). She anchored across the harbor from us, in water about twenty fathoms deep.

Here indeed, to this sheltered, island-abounding harbor, had come mighty elements of the United States Mediterranean Fleet. They would, I estimated, be here in port for about a week before leaving to conduct fleet exercises. Under this assumption, I then took the *W-7* to seaward from Piraeus, where I could continue a barrier patrol designed to intercept—for surveillance purposes —the American fleet as it moved out for maneuvers.

The Soviet submarine barrier patrol which we activated lasted an irritatingly long period of time—until Sunday, October 5. It was not pleasant to have to patrol back and forth across the approaches to Piraeus, for over a week, waiting for an enemy to move out. And it was especially annoying to realize that while we patrolled, these American sailors were enjoying their privileges ashore as tourists. The surprise came when they suddenly started to sortie from the harbor—first the destroyers, which formed a typically ineffective screen to shield the major ships—and then the heavy units. This movement on a Sunday was something I had not expected. The Voroshilov Naval Academy had for many years taught that the American Navy's regulations forbade ships from getting underway on Sundays . . . thus my amazement when the sortie of the Sixth Fleet ships was first observed. But that is another story for another chapter. Suffice it to say that we had now stalked the prey—and, if we could stay with him during the next period of operations at sea, we would indeed be "striking it rich."

4

Striking It Rich

It was shortly after breakfast and not yet eight o'clock that Sunday morning, when *W-7,* patrolling leisurely off the southernmost tip of Nisi Aiyina, became alerted to the sortie of the United States fleet units from Piraeus. Assuming conning control of the submarine, I maneuvered over to an excellent pre-planned position off the southeast corner of the island. From this vantage point, and without fear of detection, I was able to observe the American fleet departure from Greece.

As I logged in my written report to Admiral Gorshkov, United States destroyers emerged from the harbor first, all of them soon maneuvering around in obviously pre-positioned stations. The pattern of their maneuvers appeared to be the same kind of unimaginative submarine searches which the American Navy used in World War II against the German U-boats (so much inferior, of course, to the present-day Soviet submarines). I could see them through my periscope, as they plowed through the water, lurching and rolling while they alternately turned first left and then right, executing their customary "figure eights" at an average speed through the water of about sixteen knots. By ten o'clock, after fully clearing the southern approaches to Piraeus, the American destroyers had formed what appeared to be a circular sort of screen around the heavy ships, and the whole force was proceeding to the southward at about twelve knots.

From under the cover of the choppy blue sea, the *W-7* had lurked in waiting for this fleet and, with stealth befitting submariners whose captain (myself) would later receive citations for this "extraordinary service," we now stalked the Americans as their ships moved out for extended tactical operations.

Shortly before two o'clock in the afternoon, during one of our quick but frequent looks through the periscope, the large American attack aircraft carrier *Randolph* was observed to show from her signal hoist the blue and gold striped international signal flag for the alphabetical letter "G." This word was duly passed to me. I can recall the professional satisfaction I felt at being able to relay back to the watch officer the significance of what he had reported.

Over the sound-powered telephone from the crew's galley, where I was inspecting the eating utensils in company with Second Officer Rurik and commissary Lieutenant Koslov, I spoke to the watch officer, Rostopchin. Because he was the chief engineer, he had not had any extensive experience with international or Allied naval signals.

"Makar," I said with enlightenment gleaned from considerable schooling in military intelligence seminars at the Voroshilov Naval Academy, "what you have just witnessed is the assumption by the aircraft carrier of the role as pilot for the rest of the ships. Henceforth, all other ships will take their maneuvering cues from the carrier."

Second Officer Rurik, at one time a passenger on an Allied military transport vessel, corroborated this for the benefit of Koslov.

"*Da,* Yuri," he said smugly. "I myself have witnessed it many times from the surface while in convoys."

Other than officer-artilleryman Nikolai Volkonski, none of the other officers besides Rurik and myself were old enough to have had any experience in World War II, or in any subsequent Allied fleet exercises.

Impromptu class over, we continued our inspection of the crew's messing space.

Within a half hour, Watch Officer Rostopchin sent word down to me that the pilot flag had been hauled down from the aircraft carrier and that he had seen it hauled up on the cruiser *Newport News*.

By midafternoon, we were trailing lazily behind the Americans as they commenced refueling operations. The first indication we had that they were about to conduct such an exercise was when the sonar operator announced widespread increases of propeller revolutions and quickly changing bearing rates from all surface noise sources. A check through the periscope at the ships ahead confirmed that the U. S. ships were maneuvering at high speeds, apparently moving to form some kind of special refueling formation. By late afternoon, I had personally observed the refueling technique of the Americans, to the extent that I was able to log the tanker *Nantahala* as refueling *both* the aircraft carrier and a destroyer simultaneously, an amazing feat of superb seamanship. All the ships in the formation had refueled underway, and the three interchangeable screening destroyers ahead of the refueling ships were—as usual—obviously ineffective in detecting our stalking submarine. I could not help but think how useless would be the most skillful seamanship techniques of the Yankees, if we had been under orders to sink the carrier, cruiser, and tanker—all major targets.

By early evening, the Americans had apparently completed refueling operations and then went into another circular-type formation with six destroyers positioned around the heavy ships and at a range from them of about two miles.

The weather conditions for the refueling, I noted in my special report to Supreme Soviet Naval Headquarters, had been excellent for our purposes of observation while remaining undetected. The wind had been from the southwest, and the formation of ships had been heading in that direction. The wind velocity of about ten knots, in conjunction with waves of about two feet in height, contributed materially to our ability to follow astern and remain unseen despite our frequent periscope glimpses of what was going on.

At eight o'clock Sunday night, as Vasili Yukhnov was indicating our position to me on the navigational chart, the watch officer informed me that he could not account for the whereabouts of the tanker. At some time following the refueling operations, probably during our change-over of the watch, the *Nantahala* must have left the other ships in the formation, and we had not noticed it. I was furious.

"Captain," Yukhnov went on to say, "our location at this time should be about *here* on the chart."

He took his gold dividers, which his father had given him in 1956 when he graduated from the Frunze Higher Naval School, and pointed to the chart.

"We will probably be passing to the west of Crete by tomorrow."

"And then?" I quizzed.

Yukhnov frowned and twisted the dividers around, tapping them quickly against the palm of his left hand as he groped for an answer. None forthcoming, I volunteered my guess.

"It is my thinking that the Americans are leading us to the south of Crete for their fleet exercises."

Yukhnov's eyebrows moved higher, and an even larger frown came across his forehead as he sighed. He must have been thinking that at the least, he could have ventured such a prognostication, rather than let his captain say something now seemingly so obvious.

During the night, the concentration of American naval power passed to the west of Crete, and at two-thirty o'clock in the morning (it was now Monday, October 6) this formation turned toward the east—first on a course I estimated to be about 145 degrees true, and then, about an hour later, to a course of about 105 degrees true. We were still following the aircraft carrier *Randolph*, the cruiser *Newport News,* and several destroyers. Speed of the American ships had increased to sixteen knots during the night, but this did not interfere with our surveillance of the formation. On several occasions, we had to get up on the surface briefly and run at high speed, accepting the chance possibility of being spotted. This action was necessary so as not to drop too far behind. For the greater part of the night, however, we snorkel-trailed at high speed. As a result of this high-speed running, we were able to get only a partial battery charge by morning.

At about 9 A.M. on October 6, the *Randolph* was observed to pick up speed and commence launching aircraft. There was a generally calm sea with evidence of only slight breezes from the east. Flight operations lasted nearly all day, and were concentrated in a relatively small geographical area of the sea. At one point, the carrier turned and appeared to be heading straight for us at over thirty knots. As it developed, however, at no time that day were the Americans ever aware of our presence.

By late Monday afternoon, the U. S. ships had dispersed, abandoning their previously employed "tight" formation which we had found so easy to track. Rather than to attempt following one of these ships as they accelerated to high speeds (in fanning out to what must have been a scattered fleet disposition), we merely stayed in the area and headed slowly and quietly southeast.

At five-thirty in the afternoon, however, our luck shone bright. Plowing across our path at high speed came a large supercarrier, the huge white and black numerals 59 painted on her "island" superstructure. A quick referral to our intelligence sheets, by Second Officer Rurik, revealed this stranger to be the new American attack carrier *Forrestal.* In company with this colossal moving aerodrome was an older type American destroyer, which steamed parallel to the carrier but at a greater range away from us.

The *Forrestal* and her ancient destroyer in company passed nearly overhead at 6 P.M. But by that time, the *W-7* had changed depth rapidly to below three hundred feet and was safe from detection—there was a thermal layer between us and the surface, which I knew would preclude our discovery except at very close range. And yet, I chuckled, had we desired to sink this pride of the U. S. fleet, we could have done so—and right under the nose of her "protecting" destroyer. This opinion was, of course, transmitted in my written report at the end of the cruise.

By 9 P.M., we found the sea around us had been vacated by the Americans. Boldly, we probed the atmosphere with an electronics receiving antenna, and picked up a rash of signals. From these, my signals officer was able to determine that the cruiser *Des Moines* was somewhere in the area, together with many other new ships. But until the following morning, we were to have no particular excitement. The battery was fully recharged during the darkness and when dawn came on Tuesday, October 7, we were still moving eastward at slow speed.

Not much after 9 A.M., sonar informed me that there were now echoes being received from many ships on a wide range of bearings. However, neither the operator nor Rurik could tell what speeds these ships were making. It appeared obvious to me, then, that they were attempting to conceal the true revolution count of their propellers. Could this be taken to mean that somehow we had been sighted? Or perhaps that our presence was suspected? I gave the orders to go deeper and rig for silent running, so that we might possibly hear better—maybe find a good sound channel.

By ten-thirty o'clock, there seemed no danger still existing. I therefore brought the submarine back up to periscope depth for a visual check of the area. I could see nothing around us, though I searched several times in a complete circular arc. The sea was dead calm, not good for submarine close-in periscope observation because of the probability of detection. Our position was roughly south-southwest of the southeastern tip of Crete, at a range of just about a hundred miles. I decided that we had lost the Americans. I ordered the radar intercept antenna raised. From it, this time, we received nothing of any help.

But at a few minutes before eleven o'clock, having returned to below periscope depth for better listening, sonar abruptly reported hearing loud screw noises and echo-ranging. *W-7* was brought up quickly to periscope depth again. I looked along the bearing of the screw noises and echo-ranging. Less than eight thousand yards away, and heading straight at us, was a destroyer!

"Down scope! Take me down to 275 feet! Will that be under the thermal layer?"

Rurik answered me. "Yes, Captain, the layer is at 175 feet."

The noises from the approaching destroyer grew louder. We now leveled off at 275 feet and were rigged for silent running again. The echo-ranging pulses were growing more rapid and frequent. Surely we *must* have been detected. It now appeared certain that the destroyer's sound beam had found us.

"Estimated range to contact, fifteen hundred yards," Rurik reported, "closing fast."

"Very well, fire a false target decoy from the after-torpedo room," I responded.

Twenty seconds passed.

"Away decoy!" a report flashed back to me.

I turned up the listening equipment noise amplifier.

swswswswswswsSWSWSWSWSWSWSWSswswswswswsws

. . .

"He just passed down our port side, close aboard," said Rurik, frowning tensely. His heavy, straggly black eyebrows were distorted in a reflection of anxiety matched only by the nervous worry etched in the face of Lieuten-

ant Commander Sverdlov, who had now stationed himself close to the navigational chart desk.

"Why do we put up with this role of the hunted when
we could so easily destroy this American? How better for
us to teach them a lesson! How I hate this cringing, this
evasiveness, this hiding from the pursuer! It is so unnecessary! How do we know that he will not dump some
depth charges upon us? He could do so, and report only
that he was involved in a so-called 'training exercise.'
I say, when something like this occurs, let *us* assume the
initiative and take the offensive. Captain, I am giving you
my professional opinion!"

It was the political commissar, offering his armchair
strategy once more. I decided to ignore him in this latest
effrontery to the concept of strict obedience to military,
as opposed to Communist Party orders and authority. We
now all waited for indications that the destroyer was circling. This would have meant she was preparing for a
reinvestigation of her contact. But now, by some miracle,
the destroyer's echo-ranging ceased. Was the American
now listening for our propeller noises? We continued our
course, away from the previous action spot. And, for
some unaccountable reason, the American lost us. Instead of circling around to come in overhead of us again,
the destroyer moved further and further away. Perhaps
he was confused by the decoy. I suppose I shall never
know.

I glanced at the chart. Yukhnov's gold dividers dangled
from a makeshift cradle. I lifted them and measured off
our estimated navigational position. It was latitude
33° 35° north, longitude 26°02′ east, roughly halfway
between Crete and the Mediterranean coast of Egypt.

It was much later in the afternoon—close to supper
time, when the unexpected smell of frying onions, liver,
and bacon first began to permeate the submarine—that
I took a long look through the periscope and saw the *For-*

restal wheel around toward the northwest and pick up
speed. Her track placed her on our starboard bow at a
range of about seven thousand yards. The old destroyer
which had been with her the previous day appeared to be
still in company. I watched one aircraft take off, as the
mammoth moving airfield plowed through the sea looking very much like a gray dachshund with a bone in her
mouth. We slowed to three knots and maneuvered
to present as small a target as possible to both the carrier and the destroyer by keeping our bow pointed in
their direction.

Presently, the carrier and her escorting destroyer
turned and headed eastward. In case they intended to
conduct further flight operations later, I decided to turn
northward so as to intercept them. The wind direction
was still from the northwest and the carrier would have
to head that way if she were to operate more aircraft.
Leaving the conning station in the hands of the watch,
I made my way back to the galley. It annoyed me that
the cook had obviously disobeyed my orders of long
standing, about frying greasy foods while we were submerged. To my consternation, commissary Lieutenant
Koslov intervened before I could reprimand the cook.

"Captain," he said apologetically, "I am sorry about
this. I know your orders, but Lieutenant Commander
Sverdlov came in here this afternoon and gave orders that
we would have fried liver, onions, and bacon tonight.
He said it was an irrepressible desire on his part and that
the crew would appreciate his innovation in the menu."

Sverdlov himself now appeared, his pallid features
dominated by a look of obvious contempt for my authority.

"Lieutenant Commander Sverdlov," I seethed, "perhaps you are unaware of my reasons for not wanting food
fried except by my express permission. The odors and
small grease nodules which erupt from greasy food fry-

ing can cause undue discomfort to the crew when submerged."

The contemptuous expression on Commissar Sverdlov's face became fuller, sensuous, and more apparent. The insolent eyes stared; the equally insolent lips moved, and their contumely convulsions introduced such arrogance that I was motivated to strike him physically.

"In my opinion," he said, "the morale of the crew demands a significant change in the bill of fare. As the officer specifically charged by the Supreme Soviet with the morale and well-being of the men, I have decided that onions, liver, and bacon would be most appropriate for supper tonight."

"Mr. Sverdlov," I retorted firmly, "you are aware that you are the political administrator on board this boat. *I* am the commanding officer and it is my duty and responsibility to ensure the good morale and well-being of the crew. I will not have you or anyone else interfere with the menus once I have approved them."

The commissar's wan features colored somewhat. He raised one of his thick, pudgy forefingers and, waving it vigorously at me, issued a humiliating warning: "Captain, when I return to Moscow, you may be certain that your indecorous wording to me will be the subject of a special report to Vice Admiral Grishanov."

While this conversation was going on, Rurik, sitting in the wardroom and bothered by the greasy odors, which had been sifting into the wardroom through the fan duct, had decided he could stand it no longer. Eyes watering from the onions, he had pulled out one of his polka-dot handkerchiefs and was busily wiping his eyes when he appeared at the forward end of the galley.

Sverdlov, climaxing his defiance, had just taken a plate filled with sizzling onions, liver, and bacon, and was shoveling food into his mouth when Rurik stepped into the small compartment. Through watery, running eyes, the Second Officer glowered at the commissar. The latter returned his gaze. As he munched a thick piece of liver covered with greasy, fried onions, Sverdlov's pale blue eyes focused on Rurik's polka-dot handkerchief. To his mind as he watched that handkerchief mop up the tears streaming down the Second Officer's face, came the vision he had fostered of Rurik's use of that handkerchief on a previous cruise.

The thought was so hilarious to Sverdlov that he wanted to tell everyone how funny it was. Yet his mouth was so stuffed that he could not, and furthermore, the whole thing seemed so ludicrous to him that he was unable to swallow. When he finally burst into explosive laughter, the contents of his mouth—the half-chewed onion, liver, and bacon—catapulted across the narrow space and splattered over Vladimir Rurik's face and chest. The unintended victim of this spontaneous development did not see the humor of the situation. In a flash of surging rage, he took a step forward and thrust his thoroughly soaked handkerchief into the wide open mouth of the laughing Sverdlov. The force with which Rurik shoved the polka-dot rag between the teeth of the commissar was so violent that Sverdlov gagged. A trickle of blood appeared on his upper lip. The soggy handkerchief was too much for the suddenly squeamish stomach of the commissar. As he staggered back, he coughed convulsively, and then vomited. The already odious atmosphere became unbearably sickening.

Koslov, his stomach notably delicate anyway, fell first victim to the combined odors of the food being prepared and the vomit. His eyes bulging, Yuri paled, clapped his hand to his mouth, and rushed headlong to the galley sink.

The convulsive eruptions, together with the malodorous and steadily increasing odor, were too much for poor Rurik. With a groan he rushed to join Koslov at the galley sink.

The situation was untenable even for the captain. I turned quickly and fairly ran to the conning station, where I hoped to forget the mess in the officers' galley. I would leave the offender, Sverdlov, to his "fellow officers." Sverdlov, I felt uneasily, would add this to his grievances when he returned to Moscow.

At about 7:30 P.M., I was still standing at the conning station. The *W-7* was at periscope depth and heading on course north. I was hopefully awaiting some indication that we would soon come upon the carrier or other fleet units again. Presently sonar passed the word of loud propeller noises to the east, all becoming rapidly louder. I gave the order, "Up periscope!" and then quickly trained the periscope around to the noise bearings.

Over the horizon and at a distance of about five miles, I could see the red truck lights of a large ship. With her appeared to be two smaller vessels, one on the port beam and the other astern. It was the carrier again—no doubt the *Forrestal*. My maneuvering for another interception had worked! The enemy's movement was steady and positive. As the carrier came steadily closer, I quickly changed the course of *W-7* to present a small target aspect, in order to reduce the possibility of our being detected.

One thing which had always intrigued me was the rumor that the Americans actually launched and recovered high-speed aircraft from their huge carriers at nighttime. Frankly, neither I nor most Soviet officers believed that this was done other than as an emergency measure. It was, then, a great surprise for me to stare through my periscope at these extended night flight operations being conducted. All the more amazing to me was the fact that although I could see no lights on the carrier decks, I could see the seemingly endless assembly-line landings of jet aircraft. Each plane's exhaust burned bright and yellow against the dark sky as it circled and then came in to roost on the *Forrestal*'s deck. Finally, the carrier with her

escorts turned and headed away to the eastward again.
Flight operations were over for the night. I was elated
and satisfied at the success of our surveillance.

The navigator, hearing me state this, invited me to
check our estimated position as of nine-thirty o'clock. I
did so. According to his calculations, we had been at
34° 06′ 03″ north latitude, and 26° 13′ 02″ east longitude. A glance at the chart showed this to be most credible. We were still between Africa and Crete, churning
up waters through which the fleet had been moving since
the exercises had begun.

For the rest of the evening, we snorkeled and
charged our batteries—until two o'clock in the morning.
That was when radar intercept as well as sonar informed
us that all fleet units were again converging. Since nothing was visually apparent, I decided to risk using radar
to find out the range and disposition of the Americans.
Several quick rotations of the radar antenna, and I saw
all I needed to know. The American fleet was forming up
some seventeen miles away, in what appeared to be another refueling disposition. We in *W-7* watched silently.

At four o'clock that morning, carrier flight operations
resumed. This time, I could see the blinking red lights on
the aircraft as they zoomed off in the distant sky. And
all the following day, *W-7* witnessed full-scale fleet aircraft operations. These lasted until nearly nine-fifteen
o'clock in the evening! I marveled at the stamina of the
American flyers.

But the U. S. Navy does not maintain its amazing air
superiority at sea without paying a price. I was witness
to one payment. It occurred at eight o'clock that Wednesday morning.

As the huge, powerful-looking *Forrestal* steamed by
us at high speed, through fairly calm seas, I was peering at her through our unobtrusive periscope, watching
her conduct further flight operations. They fascinated
me.

Suddenly, without warning, one aircraft—it looked like one of the U. S. Navy's *A4D-2* types—crashed off the stern of the fast-moving carrier. When this happened, I realized that all eyes on the *Forrestal* would be on the downed plane. Therefore, I continued looking at the accident—from about three thousand yards away. Great clouds of white steam billowed forth from the carrier's funnel as she came to an amazingly rapid stop in the water. Finally, she lay to within a half mile of the crash scene, while one of her helicopters maneuvered over the partially floating wreckage. About ten minutes later, the plane sank—and I am certain that the helicopter did not rescue the crashed flyer. He went to the bottom in his cockpit.

The high-speed approach of a rescue destroyer cut short my spying on this scene, and we went down quickly to 290 feet—well below the thermal layer.

This incident occurred about sixty miles north of the African coast, and approximately 115 miles south of Crete. In passing, I might mention that when Commissar Sverdlov relayed the news of this plane crash to the crew, he told them that "it occurred some 780 miles due south of the Transylvanian Alps, one of the last strongholds of superstitious simple-minded Christian native-folk."

When flight operations had been completed on Wednesday night, the Yankees steamed along in a formation using what might be described as a semicircular destroyer screen for protection against submarines. Their base course was now westward and their speed about twelve knots.

The wind, at one time from the northwest at about ten knots, increased as the night wore on. By daylight, a stiff wind from the southwest had combined with ten-foot waves. These made it possible for us to maintain contact with the Americans by cruising on the surface, yet with little chance of detection.

On Thursday, October 9, we were witness to the largest fleet replenishment exercise that I had ever seen. The surprising point to me was that it appeared to be the entire Sixth Fleet refueling and reprovisioning at sea! I had not expected that my surveillance of the American fleet would bring before my eyes such a tremendous concentration of power.

During the night preceding the dawn on Thursday, the fleet had been slipping farther and farther away from us. Despite the fact that the high waves permitted us to pursue the Americans by cruising on the surface at fifteen knots, they were steaming at an even greater speed and it was possible only to maintain electronic rather than visual contact as the night advanced. Shortly before noon on the ninth, however, the fleet turned to the south-southwest. This resulted in my intercepting the entire armada —in fact, the *W-7* was caught in the middle of this logistics formation as it plowed southward.

Penetrating the formation's destroyer antisubmarine screen proved to be no problem. Sonar conditions were poor for surface ships' underwater echo-ranging equipment, and we merely moved in under a protective layer of cold water until I knew that we were well inside the destroyer screen. Then I came to periscope depth and maneuvered through and between some of the major elements of the fleet. As I spotted hull numbers or ships' names, I called them out to the quartermaster, who logged them while Rurik stood close by with his intelligence folder, identifying by name those ships whose numbers I called out. When we had disentangled ourselves from within this maze of naval tonnage, the logged names of ships I had peered at through periscope cross hairs made up the bulk of power in the American Mediterranean Fleet.

When I wrote my report to Admiral Gorshkov, I stated that had this been wartime, the Soviet Navy could have rejoiced in the certain sinking of the United States ships *Forrestal, Randolph, Des Moines, Newport News, Rigel,*

Altair, Wrangel, Mississinewa, Waccamaw, Du Pont, Benham and *Abbot*. Although I was aware that other ships were present besides these, none came directly dead center into my vision through the periscope other than those mentioned above.

Prior to six-thirty in the evening, the great armada dispersed in several directions. *W-7* now moved northwestward at six knots and spent the night fully recharging batteries.

By breakfast time on Friday, October 10, we had moved into the southern Ionian Sea, still maintaining electronics contact with the *Forrestal* and the *Des Moines*. We were able to intercept several uncoded messages from COMSIXTHFLEET (Vice Admiral "Cat" Brown, whom Admiral Gorshkov was later to mention as a potentially good candidate for sinking), as well as from minor commanders and unit officers. By midmorning, it had become obvious to me that the Americans were involved in a large-scale aerial strike exercise. Their carriers were conducting constant launchings and landings of aircraft, and all ships in the fleet were widely dispersed. Perhaps this was one of Admiral Brown's "dry runs" in preparation for an assault on Russia! I became worried. The United States was demonstrating such fine seamanship and such excellent aerial assault capability that I knew we would have to knock out the Sixth Fleet at the very first, if relations with America degenerated into war. Otherwise, Russia would suffer from the cold efficiency of this fleet's tremendous aerial striking force. These thoughts were included in our final cruise report to Naval Headquarters.

The brightest spot in my entire report centered on the U. S. Navy's obvious nakedness in submarine countermeasures. The very fact that the Soviet submarine *W-7* had been able to operate at such close quarters to the American fleet, and had remained in such proximity undetected for so long, was ample proof that the Americans are weak in antisubmarine capability. Fortunately for

Soviet Russia, not much has been done to improve America's readiness for antisubmarine warfare since that 1958 Mediterranean cruise of the *W7*. However, since 1958, Soviet progress in submarine development has been accelerated. Again, it is probably to Russia's advantage that the American naval hierarchy has chosen to publicly disbelieve the statements of Premier Khrushchev and others on the new advances in Soviet submarine capability. In fact, when the American Navy's Pentagon chief refused a large amount of money in 1960 that the representatives in Congress wanted to appropriate for antisubmarine research and development, the Soviet naval headquarters were delighted. At the time, Admiral Gorshkov and his principal fleet commanders had met to discuss the American shipbuilding program. Gorshkov is alleged to have said to Kasatonov and his other commanders, "The United States Navy cannot be explained. They know well enough that our large underseas fleet is several times as huge as the U-boat forces with which the Germans almost won the war in 1942. Yet their admirals oblige us by ignoring our most significant weapon. They went to the American Senate and dissuaded them from appropriating funds for improving American antisubmarine readiness. In fact, these admirals rejected three brand-new destroyer escorts and some nuclear attack submarines. And why? To make sure that the Congress of the United States would let the American Navy have another big aircraft carrier. Let's drink a toast to their number one admiral, Old Walrus Butt!"

By Saturday, October 11, 1958, I had witnessed enough of the American fleet's Mediterranean operations to set course for Vlone. Our last contact with the American ships was when we intercepted one of their uncoded wireless tactical messages on Sunday morning. Apparently, they were forming up into a column for transit of the Strait of Messina, and the *Forrestal* was to lead the procession.

We entered the Albanian harbor of Vlone four days prior to our operational deadline for doing so. It had been a most memorable cruise. We had—as the Americans say —"struck it rich." And now I was to discover that my premonitions about my immediate future were accurate.

No crystal ball could have predicted the events surrounding my arrival any better. Five weeks after Admiral Vladimir Afanasyevich Kasatonov, the Black Sea Fleet Commander, had relayed the word from Moscow that I was to quit the Beirut operation, I was back in the Motherland reporting to the Navy Commander in Chief himself, Admiral Gorshkov. With him in his nautically decorated office in the Soviet capital was Kasatonov. Together, they sat impassively as I tried to explain how it was that the W-7 had aborted in the attempt to embarrass the United States.

Gorshkov, although a Party man to the marrow, is nonetheless a good naval officer. He was quick to excuse the failure in Beirut upon my statement of the facts in the case. My presentation to both him and Kasatonov decried the presence of the bungling commissar, and I told them that only a court-martial of my erstwhile Third Officer would satisfy me. Gorshkov's reaction was noncommittal, but it was noteworthy that neither he nor his immediate subordinate condemned me personally for the failure of the expedition. Instead, Gorshkov sat amiably listening to my entire account of the cruise—from beginning to end —and when I had finished, he ignored Soviet military protocol by offering me a Chesterfield cigarette.

"Captain Zhdanov," said the Navy chief thoughtfully between contemplative puffs on one of his American cigarettes (which since World War II he has had supplied to him regularly by diplomatic couriers), "I must tell you that on the basis of your failure to accomplish your original mission, I had been prevailed upon to remove you from the list of officers qualified for command at sea. In

the absence of amplifying news reflecting on the incident
as reported by the American papers, we here at Headquarters did not see how you could have avoided detection."

Admiral Kasatonov, a delegate to the 20th Party Congress and ever mindful of his status, saw an opening and
joined in the conversation:

"We felt that you would compromise the position of
the Motherland!"

Gorshkov, holding his cigarette between the thumb and
index finger of his right hand, now caressed his dangling
array of medals with the other hand. His groping fingers
ferreted out the decoration of which he was known to be
most proud, the Order of Kutuzov, First Class.

Stroking the medal slowly, he continued his talk.

"Luckily, there *was* no detection and no compromise.
That is to your advantage. However, it is because of your
outstanding operations later, in spying on the American
Sixth Fleet during their war gaming exercises, that I am
disposed to ignore the most pressing demands of others,
who have conducted an investigation into your treatment
of Lieutenant Commander Sverdlov . . . as well as into
all aspects of your performance."

Kasatonov leaned forward in his chair.

"You must surely know," he confided, "that Lieutenant
Commander Commissar Sverdlov, upon his arrival back
in Moscow, wasted no time in branding you unfit for command of an attack submarine."

Although I had known that he would complain about
me, I had not fully realized the extent to which he would
go to ruin me.

"According to Sverdlov," interrupted Gorshkov, "you
should have responded to his pistol firing in the manner
a good Cossack would respond to a bugler sounding the
Charge!"

I knew that Admiral Gorshkov had never personally

liked the idea of having political commissars attached to men-of-war. But Gorshkov's easy, unassuming outlook on life precluded his fighting the problem. He recognized that his own rise in the Navy, under Stalin, had resulted largely through his own acceptance of Communist doctrine; he also recognized that Vice Admiral Vasily Grishanov, the Supreme Navy Commissar for Communist Administration, was a power to be dealt with. Grishanov, as a matter of fact, was not even answerable to Gorshkov, despite his inferior rank. The divorcement of commissars from normal naval discipline extended even up to the highest levels.

"My dear comrade," whispered the Commander in Chief of the Soviet Navy as he blew a great cloud of smoke through his large nostrils, "by your exploits against the United States Sixth Fleet, you have done our cause the greatest of good. Now that we know more about the American methods of operation in the Mediterranean—thanks to you—we shall better know how to deal with their stupid Admiral Brown, the one they call 'The Cat.' One day while he is reading his archaic Bible in that nice, big, comfortable bed of his aboard that cruiser you so often watched through your periscope, we may deliver to him the shock of his useless life!"

Admiral Gorshkov's friendly eyes opened wide.

"And you, Aleksandr Ivanovich," he chortled, "may be just the man to someday give him such a present!"

The lump in my throat prevented me from even saying thank you to this man who held my future in the palm of his hand.

Gorshkov took one last inhalation on the remaining inch of his American cigarette and, as he squashed the stub against an ashtray with an unnecessary display of power from his thick, pudgy fingers, he added thoughtfully, "By the way, did you know that the big comfortable bed that Bible reader curls up in every night is made up for him every day by black men?"

"I thought they were indentured Filipinos," interjected Admiral Kasatonov, raising his eyebrows.

"Well, no matter, one way or the other, it makes no difference," concluded the highest-ranking officer in the Soviet Navy. "When the time of truth comes, they'll die right alongside of their capitalist masters. What a shame . . . what a damned shame!"

PART II

POWER PROJECTION WESTWARD:

Via the Red Underbelly, to the American Backyard

5

"RED SAIL NINE"—How It Began

☐ The rendezvous with Glenn occurred during the longest cruise ever undertaken by a Soviet submarine. It started on the bitterly cold night of January 29, 1962, from the Russian ice-free port of Murmansk, which is nestled in the northern reaches of continental Europe.

In the weeks prior to our deployment from the submarine base at Saida Guba, I had been subjected to an intensive briefing by Soviet intelligence officers, regarding American as well as Allied naval strength in the North Atlantic. Considerable emphasis was devoted to the operations of the U. S. Atlantic Fleet carrier-based antisubmarine forces. These were known to be conducting almost constant exercises on the high seas. Aside from a brief commentary on shipping volume around the British Isles, and a discussion of international traffic likely to be using the sea lanes of the Atlantic during the ensuing months, there was no indication at the time that we would have anything to do with the American astronaut.

On the last day in port, during the forenoon, Captain Georgy Novgorod, Chief of Staff for Political Administration (i.e., Commissar) to Admiral Andrei Trofimovich Chabanenko, escorted me to Submarine Headquarters. Awaiting me was iron-faced Admiral Chabanenko himself, Commander in Chief of the Northern Fleet, together with several of his staff. After a succinct and most humorless introduction, the admiral stated that on the recommendation of the Navy over-all Commander in Chief (Admiral Gorshkov) I had been selected to conduct this most secret operation. The code name was to be "RED SAIL NINE."

"Captain Zhdanov," declared the Northern Fleet chieftain, "you have of course already received the first part of your instructions for 'RED SAIL NINE.' I understand that the loading of all supplies and equipments, including special armaments, has already been carried out. You know the geographical oceanic points through which you will pass on the first phase of your cruise. Captain Anatole Chichagov, my staff operations officer, will point out to you the refinements of the situation. What I desire to emphasize is that you do not open your sealed orders until you have fully complied with the provisions of your presently effective instructions."

He nodded to one of his staff officers. A stocky, balding Mongol bowed slightly from the waist. I presumed that this was Captain Chichagov. I had not previously known him, and gave little more than momentary thought to the fact that the new staff operations officer was a Mongol. I knew that hundreds of years of intermarriage between Slavs and Mongols had resulted in Asiatic facial characteristics in many Russians bearing Slavic names. Chichagov, between tightly compressed gold-plated teeth, announced that the dark red sealed envelope which he handed me was MOST SECRET. I would now be pleased, he rasped, to follow him on the chart as he outlined the first part of the forthcoming cruise. Taking a wooden, bullet-tipped pointer from an assistant, the speaker then moved across the room to a huge wall map of the North Atlantic and Baltic Sea regions.

After bowing once more Chichagov tapped the colored chart on the wall and began:

"As orders have indicated to you, the *F-689* will depart tonight from Kola Inlet for an extended deployment. Ostensibly, you will be prepared for a ninety-day patrol. This information you may disseminate to your officers

and crew. Just prior to getting underway tonight at about
10:45 P.M. (which is the time that seven fishing trawlers
will also be standing out of the inlet heading in the direction that you will be going), be prepared to embark two
passengers. They will be very important to your ultimate
assignment. But they have been instructed to say nothing
about their roles until after you have opened your sealed
orders. For your information now, they are civilians, and
are considered to be experts in the fields of agriculture and
economics. Perhaps you have heard of them. Professor
Boris Bogucharovo, from the University of Moscow, perhaps the world's foremost authority on improved mass
farming techniques; and Professor Stepan Alexovich
Pozdeev, formerly head of Moscow University's Economics Department, who is more recently identified as one of
the brains behind the new science research city of Nauko-
grad, in western Siberia, near Novosibirsk."

So! I was to have two very important civilians—intel-
lectuals—on my boat! As I focused my attention on the
large, colorful chart to which the briefing officer was now
pointing with his stick, I wondered what the mission was
of these two top scientists. I reached into my coat pocket
for a Turkish cigarette, but remembering that Admiral
Chabanenko loathes smoking, diverted my movements so
that it appeared that I was merely looking for a handkerchief. Captain Chichagov was now outlining the projected
track I would be taking.

"You will use a speed of advance of ten knots. At this
point here, on the chart," and he tapped the place on the
map, "you will rendezvous with a second group of Soviet
trawlers. The first group of trawlers escorting you out of
Murmansk tonight will merely be doing this to conceal
your movements; you will, of course, cruise on the surface tonight in their midst. No one other than friendly
eyes will suspect that you are underway. But later tomorrow, you will be on your own until you meet up with the

other trawlers at Point 'A.' Needless to say, you will stay submerged during daylight hours in order to avoid possible detection."

The wooden pointer was now tapping the chart at the place the Mongol had said was Point "A." I noted that it was approximately forty-five miles due northeast of North Cape, Norway, in the Barents Sea.

"The *F-689*," said this balding near-image of Yul Brynner, the American actor, "will then proceed to Points 'B' and then 'C.' "

The wooden pointer flashed laterally across the wall chart, stopping at points marked "B" and "C."

"Your mission during this phase of the cruise will be to conduct undetected training operations. You will test the practicability of trawler escorts for covert military operations, and you will collect general intelligence data on British and American naval units if opportune. Unless you are otherwise advised, you will open your sealed orders when you arrive here."

The bullet-tipped stick struck the wall chart a vigorous blow at a point about two hundred miles northwest of Ireland. It was marked "C."

Admiral Chabanenko now arose, nodded to his staff operations captain, and then, facing me, said: "I am hopeful that you will do as well as you did in the Mediterranean in 1958. If you have no questions, may I say good luck?"

The briefing was over. Along with the other staff assistants to Admiral Chabanenko, I was on my feet. Since neither the admiral nor the others moved, I recognized that the withdrawal from the scene was left to me to accomplish. With a small, stiff bow, I took the red envelope and, backing away two paces, thanked the admiral for his kindness. Then, turning toward the door, I strode out. A staff car was waiting to take me to the submarine piers where the *F-689* rode to her mooring lines.

As the *F-689* splashed gently through the mild swells
and small wavelets of the cold, black Barents Sea north
of Murmansk, I pulled the fur protective pads of my parka
up around my cheeks to shield my face from the cold
night sea breeze. I was on the small open bridge with the
officer of the watch. The submarine was proceeding according to plan, now on course 315 degrees true, on a
track which would take us along the northern tip of Europe toward the Norwegian Sea. We were maintaining
our station in the vicinity of the trawlers which had left
port with us, and which would "escort" us for the next
few hours. Then, with an entirely recharged battery, we
would continue the first leg of the voyage by ourselves. I
scanned the dark sea around us. The fishing trawlers were
carrying their usual lights—and so were we, as a night-
camouflaged member of this little group, displaying identical illumination. Little chance, I thought to myself, that
we would ever be suspected to be what we really were.

In fact, the Second Officer had made sure that the submarine's side numbers had been removed, shortly after
getting underway. Now, without the large white block letters *689* gleaming on the side, it would be most difficult
for anyone to identify the dark green hull.

6

Away the Trawlers

☐ JANUARY 29, 1962.

One of the *F-689*'s escorting trawlers, the *Mosalsk*, had made headlines in 1960 when she had entered a United States port. At the time, she had been engaged in oceanographic espionage against the United States, but her publicly proclaimed mission had been "fishing." It was a coincidence that one of this trawler's officers in 1960 would now be on board my submarine, the *F-689*; his name was Ivan Baliuk. He was now my intelligence and underwater sound officer. I felt fortunate that I had him, for he brought to us an expert knowledge of hydrography, much of which he learned while serving as hydro-electronics engineer on board the *Mosalsk*.

At this point, it might be wise to briefly discuss such vessels, for they are interwoven with Soviet submarine probings in militarily important areas of the world. And I consider it essential that the reader fully understand that these fishing trawlers of Russia, which operate so methodically and with such precision near American and Canadian waters, are primarily concerned with accumulation of intelligence. This is also true of the trawlers which operate in the waters north of the United Kingdom, extending roughly from Iceland to the territorial limits of Norway. Additionally, they are used in active measures laying the groundwork for offensive naval action against the United States.

The Soviet Union, in its vigorous bid for maritime predominance, is relying in part on her growing fleet of oceanographic survey vessels, research ships, and combinations of both, camouflaged as trawlers, to outstrip the United States of America in seapower. It is therefore necessary to consider this new breed to better understand the concurrent role they play with the Soviet submarine fleet in espionage from oceanic environments.

Many of the thirty-five-hundred or so oceangoing trawlers are active against the United States, and are manned by Soviet naval officers, seamen and technicians. Their numbers have been multiplying steadily since the end of the Stalin era. Yet fortunately for the men who dominate the Kremlin, most Americans are either blissfully unaware of the espionage which these vessels conduct, or uninterested. Russian intelligence believes that even when the press of the Western world has spotlighted "incidents" involving Soviet trawlers, the American people themselves have shown little more than passing interest in the matter. The American Congress seems to be apathetic, the American State Department indecisive, and apparently, even the American Navy itself does not seem worried about the possibilities that these trawlers and other "peaceful" ships are primarily concerned with military operations.

The Soviet ambassador to the United States has told Premier Khrushchev that he and his military staff believe that the American naval authorities are cognizant of Russian activities in this field. But at the same time, the ambassador has told Khrushchev that the U. S. Navy probably will not take any countermeasures. Perhaps the overriding reason, at least in the minds of the observant Soviet staff in Washington, is that drawing attention to areas of naval weakness associated with oceanography, sea exploration for military purposes, and antisubmarine warfare, might detract from the congressional readiness to appropriate huge expenditures for such programs as super aircraft carriers. This, according to the ambassador and his advisers, the air-minded Pentagon admirals would not want.

Of course, when one of our Soviet trawlers erupts into

international newsprint, the American naval authorities do have statements to make to the press.

For instance, back in the last days of April 1960, the Soviet trawler *Vega* maneuvered into a position approximately sixty miles south of Long Island, under orders from Soviet Naval Headquarters. The mission was twofold: to spy on the new United States nuclear Polaris submarine *George Washington,* which was slated to test-fire her consignment of practice ballistic missiles; and to pick up and record the characteristic sounds of that submarine —which presumably would later be operational in waters near the Soviet homeland.

The 230-foot-long *Vega,* equipped with the latest electronics devices in use (radar, electronics intercept and radio-direction-finding equipments, sonar, portable hydrophones for underwater listening, and high-powered radio sets) succeeded in her mission. At the time of the testfirings, she was less than two thousand yards from the nuclear submarine! Since our trawlers ostensibly are out after schools of fish, the fact that they are equipped with new long-range underwater listening and electronics video consoles can be justified. It would not *necessarily* mean that they are out after submarines. Nor would it prove that they do not use their equipment as aides in better understanding the sea and its environment (bottom, water temperature gradient, etc.) in the areas in which they operate. However, Russian trawlers do operate in and near the large U. S. Navy exercise locales and consistently extract invaluable information from the Americans. For instance, the *Vega* has been credited with determining the precise frequencies of many U. S. electronics equipments. Such knowledge would be necessary for many wartime applications.

After successfully spying on the *George Washington,* the *Vega* moved southward, and the following day was off the main U. S. Atlantic base at Norfolk, Virginia. There, several merchantmen recognized her and (presumably) advised the American Coast Guard of her presence in the area. With the word thus publicized, the American Navy apparently decided to reveal the earlier part of the story, and released news bulletins describing the presence of the trawler in the Polaris test-firing area the previous day. The news services of the world were then treated to the word that the Soviets could have measured the time it took for the ejected projectiles to reach air re-entry, the firing interval, and the identifying sounds emitted from that particular submarine.

It is of interest, too, that the vehicle discovering the trawler's presence was a blimp, of the type used in World War II for antisubmarine patrol work. But very recently, and not very understandably, the American Navy decided to dispense with lighter-than-air craft. Such additional good fortune for the Soviets!

At an earlier date, there was considerable publicity over an American boarding party which inspected another Russian trawler, the suspected culprit in the breaks of the transatlantic cables off Newfoundland. Actually, the trawler the American sailors boarded was *not* culpable. She was a mere decoy. The perpetrator of the deed was a friend and classmate of mine from the Frunze Higher Naval School, Vladimir Romanov. As commanding officer of a Soviet submarine operating in concert with five trawlers off the St. Georges and Grand Banks, Romanov was attempting to plant various special electronics devices near the cables when his equipment became fouled. The ensuing difficulties experienced by Romanov in trying to extricate himself resulted in the cables being cut. This was done without malice, however, although the American press suggested that perhaps the Soviet Union had intentionally cut the cables. It may be of interest, nonetheless, to know that the devices he was planting were for future use against America in the event of war.

Another incident involved the Soviet trawler *Poexobo*. She was part of a twelve-ship squadron leaving Murmansk in April 1960. Their job was to conduct surveillance of the American submarine operating areas off New London, Connecticut. However, *Poexobo* was ordered detoured via the north coast of Iceland. Her mission was to evaluate the radar efficiency and effectiveness of U. S. radar stations in the vicinity. But on May 19, an Icelandic patrol boat discovered the trawler at anchor in a cove near the radar station, and sent a boarding party to her. The *Poexobo* skipper claimed engine trouble as an excuse for being there, and nothing further developed—other than widespread publicity. The trawler subsequently proceeded to join her sister vessels along the American continental shelf.

Apparently, the American Air Force, ever alert to embarrass the Navy, has been responsible for fairly widespread publicity covering the Soviet trawlers which have operated near the Air Force's Texas Towers. These mammoth radar warning towers, rising out of the sea near the edge of the American continental shelf, have indeed been the focal point of attention of Soviet maritime observers ever since they were emplanted. Other Soviet craft have operated near the island of Nantucket, and some twenty miles off Chatham, on the "elbow" of Cape Cod.

Many of the squadrons of Soviet trawlers at sea operate under the definite control and command of task force commanders, who utilize each of their ships for specific primary purposes. Of course, in order to preclude the exposure of their cardinal purposes, most of the trawlers actually engage in bona fide fishing activity. Thus, the Soviet Union's vast fishing armada has returned to Russian canneries with probably more fish than the Americans and Canadians combined have brought back in identical periods to their own shores.

Sometimes, however, the position of our Soviet vessels, intent on obtaining intelligence, or in laying false bottom reflectors, or other devices in vital areas along America's continental shelf, cannot be supported by the excuse that the trawlers involved are only "fishing." For instance the *Vega*, when spying on the *George Washington*, was in waters which are most seldom, if ever, used by foreign flag commercial fishermen. That area off Long Island is almost constantly used for maneuvers of U. S. submarines and hunter-killer destroyer forces from nearby Newport.

Additionally, the milking of vital information from the Texas Towers, one of which is located about 110 miles east of Cape Cod and the remaining one more nearly east of Nantucket island, has provided the Soviet Union with enough data to make it possible to negate the effectiveness of those towers in the event of hostilities between Russia and America.

On June 11, 1961, a Soviet trawler entered Boston Harbor officially bent on procuring medical treatment for her captain, Artsev V. Grigorievich, who supposedly was suffering from gastritis. Also brought ashore for medical treatment was a seaman, Nicolai I. Kulakov, who reportedly had sprained his back when the trawler dropped anchor in lower Boston Harbor. Actually, the "seaman" was Lieutenant Ivan Nicolai Kulakov, special intelligence officer whose basic mission was acquiring graphic knowledge of the approaches to and confines of Boston Harbor. For the Soviet master naval plan calls for the penetration of all important American bases by Soviet underseas craft in the event of a war. There is nothing Soviet submariners would rather do than surpass the great submarine exploits of World War II—the penetration of Scapa Flow by the German U-boat or the depredations of American submarines in Japanese home waters. Boston Harbor, of course, is militarily important in that it houses the United States Naval Shipworks, and is also the home port of at least one missile cruiser.

In one other notable case, a Soviet trawler—in this case the *Mosalsk*—had been engaged in surveying the ocean beds off the New Jersey coast, when one of her junior officers became ill. Rather than seek American help for an officer of the Soviet Navy, it was decided to say that he was a mere fisherman. True enough, Ivan Baliuk was a fisherman—but he was fishing for more than menhaden. As a specially trained hydroelectronics engineer, he was aboard to fish for some clues concerning America's anti-submarine defense capabilities. (As a matter of fact, the annual fishing run on menhaden had not yet commenced in these waters.) The mother tender, a larger Soviet ship, radioed Argentia, Newfoundland, to request permission for the trawler to put in at Atlantic City in order to get medical attention for an ailing *seaman*. Thus, on May 21, 1960, the Soviet Navy "trawler" *Mosalsk* entered port at a well-known American resort and procured medical services for a sick "crewman." An interesting sidelight on the news articles appearing all over the world at the time, concerning this incident, is that the two women reportedly serving on board the vessel as marine biologists were, in fact, what the news reports claimed they were. However, they were also on board because new prevalent thinking in maritime and naval circles in the Soviet Union suggests that male seamen will perform better with a biological incentive at hand!

7

"Who's Who"

☐ JANUARY 30, 1962

It was past midnight. The sleek, dark green, long-range underseas craft responded gently to the mild sea swells coming down from the north. Occasionally, the bow would emerge headlong from the recesses of one of these swells, and a swiftly passing image of white foam would swish along the sides of the submarine. The lookouts and watch officer frequently turned their parka-protected faces away from the wind and sought what relief they could from the cold salt-air blasts. The escorting trawlers and my new streamlined three-engined diesel craft were cruising effortlessly along a set course of 315 degrees true for the rest of the night. There was no further need for my presence on the open bridge.

Taking the watch officer's elbow, I nudged him and indicated my intention to go below.

"Keep a sharp lookout for any other shipping, and let us have no collisions with the 'fishermen,' " I bellowed.

The man I left in charge needed no such admonitions. He was an officer I had previously trained in the Mediterranean. Officer-artilleryman Nikolai Volkonski, now Lieutenant Commander and Second Officer for this cruise, acknowledged my warning with a cheery, "Aye, aye, Captain," delivered through teeth whose chattering revealed the cold chill of his body.

"Send one of the lookouts down to the wardroom to get a ration of brandy for each of you," I said, fully aware of how frigidly cold and hence inefficient a watch crew can be when exposed to the wintry winds. And then I jumped

down, out of the freezing outside, into the warm inside of
a Soviet submarine whose crew had not gone to sleep, but
who, significantly, were up and talking. Some were joking.
Others played games. Generally, all seemed to be in high
good spirits, befitting a seagoing group just commencing a
voyage which promised considerable adventure and excitement.

In the small, cramped conning station under the open
bridge from which I had jumped, the navigator was bent
over his charts. The only light came from the dim, red-
coated fluorescent bulbs. Removing my heavy-weather
outer garments, I threw them into my specially constructed
personal locker, adjacent to the navigator's chart table.

"I have provided a list of navigational lights for the
watch officers," the navigator broke the silence.

He was fresh from the Voroshilov Naval Academy's
junior course in submarine navigation, and had been the
beneficiary of a previous trawler cruise to Newfoundland
and the Grand Banks. He was thoroughly familiar with
Soviet naval activity in that region, and had even become
familiar with Halifax . . . Halifax! wartime assembly
point for American convoys in two world wars!

His shock of wavy blond hair, like Rostopchin's, was
complemented by Scandinavian-like blue eyes and a ruddy
complexion. His name was Sergei Nikolovich Mikhailoff,
and his forebears came from Moscow. His father had been
a minor nobleman and Army officer under the Czar's
regime, and his mother had been the only daughter of a
Moscow gold merchant of the Second Guild. Mikhailoff
was well connected, even in Soviet Russia, for his childhood nurse was married to a man who had become a per-
sonage in the Communist Party hierarchy. Hence, Mikhailoff was able to bend the ears of several key members
of the Party. Doubtless this partially accounted for his
demand as an aide to flag officers in the Navy, several
of whom repeatedly sought his services. He had been assigned to me for this cruise at the direct order of Admiral

Gorshkov, who let it be known that he wanted his best officers to have roots at sea.

"Thank you, Lieutenant Mikhailoff," I said, unbuttoning my shirt collar and smiling. "By the way, I will want to dive before daylight—then we can snorkel along."

"Aye, aye, Captain." It was the cheerful response of a man happy to be off on his first important submarine cruise, and cognizant of his considerable responsibility for its success.

"By the way, Nick," I said, "in case the watch officer forgets, I'd like you to see to it that every other hour commencing now, the exposed watch personnel get a ration of brandy."

Mikhailoff smacked his lips approvingly.

"Perhaps I should go up to make sure they comply, too," he said expectantly.

"Very well, Mr. Navigator," I said soothingly, "but whatever you do, please be sure not to expose yourself. It's much too cold up there and you'd be so unnecessarily uncomfortable!"

My frown gave way to a broad grin and Sergei Nikolovich Mikhailoff threw his head back, chuckling.

In reflection, I suppose that this interchange was indicative of the tone set throughout the *F-689* during this cruise. It was a good crew, a happy crew. The men were well trained, and daily became even better trained. Constant drills in casualty control and battle stations brought our team efficiency to its highest possible levels.

Only two officers in the submarine gave me any cause for concern at any time. One was my new gunnery and torpedo assistant, Officer-artilleryman Lieutenant Nesvitski Igorovich Glinka. He was a tremendously personable young officer, with a ready wit and glowingly delightful sense of humor. His jet black hair and expressive brown eyes, combined with his flashing white teeth, made him the object of much feminine attention in Murmansk, as had been the case when he was a cadet at the Frunze Higher

Naval School. There, he was an extremely popular under-
graduate and in great demand by the mothers of daughters
sired by the more important Communist Party members.
That he might marry one of their daughters was an obvious hope held by many such mothers. But he managed
to graduate without committing himself, and moved on to
the Northern Fleet Naval Headquarters Staff. While there,
his appeal to the local young womanhood was so pronounced that the Chief of Staff, hearing of his constant
attention more to social life than to the increasingly powerful Soviet Navy, assigned him to my boat for a cruise
which supposedly would give the girls a breathing spell.
Concurrently, it was hoped that young Glinka would become a good sea-rooted naval officer. More importantly
to me, I hoped that he could be made into another outstanding submarine officer.

My other "problem" was Georgy Mikhailovich Lvov,
recent aide and flag secretary to Vice Admiral Grishanov,
the top political commissar. I now know that the complexion of all commissars is the same. They are of one
mold. They are Communist Party adherents and members
who live in rigid mental conformance to the most narrow
patterns of behavior. But Lieutenant Commander Lvov
was fundamentally a jovial, pleasant chap to have around.
He was generally well thought of by the crew, with whom
he never failed to joke and tell stories in addition to giving
his daily political lectures. The wardroom officers were at
once beguiled by his friendly attitude and contagious
laughter the moment he reported aboard. My relations
with him were, to say the least, interesting at all times, but
certainly at first, most cordial.

With a parting smile to Mikhailoff, I left the conning
station and went below to the control room, thence forward to the underwater sound room. There, the sonar
operators were converged around the sound console.

"Listening to recordings of the propeller noises of U. S.
submarines for practice, Captain," spoke up Lieutenant

Ivan Dedusko, my newest officer and the electronics officer for the boat. Under his arm he had a Soviet naval manual entitled *Underwater Sound Manual, Naval and Merchant Log,* which recorded the revolution counts of compiled ships' propeller rotations at varying speeds. Based on actual encounters with each ship listed, this manual was the brainchild of a classmate of mine, Commander Peter Dmitrich Guragin. In 1949, he prevailed upon the Chief of Staff to the Commander in Chief to inaugurate a ten-year program of sound surveillance for ultimate use of the Soviet underwater squadrons. Part of this program called for a continuing report and logging of all foreign and friendly ships, both merchant and naval, relating to their sound characteristics in water. Such an aid as Dedusko now had, therefore, could be attributed to no little forward thinking and imagination on the part of the new generation of naval officers defending the Soviet Bloc.

"Good. Good, Lieutenant Dedusko," I acknowledged, and then added, "Better get acquainted with the sound characteristics of some of the British destroyer classes. We may have some need to identify them shortly. As you know, we shall be passing down the west coast of Norway, and continue southwest past the United Kingdom. The British fleet still conducts some exercises around their islands—and while I'm thinking about it, don't forget we may run headlong into that new American antisubmarine group which I understand is stationed somewhere in the area between Iceland and Norway. That outfit is assigned the specific job of discovering any of us who may be conducting what they call an 'egress' from our Northern and Baltic Fleet bases into the Atlantic."

This last remark sent the sonarmen and Dedusko into uproarious laughter. This was good. Morale was excellent. I left them and proceeded on a tour of the submarine; I wanted to see that everything was battened down for sea and that the ship was in good shape for all eventualities. Walking through the after crew's berthing space,

I observed a group of sailors playing one of the more popular Russian card games. A chess game was also going on in another section of the compartment. One of the players was a young lad with bushy, strawlike hair, whose large blue eyes and friendly smile were to make him a favorite of the commissar as well as some of the other officers as time went on. He was originally designated as special clerk to the Second Officer, but before long, Commissar Lvov requested that he be assigned to him exclusively to help with the manifold political reports and training which the latter had to make. The young lad's name was Alexei Kryzhanovski.

Chief Petty Officer Igor Novikov walked up.

"Good evening, Captain," he said, in the firm tones which showed his self-confidence and that middle-aged matter-of-factness which can come only from having arrived securely at a predetermined goal in life. He was a man who knew submarines; they were his whole life—besides women and vodka when ashore. He enjoyed an outstanding reputation within the Soviet submarine fleet as a top-notch chief petty officer at sea. Unfortunately, he suffered from an unenviable reputation as a man whose proclivity to vices ashore kept him in continual hot water.

"I want to make sure that the boat is ready in all respects for rough seas," I said.

"The boat has been fully checked by me personally," announced this heavy-set human study in contrasts.

"Fine, Chief. I wouldn't want any of the new men to see us go to sea in any but tiptop shape."

"No sir, and tomorrow, I'm starting basic submarine orientation courses for the brand new ones," Novikov volunteered.

"Yes, and I shall make sure you are well supported, Chief," I said, adding somewhat thoughtfully, "and not a day shall pass without us going through every conceivable kind of simulated casualty drill for the entire crew."

I moved on back to the engine room. My eyes were be-

ginning to water from the exhaust fumes. Combining with
the smell of lube oil and human bodies confined to warm,
limited spaces, the air seemed rank and oppressive. This,
of course, was typical—and my sensitivity to it would
pass with the next few days. Always, the initial hours inside a submarine underway prove to be somewhat unpleasant. But the human structure is such that it can ac-
custom itself to unusual conditions and even unpleasant
environments. All that is needed is the passage of time.

The first man I saw inside the engine room was a young
diesel engineer, whom the obnoxious fumes had obviously
defeated. He was squatting in a corner, red-rimmed eyes
glistening in an abundance of tears, which were streaming
down his cheeks. In his hands he held a galvanized iron
bucket; the gastronomical upset he was experiencing demanded such a receptacle.

Watching a battery of engine performance dials was the
engineering officer, Makar Rostopchin. Nikolai Volkonski
and he were the only officers from my previous association
in the Mediterranean episode whom I had requested be
assigned to me for this cruise. Rostopchin had done such
an extremely good job with the *W-7*, in keeping her engineering plant in superior material readiness, that I
wanted to have him with me on this longer and perhaps
more important voyage. I had seen to it that for his outstanding performance in the *W-7*, he was given appropriate recognition. This took the forms of promotion to
lieutenant commander, and award of a fleet citation
signed by Admiral Gorshkov himself. (I had been responsible for Volkonski receiving the same honors; my old
Second Officer, Rurik, had been promoted also—to commander—and now had his own W-class submarine in the
Pacific.)

"Makar," I called out, raising my voice high enough to
overcome the resoundingly noisy pulsations and throb-
bings of the engineering plant, "as usual, I will want to
snorkel whenever there is no danger of detection by un-

friendly eyes. Until we move into congested waters, I plan to snorkel in the daytime. Be ready to cease snorkeling at any time when so ordered by the conning station, however. On this first leg of the cruise, feel free to conduct all types of engineering casualty drills, but request my permission before doing so."

Makar Rostopchin touched the visor to his grease-blotched old "steaming" cap. His blue eyes sparkled. He was in his element. He spoke up.

"We're in good shape, Captain. Good shape."

I questioned him. "We've got all our spares and extras in case of breakdowns?"

Rostopchin's smile eased a trifle, and he frowned slightly.

"The supply officer managed to get us more than a full supply of spares in most cases, but Base Supply only had a limited number of engine injectors for us. That's the only item we may be short in."

The chief engineer sensed my concern. His face cleared.

"But don't worry, Captain," he roared, "we're going to take care of this plant just as if it were a newborn baby." He walked over to a centrifugal lube oil pump, threw his head over his shoulder so he could watch me, and then embraced the pump, patting it and stroking it in a histrionic play for laughter.

"Mother love will take care of everything," he yelled, his boisterous voice rising high above the engine-room noise. He was amusing to me sometimes, this half-Jewish descendant of Russian nobility, but more importantly, I valued his engineering skill. Satisfied that his attention to the engineering plant would indeed be not unlike mother love, I turned and left. I moved forward through the crew's spaces, bound for the "officers' country." En route, I engaged in small talk with various enlisted men. Such procedure was habitual with me (but not so with most other captains). I believe a commander can best command who "has his ear to the mess decks," so to speak.

It was close to 2 A.M. when I collapsed into my chair in the wardroom and accepted a cup of hot brandied coffee from the only enlisted man I had sought for this cruise from among the old complement of the *W-7*. Rodion Trubetovski, my old commissary-porter, had been ordered to my continued service at my special request. He had reported aboard with considerable emotion, feeling it one of the greatest possible honors in his life, to have been especially sought after by his former commander and master.

His father having formerly been a butler in the home of one of the Cantacuzene princes, Trubetovski had been well schooled in the traditional relationship between servant and master. The fact was that he enjoyed his role in life, and often said that his father had always regretted the abolition of the old system in Russia. Some of his father's philosophy had filtered down to Rodion. He never tired of repeating it to anyone who would listen—but only when he was sure the commissar wasn't listening. Obviously proud of his family heritage, he would lift his head proudly and say, "If it weren't for the fact that there are men who *have* power and wealth, think how many people working for them would have no jobs!"

Professor Boris Bogucharovo was already seated at the wardroom table. He was pale and perspiring, the little beads of sweat on his forehead now and again mushrooming into droplets which sloshed down his sick-looking face. His bald pate glistened; his large black eyes, scarlet-ringed and watery, gave him a ghoulishly offensive, if not frightening, look. His bulbous, peasant type proboscis, featuring huge, cavernous nostrils from which reeled strands of unusually long black hairs, dominated his countenance. On my entrance, he looked up and said, "If *this* is what the whole trip will be like, I don't think I can make it!"

I restrained my impulse to laugh. It was obvious that the Professor of Agriculture was miserable. Doubtless, this was his first voyage at sea—and if that weren't bad enough, it was in a submarine. Even senior and experienced submariners fell miserable sometimes, especially in the first few days of each cruise. The combination of fumes from battery gassing, cooking, fuel oil, and plain lack of fresh oxygen, is normally sufficient to induce strong headaches in most men; to a man alien to the rolling and pitching of a surfaced boat at sea, the complete combination can be overpowering.

I suggested to him that he might feel better if he went up to the open bridge and got some fresh air. After that, he could go to bed and try to sleep. He needed no further encouragement.

When he had left, I smiled at the other officers present. Baliuk, the intelligence and underwater sound expert, had been talking to another officer whose previous experience had exposed him to cold-war spying against the United States. This was Ivan Nicolai Kulakov, now my operations officer. It may be recalled that he had surveyed Boston Harbor in June 1961 under the pretext of having a back sprain.

To both of them, I voiced my hope that they would find submarine operations on this, their first submarine cruise, to be at least as exciting as had been their previous trawler experiences.

"We are glad to have such experts in American harbor intelligence with us," I said rather jokingly to them.

My remarks seemed to embarass them both, so I decided to pass on to them some of my more definite and sincere thoughts.

"The Soviet Union," I observed, "owes a debt of gratitude to the trawler navy. They are the unsung heroes. You who were on board such ships know what I mean."

Kulakov blushed. I had previously heard that he was an extremely ambitious young man, and it was his most prized dream to some day command a Soviet submarine in a move against shipping and the naval shipworks in Boston.

"One day, perhaps I shall not be just another 'unsung hero,' " he bleated.

"I am sure you will not," I replied quickly.

"But what I wanted to say was that without the magnificent efforts of the trawlers, we would probably be as far behind in oceanographic research as is the United States."

Kulakov smirked.

"The United States! The United States! To mention them when we talk about oceanography is most humorous. Did you know that last summer," he continued, with words becoming faster and more mouthed, in his obvious excitement in expressing himself on a matter with which he felt strongly identified, "last summer, yes, right after I returned from that trawler expedition off the Boston area . . ."

"By the way, how were the beans over there?" It was Lieutenant Nesvitski Igorovich Glinka, his white teeth flashing in a broad grin as he stood at the compartment door.

Kulakov gave no indication he had heard anything, and pressed his delivery.

". . . right after I came back from Boston, I was sent to Paris as an aide to the senior Soviet representative at the international oceanography conference. The Americans there . . ."

"I say, Ivan Nicolai, what about the beans? What about the beans?" It was the new officer-artilleryman, again playing the comedian. This time, Kulakov looked up, acknowledging Glinka's presence. He was not easily beaten.

"My dear Nesvitski Igorovich," he intoned, "you may not realize it, but do you know that while you were sampling the boudoirs of the boldest of the hussies, *I* was sampling the future battlegrounds of the boldest of the bold?"

An uproar of laughter made Glinka hesitate. Having

thus gained the initiative, Kulakov hastened on to complete his squelch.

"Beans?" His eyebrows rose as he continued.

"Beans indeed! While I was ashore, I had *other* fare. There's no doubt that you, as a connoisseur, would have appreciated it, too. The nurses in Boston were lovely, simply lovely. As I say, why should a man content himself on *beans* when *meat* is so available?"

This was not the kind of language or humor that I wanted to have in my wardroom, and I was about to censure Kulakov for his lack of propriety when he raised his hand as if to restrain anyone from so admonishing him.

"Let me say that right after I returned from the trawler expedition, I was sent to Paris for the October international oceanography conference. The Americans there were headed by a civilian assistant to the Secretary of the Navy, an amiable academic type who wanted everyone to know that he was above all a man of good will and a scientist. Fortunately for us Russians, his delegation was ineffective. I cannot understand for the life of me why the United States sends such disorganized representation to an international meeting. I don't see how their trip to Paris could have been worthwhile."

Kulakov rolled his eyes suggestively.

"Did the Americans gain anything at all from this conference?" I was intrigued by this accounting of how the Americans had conducted business at so important a gathering.

"Frankly, if it hadn't been for a few of his staff and advisers," said the man who had been there, "I don't think the Americans would have known if we had laid claim to most of the American continental shelf."

"You might have done so, just to see what their reaction would have been," chimed in Glinka. "After all, you could have said that since we were the first nation to *explore* the underseas areas off North America, the geographical areas could *properly* be considered ours."

"The point is," said Kulakov, "the Americans had no firm leadership at that conference. No one to protect the Yankees' basic interests. Except minor advisers, and of course they could only advise. But it was almost unbelievable. Here they were, those Americans, with . . ."

"Let's be glad," I interrupted. I thought the discussion had become repetitious. "Let's be glad *we* have firm leadership when we deal with the complacent representatives of the imperialists."

8

"Who Rules the Heartland . . ."

☐ It was dawn, and the date was January 30, 1962. The oncoming watch officer sent word down to me that the trawlers had now veered off to the northward as planned, leaving us to proceed independently along our predetermined track heading northwest. He requested permission to submerge to snorkel depth within the next fifteen minutes. I was slightly irritated that the watch officer had not merely indicated his immediate intention to submerge, for my night orders had been to submerge for snorkeling at daybreak. However, Lieutenant Dedusko was not a fully qualified submariner and this was his first turn on the bridge as my officer of the watch. With more time and training, I was sure he and the others would grow into a first-rate team who knew just what to do. I gave the necessary permission to the messenger, for relay to the open bridge. Then I went to the control station to watch.

It was shortly after leveling off at the desired depth for snorkeling that I called a meeting of all officers to the wardroom. Lieutenant Commander Lvov seated himself at the opposite end of the table from me; Second Officer Volkonski pulled himself up alongside me and to the right. Makar Rostopchin, still sweaty and grease-splotched, decided to stand against the bulkhead, leaning against the open door frame; navigator Mikhailoff sat to my left, flanked on his own left by Baliuk, Glinka, and my new supply and commissary officer, Lieutenant Georgy Rodzianko—formerly the pay and accounts officer of the cruiser *Kirov*.

Rodzianko, perhaps the youngest of the wardroom officers, had already been taken in tow by Volkonski. The latter, now that he was number two man, and as such traditionally responsible for internal administration of the submarine, had told the fledgling commissary officer that he, Volkonski, would prepare the menus for all meals. Volkonski, as may be recalled, was not only a glutton, but in truth a gourmet of exquisite refinement in taste when it came to culinary preparations.

"Gentlemen," I began, "this morning, we are at last independent of all outside friendly contacts—at least, for the time being. Before midnight tonight, we will have passed North Cape to the south, but before that time, we will have been exposed to the possibility of detection by Norwegian fishermen. That is why it is important that for our security, the watch must be alert for contacts from now on. At about evening twilight tonight, we will rendezvous with a squadron of trawlers which will then escort us around the northern coast of Norway and then southwest to a point northward of the Shetland Islands, where they will leave us. After that, we will be by ourselves again for good. We should be at Point 'C,' where I will open our sealed orders, around noontime on February 6. As you know, Point 'C' is roughly 190 miles northwest of Londonderry, Ireland. I have not the slightest idea what is in those sealed orders, so that I am afraid I cannot even hint at what we may expect."

There was an audible sigh and some shuffling of feet.

"As you all know," I continued, "this cruise is one of great national importance, and I expect every man will perform to his utmost to insure our singular success. For such results, we can expect the very highest encomiums to devolve upon us. From my past personal experience, I can tell you that Admiral Gorshkov himself will not be unmindful of your contributions. We shall not even talk of failure in our mission."

I looked searchingly at each officer. I wanted each man to consider himself the personal object of my talk. The eyes of each man, in turn, met mine—and I was satisfied that they understood me.

Looking at Volkonski, I bade the officers commit to memory my special patrol instructions. He, in turn, asked for permission to make a statement, and upon my nod of approval, declared that the chief clerk would provide all officers with copies immediately after the conference. This written document, covering all actions foreseeably applicable to us, was prepared so that there would be no doubt about proper action for watch officers to take in various situations.

"Our mission from now until we join the trawlers at Point 'A,' just this side of North Cape," I said, "will be to remain undetected. I expect that today we will go through all major drills. The Second Officer has prepared a list of those drills and will disclose them in a moment."

Volkonski shifted his weight from one buttock to the other, and reached into a pocket for his memo book. This he carefully paged until he came to the place holding his list. Expectantly, he leaned forward, waiting for me to give him the floor. But I wasn't yet ready. I wanted to emphasize the movement southward with the trawlers.

"Please do not forget that this escort by trawlers," I warned, "is designed to determine the feasibility—rather, the advisability—of joining submarines to trawler squadrons for all operations in alien waters. We are to decide the practicability of mutual support in joint operations. The stage that is set for us will be one in which we will cruise together into heavily traversed enemy waters. We can expect to meet enemy warships, even antisubmarine groups. They will cast a most suspicious eye in our direction. Our job will be to avoid detection at all costs. We may expect the trawlers to assist us if necessary by resorting to diversionary tactics, slowing down or stopping, for instance, and moving about to stir up the water—if we are actually closely investigated by antisubmarine forces."

Volkonski cleared his throat. It was his way of letting

me know, in case I had forgotten, that he was ready to give his list of daily drills. Still, I was not yet ready to turn the conference over to him. There was one more thing I wanted to discuss. That had to do with the meals.

"Effective today, we will commence our regular cruising hours. This shift will mean that during daylight, most of the crew will be in their bunks. This will be best for morale as well as for health."

I stopped and looked at the several astonished faces, then continued, "Since we will normally be snorkeling at night, or cruising on the surface for short periods if opportunity permits, it will only be during such operations that we can get fresh air into the boat. This will be the best time for the crew to be up and about. It will give us more oxygen for our comfort and health during our expected long periods of submerged cruising on the batteries in daylight.

"This routine will require that we also shift our meal hours radically. Henceforth, our big meal of the day will be at nighttime—thirty minutes before the midwatch is posted, at 11:15 P.M. Breakfast will be at 7:15 P.M., and of course the final meal before most of the crew turns into their bunks will be at seven-fifteen in the morning. For those up and about during daylight hours, we will have snacks available, with soup, at 11:15 A.M."

Commissary Lieutenant Rodzianko looked stupefied. He had never heard of such a sweeping change in living habits, and was not so sure that it was "legal." This thought apparently struck him a rather hard blow, for he raised his hand as a schoolboy does who seeks recognition of his teacher. To my nod, he exclaimed, "But sir, the Rules for the Conduct of the Navy Afloat say specifically that forces afloat will, except under extreme circumstances, conduct messing at such times that the crew will find transition easiest from life ashore to life at sea, and the Rules suggest breakfast at 6 A.M., dinner at 11 A.M., and supper at 7 P.M. Of course, if your desire is an order . . ."

Volkonski spoke up. He was irritated that this young-ster would bring up the matter.

"This," snorted the Second Officer, "is not the cruiser *Kirov*, Lieutenant Rodzianko."

And that ended the commissary lieutenant's inquiries.

"But we will have one thing that they get on board the cruisers," I quickly added, watching a slight smile force it-self across Georgy Rodzianko's mouth, "and that is freshly baked bread. Let us have fresh bread for breakfast tonight!"

I turned to Volkonski with uplifted palms. He accepted the motion for what it was worth, and donated his piece. His little eyes sweeping the table, he again cleared his throat and waded into his subject.

"As the captain has said, we will have daily drills in all conceivable casualties. Today, commencing at 9 A.M., and thereafter when directed, we will have the following ex-ercises: fire drill in the forward battery room, simulated emergency destruction of secret publications, steering cas-ualty, manual working of the bow and stern planes, loss of auxiliary power, and . . ."

"And by then," I interjected, "it will be nearly noon-time, so that if we are going to shift to our regular cruis-ing schedule, I think we had best defer the rest of the drills until tonight. That will leave the afternoon, at least, for the crew to get some sleep."

To avoid embarrassment to Volkonski, I added, "But the Second Officer and I will stand for nothing less than full and determined participation in these drills. He will see to it that they are conducted, and all due reports made to me."

"There will be one group who will be given an orienta-tion briefing this afternoon, however," Volkonski went on. "That group will be the lookouts for the twilight and early morning watches. Lieutenant Baliuk will provide the instruction, and the subject will be recognition of the types of unfriendly aircraft and surface ships which we may encounter."

Balding, wide-eyed Ivan Baliuk spoke up, perhaps out of place. But then, this was an informal atmosphere, and I actually wanted it that way. Said he:

"With your concurrence, sir, I think it would be profitable for all watch officers to be present for at least the major areas that I will cover."

I saw Glinka roll his eyes. Under the table, he kicked the commissary officer, and then winked. This disturbed me.

"Nevitski Igorovich," I asked, "would you, as officer-artilleryman on board, prefer to give these briefings yourself? Perhaps they more properly belong in your sphere of responsibility . . ."

The Russian Don Juan looked sheepish and colored visibly.

"This business of recognition is no laughing matter; nor is it something we can afford to regard lightly," I continued. "Our mission—or at least part of it—will be to conduct surveillance operations, of that I am sure. You know it. But we will be worthless unless we can identify what we see. Let none of us see alien craft, and not be able to identify it as to type or class."

Nikolai Volkonski spoke up thoughtfully.

"Let me remind you all," he boomed, "that even the Germans, who always style themselves as so efficient, lost a great engagement in World War II because their lookouts and their watch officers couldn't tell the difference between British destroyers and cruisers at long range."

"The *Graf Spee* fight with the three English cruisers!" It was Rostopchin, who had been lounging against the bulkhead, and who now sought to enter the conversation.

"That," said Volkonski, "was inexcusable, for the German ship was needlessly committed to battle, and through error in contact evaluation!"

Makar Rostopchin pushed his "steamer" to the back side of his head and then reached into his shirt pocket, drawing forth his heavily ornamented silver snuff box. Opening it, he raised it to his nostrils and took a whiff.

"AhhhhhHHHH-CHEEW!"

The silver box was closed and returned to Makar's shirt pocket. Volkonski, who never had really approved of this habit, which he regarded as wholly unnecessary, focused his beady eyes at Rostopchin. The object of such a withering gaze merely closed his eyes.

There was one more item I wanted to talk about, and I now brought it up.

"Just before we left port," I confided, "I read an article in a British newspaper which had been flown to Naval Headquarters. The British were playing up the counting of over three hundred of our trawlers in the waters around the Shetland Islands. This article said that more than forty Soviet trawlers were taking shelter in the lee of the Muckle Skerry—wherever that is—and that they were recovering from a fierce storm. The important thing is that all those trawlers are being kept under sharp vigil by the British. They seem to think, and of course rightly so, that these ships of ours are spying on them to find out how much progress they are making in antisubmarine measures. We know the British are experimenting with detection devices in the area, and that their ships signal results of their tests to the shore stations nearby. That's where some of our trawlers come in. They are intercepting these messages, so that we can find out what the British are up to. Of course, what they don't know is that our ships are not only doing this, *and* catching fish, but some of them are laying special devices to negate the effectiveness of their surveillance equipment. You know, in case of war . . . I'm sorry, but I can't tell you anything more about this, because it's very sensitive information."

The commissar, who until now had been silent, leaned forward and, pounding the table, attracted attention to himself.

"We have the most powerful navy in the world," he told

the eager ears that reveled in hearing such optimistic news, "and every day we grow stronger. When our trawlers get through, what with their hydrographic and other oceanographic work, the American Polaris submarines will be viewable no matter *where* they may be," he said in confident tones.

"If I may say a word or so more," asked the commissar, and upon my nodding acquiescence, he enthusiastically continued, "Do you all know that the Western nations of the capitalists cannot—I repeat—*cannot* survive more than just a few months without using the sea lanes for the transport of vital materials and supplies? They have an actual 'lifeline' of more than sixty thousand miles of oceanic routes. It is a fact," he now lowered his voice to give the effect of a secret disclosure, "that over 90 per cent of all strategic materials used by the capitalist nations in war must be transported by sea!"

Rodzianko looked at the commissar in disbelief. He could not understand what Lvov was saying. After all, Soviet Russia did not depend this heavily on the sea. Why, therefore, did the nations of the West?

The commissar looked around the wardroom. He spotted the commissary officer's mystic look, frozen in doubt. He pursued his offensive with facts.

"For your information, gentlemen, the Soviet Union is a land mass almost unique in that within our borders or land adjacent thereto, we have practically everything we need for our own survival. We have been referred to as the great European Heartland, and a foreigner has told the world that 'who rules the Heartland rules the world.' Let us face facts, gentlemen . . . we are unique in this respect. We are truly quite independent. It is our good fortune that the United States of America is *not*. They will always have to depend upon sea transportation for their very life in peace or war—and that is where the great Soviet Navy will hold the keys to the world's future."

It was I who now put the teeth in what Commissar Lvov had been saying to my officers.

"You and I and all submariners will in wartime have the responsibility of seeing to it that America cannot use the seas. We must—and of course, we will—see to it that she chokes to death. It will be economic strangulation. A war at sea. Not necessarily a nuclear war against the big metropolitan complexes. But a war of steady and deadly attrition of the Western Alliance's merchant marine. And then where will they be? They will be crawling to us for mercy and for terms."

"But," interjected the commissar, "if it is to be a nuclear war, we are ready. The ocean survey ships and the trawlers have already paved the way for our own missile-launching submarines."

And so the discussion went. It was typical of the daily wardroom sessions over which I presided, together with the commissar, in an effort to properly and most thoroughly indoctrinate all officers with Soviet naval and political thinking. Each day, Lvov would also talk formally to the crew in its mess, telling them what the Party line was on practically all matters, even involving life itself.

At about two o'clock in the afternoon on January 30, the watch officer called me to the conning station and asked me to look through the periscope. Sonar had picked up the light, fast propeller noises of a contact they classified as probable warship, and the watch officer had trained the periscope around on the appropriate bearing. What he saw gave him a thrill—and he had wanted me to share that thrill with him. So I took a look.

Through the cross hairs of the periscope I viewed a fast, onrushing destroyer. She was sleek and powerful-looking, with two large tripod masts and short, low-slung funnels. Her bow appeared to literally tear the water apart with a tremendous white surge of foamy brine. I recognized her immediately as one of our own *Kotlin* class destroyers— one of more than two dozen of this type now spearheading

Soviet antiair and antisubmarine shipbuilding programs in destroyers. I congratulated ourselves for having such modern, speedy ships. And I could not help but think that the destroyer I was watching was faster, more powerful, and more sleek than America's new oversized light cruisers which they are calling "destroyers."

I faced the watch officer. It was Dedusko again.

"Lieutenant," I said, "too bad you aren't rigged to take a photograph of her as she goes by."

Then I went aft to check the engineering spaces and to see whether any additional personnel were feeling sick. Before I had completed my tour of those spaces, however, I received word from the watch officer that they had picked up another *Kotlin* class destroyer, which appeared to be follow ng the first. Both were headed eastward, and they no doubt were returning to port. This second destroyer, according to Lieutenant Dedusko, would be duly recorded by periscope photograph as she came by the closest point of approach. I was delighted with the watch officer's action. His acuity pleased me. It omened well for the future, I thought.

At exactly 8:05 P.M. we rendezvoused with eight Soviet trawlers. The join-up completed, we headed west-southwest, now moving from the Barents to the Norwegian Sea.

9

From Wireless, Food for Thought

☐ On joining up with the trawlers, I had sent out by wireless on our whip-antenna a message to the escort leader. The message was, I thought, particularly appropriate for the occasion: "Westward Ho!" This was really Glinka's contribution. He had offered it while we were in the wardroom earlier that day, as a possible smile-catcher. Most of the officers present, although tired, readily responded to his offering of wit.

From the leading trawler, a ship named *Dobrinya*, came the reply: "On against the foe."

It was obvious that the officer in command of these trawlers was in no mood for humor; the response he gave was decidedly belligerent and determined—which actually could be expected of a dedicated Soviet naval officer. For there is little amusement in Russian military minds concerning the current cold war. The fact that Soviet Russia is committed to world conquest by every conceivable means, inclusive of war of any magnitude, is sufficient and compelling enough for Soviet naval and military men to view their job most seriously; after the reply from the trawler, I had misgivings about whether I had been too light and airy about the whole business. Perhaps I should have offered a toast to the final victory of the Cause. I'm glad now that I didn't. But at the time, I brooded about it. I didn't want anyone to consider me facetious about anything as grave as our pressing homeward to the Americans this important spearhead of Communist power.

A day and a half later, we would be heading southwest —straight for the Faeroes and the Shetland Islands, the home waters of the United Kingdom. I remember looking carefully at the navigator's charts and feeling intense satisfaction at my command of this independent unit of Soviet striking power. We would move stealthily but surely against the one-time center of capitalist imperialism. Closer and closer to the island realm which for centuries has dominated and enslaved so many peoples. These were my thoughts. I pictured the Queen of that once-giant Empire, standing as the news pictures so often depicted her, on the balcony at Buckingham Palace, waving to the crowds. For a moment I was unexplainably seized with a small doubt, though. Where I had routinely thought the British people themselves probably were begging for release from their capitalist masters in the famous "Establishment," I now tried to reconcile this supposed desire of the English masses with the strangely incongruous sight of the milling mobs of cheering peasantry who invariably are pictured below the Queen as she stands there on the balcony waving her handkerchief. I didn't understand it. Why would those fools be cheering her? Didn't she represent a decadent and rotten system which the masses resented? How could oppressed people support her? Involuntarily, I shrugged. Those British! How could *anyone* ever understand them?

JANUARY 31, 1962

The afternoon wireless receipts came in while I was taking a nap. Although we were submerged and snorkeling, our wireless antenna had been raised at the properly appointed hour for interception of Soviet naval messages to all our ships in the area. I was particularly interested in the news stories. They were all editorialized versions, to be sure, of news reports from worldwide sources. But they served a vital purpose in getting our people motivated for the great class struggle in which we daily are becoming more deeply involved.

I sat in my stateroom musing over the news stories. The more important ones I remember . . .

There was the one about Alexei Adzhubei, Khrushchev's son-in-law, who is the Soviet's latest propaganda weapon against the capitalist society. The story was datelined *Tuesday* (the day before), and said that Adzhubei had broken bread with President Kennedy in the White House. This was his second visit to the United States, the first one being in the fall of 1961. Tass described the January luncheon in the White House as a definite evidence of America's change of attitude within the past several weeks —and offered the thought that "with Adzhubei in the White House, all's well with the world."

Another news story from Tass concerned the United States nuclear cruiser *Long Beach*, which was then visiting Le Havre, France. The account seemed amusing to me. It went something like this:

"Suddenly into the dreary provincial port of backward France called Le Havre, a nuclear ship has become a reality. For here in this medievally unprogressive French gateway to the sea, amid the mud and sand of the still uncompleted Quai Floride, near the center of the town, a crowd of excited Frenchmen have been appraising the unfamiliar shape of the U.S.S. *Long Beach*, America's belligerent contribution to the world and the first nuclear-powered cruiser in the world, on her first visit to Europe.

" 'Like a python that's swallowed a goat,' as one intimidated French peasant described this mammoth American war machine come to frighten the French masses into backing up American imperialist dreams.

"The interior of this leviathan of atomic horror is like a palace. Perhaps it is only fitting that the capitalist drones who serve in her, who will train to deal death and mutilation to many, are ensconced in palatial living accommodations. They probably require such surroundings in order to forget their criminal mission in life."

The same news story then went on to discuss the British

nuclear project of two submarines abuilding, the French idea for a nuclear-powered oceanographic research ship, a Norwegian plan for construction of a twenty-thousand-ton bulk carrier for ore or wheat (apparently a project being worked on in Sweden), and a sixty-five-thousand-ton Dutch tanker being built in Holland.

Another news item, which I recall reading on the message file at the time, was a translation of an English "intelligence report," which had supposedly been printed in the British newspaper, the London *Daily Express*, on January 30. It went something like this:

"A system of filling stations around the world, at places such as Ascension Island, Gough Island, Masirah, Guam, Christmas Island, Labuan, etc. . . . .

"These filling stations on a chain of islands will be the key to Britain's new defense strategy. It will enable thousands of troops to be brought home from overseas. It will allow troops to fly from Britain to anywhere in the world if trouble brews . . .

"In this way, defense chiefs are confident they will be able to fulfill their military commitments to the Commonwealth."

Then the news account editorialized, saying that at long last, the British economy, hounded as it was by greed and corruption of the privileged classes, was finding it mandatory to remove her imperialist troops from the oppressed parts of the world. Her reliance on airborne "filling stations" and airborne transport of her troops for future action was, according to the Tass editorial write-up, "good news for peoples' armies everywhere. After all," the account read, "with capitalist strength evacuated from the actual scene, it will be hard if not impossible to bring it back in force against a determined opposition from the people."

I thought about this for a while. I was certain that Tass was correct. And, when the airlift failed to bring the troops and supplies needed by these capitalists to defeat the increasingly surging peoples' armies, then what? They would have to fall back upon the traditional carriers—sea transports, in order to bring their strength to bear where Red inroads are made. Tactically, this will be impossible for the Western capitalist allies to do in any future test of strength. The Communist world is prepared to use the great resources at her disposal . . . and the powerful underseas fleets of Soviet Russia, Red China, and lesser peoples' navies will surely block Western use of the seas.

Of especial concern to me was one dispatch saying that the American Navy was considering formation of an Indian Ocean fleet. Apparently, this has stemmed from the British failure to maintain a warship squadron in eastern waters; a gap therefore exists between the American Sixth and Seventh fleets. This, the admirals of the United States would like to have corrected. They would like to have a fleet in those waters so that the U.S. can "show the flag" on what they call "good will" trips to underprivileged ports in the area. This would not be in Russia's best interests, of course, as it would mean the current Soviet effort in this same field would have to be increased. One of the last really beneficial Soviet cruises where Red ships of war made "good will" calls in the East was back in November 1959, when a Soviet cruiser and two destroyers went heavily laden to Indonesia. On board were models of sputniks, luniks, and other Soviet technical gadgetry, all designed to prove to foreigners the great importance of Soviet friendship.

Still another news story was a secret analysis of a then current British article by an English writer, appearing in the Manchester *Guardian*. This article had said that "as generators of influence, strategic air forces are peculiarly useless."

I thought about this for a bit. It seemed true. For I am certain that the strategic bombers of the American cigar-smasher, General LeMay, will never have a chance to deliver their cargoes of death and agony to Soviet Russia. The missiles of which Khrushchev has so often spoken are not believed to be in existence by the Americans, however. Yet I have seen the antimissile complexes in Soviet Russia, and I have seen our capability for handling manned bombers of the famous American Strategic Air Command. I am convinced that the day of effective bombing by manned aircraft, against such a power as Soviet Russia, is gone forever.

The article went on to quote something from this English paper which I thought most thought-provoking.

" 'One of the really disturbing aspects of American defence policy is its tendency to assume that theirs is the classic line of military development and that others must inevitably be following it. They are now prepared to acknowledge that the Russians might be somewhat ahead in certain categories; but they are so big, so wealthy, and so ambitious in their own military development that they cannot believe that anything really fundamental can be going on in the Soviet Union which has not crossed their minds. They appear to dismiss, for example, the possibilities of the vertical take-off transport which might very soon give a nation the ability to put troops on any point it chose on the surface of the earth. Many other possibilities exist which, like the atomic submarine, might confer entirely new or predominant forms of military power.' "

The Tass release on this British news article then went into the secret analysis prepared for Soviet command readership. As best I can recall, it pointed to the fact that the Englishman was certainly correct in his argument that American military planners are loath to give Soviet Russia any credit for new fundamental advances in armaments or weapons technology. It mentioned the fact that although Soviet Russia has long been embarked on hydrofoil design and employment of such vehicles in coastal and now oceanic waters, the United States has equally long looked upon this Soviet interest with a most condescending eye.

Finally, the analysis went on, the United States is following the Soviet lead in hydrofoil development. Luckily for the Soviet Navy submarine fleet, it continued, the American effort is still in low, low gear, and will not be anything to worry about for several years. Big American vested interests are responsible for the failure of the Americans, the commentary said, to get into anything as revolutionary as hydrofoils for antisubmarine purposes. An insight into U. S. Navy reluctance to move ahead vigorously into this field was provided by the word that the American Navy was actually prodded into large-scale experimentation in hydrofoils by the recent American Commerce Department's introduction of a large oceangoing hydrofoil which may be used for trans-Caribbean crossings. However, the Tass editor wrote, the Russian hydrofoil designs and capabilities are far ahead of the Americans. It is our good luck, the analysis said, that the American Navy refuses to face the facts.

On this comforting thought, I folded the news releases back on the clipboard and lay down to catch some sleep before breakfast. It was past midafternoon, and evening twilight was only a couple of hours off.

10

Some Facts about Submarines

☐ Seven o'clock in the evening came around much too soon. It seemed impossible that commissary-porter Trubetovski could already be going around waking the wardroom officers for their first meal of a new working day, but that was what I could hear him doing. I felt exhausted and most unlike moving, much less getting up. My eyes glanced at the bulkhead clock. It was nearly "breakfast" time, all right. I rubbed my eyes and yawned. Still January 31, 1962! What a long day. And it was not yet over. The actual working day would commence directly after eating.

With a massive and determined effort, I rolled over and up. Quickly tucking my shirt in and rearranging my overall appearance, I stepped over to the washbasin and went through my ritual for inducing thorough wakefulness. In a matter of a couple of minutes, I had splashed cold water on my face, dried, brushed my teeth with a peppermint-flavored toothpowder, combed my hair, and patted some lotion on my cheeks. Normally, I would have used the lotion after shaving, but the previous morning's shave would be sufficient for the remainder of the day. Besides, I was considering letting the crew grow beards to help conserve fresh water. If I did that, I would certainly want to set the pace for the men.

At the wardroom table, I was joined by all except Mikhailoff. He was on watch. The economist, Stepan Alexovich Pozdeev, was there but said he wasn't feeling very hungry. As a matter of fact, he looked pale and depressed. It was obvious that the combination of fumes and lack of fresh air had caused him unusual discomfort. But he was bravely trying to join in the wardroom meal hour, which served also as a social break for everyone, and I tried to encourage him.

"Professor Pozdeev, the secret of our success is that we eat well. You look as if you could be one of the most successful economists in the Soviet Union!"

"Certainly in the Submarine Force," interposed Volkonski.

The first course had been served and it was obviously something Volkonski had relished dreaming up. Earlier, he had promised the wardroom that under his personal direction and guidance, the menus would reflect the greatest, loftiest achievements in international cuisine. It was therefore interesting to assess this first meal specifically resulting from his culinary guidance. I looked at Volkonski, the Gourmet's Pride. He was toying with the hot-pitted prunes, each stuffed with a small, oyster-like carp eye; and his teaspoon was busily probing each prune as if the connoisseur himself wanted to personally insure the presence of the seafood delicacy in each prune.

"Tell me, Nikolai," I said, my fork still toying with my own first prune, "when on earth did you manage to get such a delicacy as carp eyes?"

"Only the afternoon of our departure," beamed the Second Officer, obviously feeling a pride-in-accomplishment.

"This course is something I would think my grandfather would have rather relished," volunteered Rostopchin.

"Your grandfather?" It was Bogucharovo, still looking indisposed, with eyes now underscored by dark circles. The agrarian professor, of course, could not have known of Makar Rostopchin's grandfather and his association with the royal court of Nicholas II.

Commissar Lvov, reflecting the Party line that even references to the old regime, made in public, should be curtailed, traumatically severed any possible elucidation.

"Professor Bogucharovo," he cut in, "it is good to see

you up and about. Within a few days, you will feel like an old-timer at sea. Did you sleep well today?"

The large black eyes of the farmer's teacher met the twinkling gaze of the commissar. He could only manage a polite and very fleeting grin.

"Poor chap," said Pozdeev, perhaps trying to concentrate attention elsewhere than on himself, in his misery, "my very good friend and respected associate, Professor Bogucharovo has not only been troubled with the fumes and the rank air, but he has also had a terrible case of collywobbles."

"Collywobbles! Impossible, for he hasn't had this delectable course until now," said Glinka with a flashing grin.

Immediately, the entire wardroom—save for myself and Bogucharovo—was in an uproar of laughter. To a point, it became infectious, for I found myself laughing along with them even though I had no idea what the joke was. Only Bogucharovo sat wooden-faced, no trace of mirth discernible in his rough-forged peasant features. Volkonski bent over and whispered into my right ear, "Remind me later, Captain, to tell you what the joke is really about."

When the uproar had finally subsided, Trubetovski was bringing in the main dish for this, our first evening breakfast. It was smoked salmon on freshly baked bread slices, with poached egg, fried apples, and goat's-milk cheese. On sight of this imposing assemblage of differing foods, Bogucharovo excused himself, and withdrew from the wardroom. Apparently, international cuisine was too great a step for the agrarian to take. Or at least, this is what Volkonski mumbled to me half-defensively as the professor's footsteps faded down the passageway.

Pozdeev, unlike his fellow educator, was more inclined to regard the meal as one of simple economics. This was good food, which in the Soviet Union would be quite expensive. Why not, therefore, take fullest advantage of it? He did. Before I had finished half of what was on my plate,

Trubetovski was serving him another helping of everything. Between mouthfuls, the economist sought information.

"You know, gentlemen," he began, "never having been in one of our submarines before, I am really quite thrilled. Even if my eyes do have a difficult time getting accustomed to all these gases, and even if I *have* gotten a pretty good headache from the lack of fresh air, *still* it is a privilege for me to be here with you. But I had read in *Izvestia* a couple of years ago about a very large Soviet submarine that had big windows in it, with steel shutters protecting those windows when the submarine was underway at high speed. I understand that we use this submarine for underwater research. Could you tell me more about it?"

"Professor Pozdeev," came back my reply, "the submarine you refer to was really not a very large submarine at all, considering our present shipbuilding trends. It is probable that you were reading about an oceangoing patrol-type submarine of the 'W' class, especially converted for scientific research purposes."

The professor's interest was contagious. Two of the officers started to ask questions. They came concurrently with a more pressing interrogation by the professor.

"But another article I read, in a magazine—let me see, I think it was the one called *Union Sovietica*, said this large research-type submarine with its big picture windows was Jules Verne's 'Twenty Thousand Leagues under the Sea' come true! And did not a submarine like this, with scientists sitting at work tables next to the big windows, make a sweeping cruise recently, covering about ten thousand miles?"

"We have made many long voyages under the surface of the seas," intervened the commissar. "These cruises provide us with important military as well as biological data. For instance, not too long ago, one of our modified 'W' class was operating off the South American coast. Actually, it was off Brazil . . ."

"Let me explain," I said, thinking that after all, it was I who had begun to answer the basic question, and as a professional submariner by profession rather than a political officer, I was doubtless better informed than anyone else to give accurate answers.

"Off Brazil, one of our research submarines was recently highly successful in charting areas where water temperatures differ drastically from surface to ocean bottom. This information is of great military value. As you may know, underwater sound waves—that is, sonar waves—which are used to detect submarines, are bounced back or bent when they pierce a level of warm water and strike a layer of cold water beneath. All a submarine has to do is to find an area where the underwater temperatures vary sharply, and then just dive beneath this cold layer, in order to avoid detection.

"The importance of finding such areas off the South American coast is evident when one considers that submarine action against shipping in that quarter of the world would be a necessity if a general war breaks out against the West. Also, our submarines may even find it advantageous to bombard some South American countries with missiles, if a general war came. And, of course, it is useful in landing guerrilla forces of the peoples' liberation movements there. In any event, we will be prepared in advance. Our submarines will be well placed and we will know where they can best hide.

"From your point of view as an economist," I continued, "it is particularly interesting to note that with the world exploding with such a mushrooming growth in population, finding food to feed everyone is going to be a major task. More and more, nations will have to turn to the sea for sustenance. Plant life as well as fish from the sea will become increasingly important as staples for mankind. Thus far, man has tapped only a small fraction of the resources of the oceans. We are at the beginning of a new era in science, wherein we must exploit the seas for everything available to us. It follows that the nation which leads in underwater technology, in underwater fish-farming, in scientific methods for cultivation and harvesting of marine life suitable to the nourishment of mankind, this nation, Professor, will inevitably move to the forefront in world dominion."

"And we are way ahead now!" It was the commissar again.

"Yes, we are far, far ahead of the United States—and they are the only ones even capable of competing with us at present in this race. With the help of such submarine laboratories as the one you have mentioned," I went on, "men of science will be able to understand the phenomena linked to fish life. We will be able to find the most natural fishing methods."

Volkonski, ever mindful of epicurean delights, ventured forth. "Perhaps ultimately, we shall know the main whereabouts of the sturgeon. Now *that* really intrigues me. Do you know that the sturgeon population appears to be either dying off or moving somewhere, somewhere we don't know about? This is critical. If we can't find out what's happening, there won't be any more caviar!" That said, Nikolai Volkonski looked depressed.

"But we'll always have carp eyes," sighed Glinka, his own eyes rolling pitifully.

"In any event, Professor," I hastened to continue, "the type of submarine which we use today for underwater research is the same basic type which I commanded in the Mediterranean Sea a few years ago. They definitely are not what one would classify as really large. Just medium. Our long-range 'Z' class submarines, and this type in which you now cruise—the 'F' class—constitute most of our large diesel-driven oceangoing types. Some are oilers, some are guided missile carriers. Most all can be used as mine-layers. This one of ours is an offensive or attack type armed with torpedoes. We have diesel-electric, missile-firing submarines, too, of the 'G' class. These are the ones which will threaten American coastal cities if hostilities develop. Our last word in submarine development, of course, is the nuclear-powered submarine. Many of these are equipped to launch powerful missile attacks. And I may say, proudly too, that these submarines—high-speed, deep-diving, and deadly—are the finest in the world. The Soviet Navy of the future will depend almost entirely on its submarine force for combatant offensive operations."

"How many submarines do we have now?" The professor of economics was entranced.

"In view of constantly shifting operational requirements, that is difficult to say," broke in the commissar. "But we can count on about four hundred effective subs. More than half of these are capable of conducting patrols in American waters, or operating in Allied waters against merchant or naval shipping. There's no doubt about it, we'll rule the seas—all seven of them—in the near future!"

"In the near *future*?" It was Commissar Lvov's voice, and it had taken on a quizzical tone. I got the message.

"Actually," my own tone became positive, decisive, "we have already challenged the United States on the high seas, and they have had the trident wrested from their grip. Our submarines are able to operate under their very noses, right next to their coast, and they have not been able to detect us."

I was talking of specific instances wherein I knew of Soviet boats, commanded in some cases by personal friends, which had indeed moved into the waters over the North American continental shelf. Their missions had varied from antisubmarine intelligence probing to navigational updating of our charts. And, of course, there were always the scientific research subs, such as the *Severyanya* and *Slavyanka*.

Volkonski looked at his watch, then exclaimed, "Captain, our first scheduled drill today is due to commence in ten minutes. I want to run an exercise at battle stations."

The time had passed by quickly. Nearly everyone had

finished breakfast for some while and had merely been
sitting there listening to the conversation. With a nod and
a hand gesticulation, I signaled that everyone was excused.
Then, turning around to Second Officer Volkonski, I
asked what he had meant by the promise to tell me what
the earlier laughter had been about concerning Professor
Bogucharovo's "collywobbles."

My reminder sent Volkonski off into another fit of near-
hysterical laughter. Tears flooded his eyes as each time he
started to talk, emotional instability would overcome
him and, vibrating from wholly uncontrollable laughter,
he would just shake his massive head apologetically and
with a pleading gesture of his hand try to start his story
over again. Finally, between gasps of hard-to-control eruptions of laughter, he managed to paint the picture.

Professor Boris Bogucharovo, after his first two meals
on board the boat, had gone to the pharmacist's locker
and asked the medical corpsman for something to ease
his stomach cramps. He complained of constipation. Lieutenant Glinka had overheard his request and had decided
to have some fun at the expense of the hapless agrarian expert. Walking up to Bogucharovo, Glinka had courteously offered to demonstrate to his victim how the toilet
facilities worked in a submarine.

Confiding to the big, heavy-set man that it would be
necessary for him to be fully checked out in toilet operation before he utilized such facilities, the fun-loving Glinka
led the unsuspecting professor to the compact, closed-
closet type of accommodation serving the officers' needs. It
was located in the forward section of the wardroom country. Glinka reached out and grabbed the indented latch to
the compartment door. Twisting it, he pulled the narrow
door open. What Professor Bogucharovo's black eyes saw
was an unimpressive, cold, metallic-looking functional
throne, surrounded by a maze of valves, levers, and piping.

"Notice all the valves, Professor?"

"What else besides the damned toilet stool is there to look at?"

"Well, Professor, you will have to know how to manipulate some of these valves."

The professor surveyed the various connecting links in the plumbing, and sighed.

"To think it would require an engineering mind just to relieve one's self in a submarine," he half-whispered to himself.

Glinka heard him and was spurred on.

"Well, now, it's really not *too* complicated, sir. But you must remember that one little mistake could be disastrous."

The professor's already wide eyes widened some more.

"Yes sir," Glinka went on, "on board every submarine, there are at least two valves for almost every system. This is particularly true of our many systems which are subjected to pressure. In case one valve fails or leaks, there is a standby or inner valve to prevent further damage within the submarine. Systems exposed to sea pressure are particularly vulnerable, since for every one hundred feet of depth, we have an equivalent of about forty-four pounds per square inch."

Glinka looked closely at the professor. It was obvious he was not following the line of thought.

"Yes, yes, my dear lieutenant, but to the point, to the point. I may have to use this contraption at any minute. At any minute, do you understand? Don't forget, I have just taken a cathartic! I *must* know the *facts!* Not the theory, but the *facts!* When I get in here, what the hell do I have to do?"

"Well, I'm getting to it, Professor. But I did want you to know that a mis-move on your part could, well, maybe it could sink the ship!"

Bogucharovo pulled out a handkerchief and started mopping his forehead.

"My God!"

"What did you say, Professor?"

"I said, well, I was just exclaiming . . . why? You don't mean . . . well, I didn't mean it that way, because obviously there *is* no God. So don't get any funny ideas about my beliefs. I am a stanch believer in the Marxist theory."

"Professor," cooed Glinka, enjoying every moment of the big man's discomfiture, "I would *never* deign to question your ideological beliefs. Of course," he went on, raising his eyebrows and pretending great concern for poor Bogucharovo, "I can't say what the commissar will say or do when or if he hears of this . . ."

The already uncomfortable and now half-distraught professor of agriculture looked pleadingly at the serious-looking Glinka, who was having a most difficult time restraining himself from laughing and giving the whole little joke away.

"But don't worry," Glinka's voice was now confidential, "I don't think anyone else overheard you, and you may count on me, I shall never tell a soul!"

Bogucharovo's tension-lined face could be seen to visibly relax. But his mind returned to the basic problem at hand. How to use the toilet.

"Please, Lieutenant," he asked beseechingly, "get to the point now on this contraption. The medical corpsman told me I wouldn't have long to wait, the dose he gave me was so big, and . . ."

"I understand the problem," interrupted Glinka, much entertained by his own understatement of the case. Then he continued his indoctrination of the Moscow professor.

"You see, sir, it is really mandatory that we have so many valves. If there were only a single one for each system, and it should fail, do you know what might happen?"

"Yes, yes, you've already said it could be disastrous and that I might sink the ship if I didn't know what to do . . ."

"That is correct, sir. You could flood the entire submarine."

"Well, quick, quick, tell me exactly what I *should* do!!"

"All right, sir, now take this 1½-inch pipe you see here. It is connected to the back side of the toilet, and it extends out through the pressure hull, to the sea. Note it has two valves. When the two valves are open, sea water rushes in and flushes the waste in the toilet bowl down into the sanitary tank below. This is providing that you at the same time throw open the flapper valve operated by *this* lever here . . . no, no, over here, Professor. This lever here. See? This one over here on the left. That's it! Well, now, that's all there is to it."

The professor wasn't sure he understood, and at his request, Glinka delightedly retold him the procedure for flushing the toilet, emphasizing that the professor must forcefully throw the flapper valve lever at the right moment.

"Just be sure to reverse the procedure and close all valves securely when you are finished with everything," Glinka warned.

"Well, I think I understand the problem now," said the professor, regaining his composure for the moment, at least.

"Perhaps," said Glinka as an afterthought, but himself knowingly providing the next tidbit of information, "perhaps you ought to know that if there is a slight amount of air in the sanitary tank, which was not vented off after blowing the tank dry, and you then pull open the flapper lever, the results would be horrible."

"Horrible?" The professor stood there, gaping at the toilet, the piping, and the valves.

"Yes sir. It would be a terrible experience. Ghastly."

Glinka made himself shake for a moment in feigned revulsion. The effect on Bogucharovo was predictable. His black, red-rimmed eyes again widened.

"What would happen, what would happen?"

Glinka shook his head sympathetically.

"Professor, *if that ever happened,* everything would blow back with violent force, right into your face!"

Glinka enjoyed watching the expression on the face of the now fully intimidated agrarian instructor. And now, he took steps to insure the complete success of his plan.

"Professor, I think perhaps the best thing for you to do is to come running to me first, just as soon as you have to go this time. Then I will check the valves out for you before you go in, and if you just do as I said and remember to pull that lever when you get up, you ought to be all right. But one more word of caution. When you pull the lever, look right into the toilet bowl to try and notice if anything seems to be going wrong. You know, like escaping air."

The stage was now set, but the unsuspecting professor felt comfortably assured that all would be well with the world. He asked Glinka where he would be when he needed him, and the lieutenant obligingly said he would be in the wardroom looking at the daily news bulletins.

A half hour later, Bogucharovo could be heard yelling, "Lieutenant Glinka, Lieutenant Glinka!" and a few seconds later, the portly professor came bouncing into the wardroom, much excited. "Lieutenant Glinka, now is the time. Quick!"

It was obvious he was anxious and quite concerned.

Glinka jumped up, and said loudly, "Follow me, Professor!" as he strode quickly to the forward part of the officers' country. Getting to the toilet space several steps ahead of Bogucharovo, Glinka stood half-blocking the professor's entry while with a quick movement of one hand he turned the air valve slightly, holding it open just long enough to permit a slight pressure to build up in the sanitary tank. Then, with a deft twist, he closed the valve.

As a result, any quick opening of the flapper lever would cause the "reverse flush."

Bogucharovo, standing behind Glinka at the entry to the little space, was now suffering acute discomfort. He was standing first on one leg and then the other in his desperate effort to control himself.

"Quick, quick, I've got to get in there," exclaimed the anxious professor, who was now throwing off his suspenders and unbuttoning his pants.

"What*ever* you do, now, Professor, don't forget what I told you," said Glinka, quickly stepping aside now so that the big man could arrive at his goal.

The door banged shut and Glinka stood facing most of the wardroom officers, whom he had forewarned not to miss being present for the occasion.

A few minutes passed. All eyes were trained on the door beyond which Professor Bogucharovo sat in solitary splendor amidst his unfamiliar valves, levers, and piping fixtures. At length, a contented sigh was heard to come from behind the door, and the suspense of the audience outside heightened perceptibly. Glinka rubbed his hands in playful glee.

Suddenly, there was a loud hissing, then a resoundingly explosive noise punctuated by reverberations of water and air engulfing the interior of the professor's little world. There was a loud shuffle, too, and it sounded exactly like the reflex motion of a heavy man falling back against the side of the door. It occurred simultaneously with an audible grunt and was followed immediately by a loud shout of horror and revulsion. Then came a wailing groan.

Glinka's eyes were sparkling. His, above all others, was the most delighted and satisfied of grins. He walked a couple of steps over to the door of the compartment and, with a wink at his audience, opened the door.

"Professor!" Glinka managed a tone of shock.

The sight confronting the peering eyes of the wardroom

officers who had come to witness the spectacle was every bit the show they had anticipated. Standing dejected and besplotched before them was the inconceivably revolting image of a man who had met disaster and knew it.

It was some moments before the professor was able to speak and when he did he uttered the pathetic words:

"At least, gentlemen, I didn't sink the ship!"

11

The Devil I Say!!

☐ The following day, we changed course to the south-west, on a course which would take us down the west coast (through well offshore) of Norway, between the Faeroes and the Shetland Islands, down to Point "C," some 190 miles northwest of Londonderry, Ireland. Point "C" was where I would open the sealed red colored envelope, containing the secret instructions pertinent to the remainder of the cruise.

As each day progressed, the tension and anxiety built up markedly. The crew began placing bets on where our orders would take us, what adventures lay ahead, what important mission was to be ours. Conjecture was wild. Perhaps it was wildest in the wardroom, where all the officers—well aware of my previous exploits against the Sixth Fleet—felt reasonably well assured that I had been selected for a mission of supreme importance.

I had decided to institute a beard-growing contest and, to make sure that everyone would have a good growing model to look at, waited until I had let my own face go unshaven for four days before I announced the project. It is perhaps indicative of the tactfulness or perhaps general awe of commanding officers and their prerogatives which brought about not a single word from any officer, during those initial four days, about my failure to shave. All beards, when just starting, have a slovenly looking appearance, and cause the wearer to look most unmilitary.

There were perhaps two officers who were not particularly pleased to get caught in such a contest. One was Second Officer Volkonski, whose flabby jowls seemed to have only a slight tendency to produce whiskers, although he had no difficulty at all in raising a luxuriously huge black handle-bar-type mustache. The other was Commissar Lvov, who was wholly unable to raise any kind of beard or facial growth anywhere. Upon my announcement of the contest at dinner one night, an expression of displeasure was definitely registered on the commissar's face. However, he never said anything about the matter, although a few of the officers occasionally asked him, later on, whether he was still shaving every day and thus using necessary fresh water—which in a submarine is hard sometimes to come by.

Lieutenant Dedusko was doubtless the weirdest-looking of all the officers, once his beard-growing took shape in earnest. He artfully contrived a goatee type of affair which soon earned him the greatly apropos nickname of "The Devil." With his long black sideburns and cultivated Vandyke, he indeed did definitely resemble the cold, scoffing, relentless fiend whom Goethe in *Faust* called Mephistopheles. To the crew, and moreover especially to the electronics personnel on board, Dedusko was actually a devil. He was the type who could dream nothing save electronics, and constantly, his one-track mind invented ways and means to introduce synthetic casualties to the electronics equipment in the submarine. At one point, he went overboard in his peculiar concentration on technical problems which he generated for the electronics crewmen. The situation came to my attention through the chief petty officer, Igor Novikov, who one day while I was sauntering through the boat came up to me and complained that the electronics technicians were irate over the most recent "trick" perpetrated against them by Dedusko.

This officer, according to Novikov, wasn't satisfied that all the electronics equipment was in tiptop working condition. He still wanted to exercise the crew. Thus, he had intentionally placed black tape across four relays in our major communications transmitter. The electronics technicians, called upon by the watch officer that morning to check into the supposed casualty in the wireless transmitting equipment, had worked long and hard in troubleshooting to determine the cause of the failure. Finally, they had discovered the tapes—and had become furious. Feeling it was useless to complain to "The Devil," who they knew had placed the tape there to foul the equipment, they had sought chief Novikov. He in turn had wondered what he could do about it and, finally feeling that it was a matter of morale of the technicians, had decided to apprise me of the situation. After all, he reasoned, I was the officer responsible for morale of the crew, and furthermore this intentional fouling of the communications equipment might endanger our mission.

I thanked the chief but told him that Lieutenant Dedusko was a brilliant electronics expert whose training program for his men had previously been generally approved by the Second Officer and myself. But, I added, I would see to it that the technicians would have no such further cause for irritation.

"Go tell them I was happy to see that they managed to solve the problem as expeditiously as they did," I ordered the chief. "And while you're at it, tell the men who worked on the equipment in question that they did such a fine job that I want each of them to have an extra-large choice steak for dinner tonight."

I thus succeeded in averting an unhappy ending to this particular problem. But I then called Dedusko into my cabin and upbraided him for playing games with the crew. That type of thing, I warned him, was not proper when I was sure the technicians realized fully their responsibilities in maintaining the electronics equipment in peak performance condition. Dedusko seemed a little hurt. He looked crestfallen as he sat listening to me reprimand him, and as he listened, his right hand toyed with the handle of a screwdriver which he was carrying with a few other electronics tools in a holster-like scabbard attached to his belt.

"Lieutenant Dedusko," I said, terminating my session with him, "one other thing. You are an officer in the Soviet Navy, and you are not a technician crew member. Your job is to supervise, not to get into the actual tinkering with the electronics equipment. Therefore," and I now glanced at his imposing array of tools, "it will be quite unnecessary for you to continue arming yourself with the accessories of electronics crewmen!"

Dedusko's mouth dropped. His face colored. I was knocking out the bottom from his narrowly oriented world of electrons, resistors, capacitors, and circuitry. With *him,* using the screwdriver on complicated electronics equipment was more than just his conception of his job; it was his whole life. It was all he could ever usually talk about. But I could not allow him to further demoralize the technicians upon whom I relied so heavily.

Finally, in an effort to utilize his talents to the maximum, I said, thoughtfully, that he might do well to think up new ways for electronics detection of underwater craft. By such positive approaches, I told him, he might contribute most to the Soviet Navy. Although this advice took some of the brunt off the castigation he had received, Dedusko left my quarters looking very much like a shattered man. His head no longer held high, the goatee now rested on his chest—because for him, the "fun" and joy of his life could only be achieved as stolen fruit.

The two professors declined to join in the beard-cultivation marathon. In the words of Professor Pozdeev, who spoke for both of them, it had taken many years to get mankind to give up beards, and as men of science and as representatives of a forward-looking Soviet economy, they could not in full justice to their concepts of progress become involved in such retrogression. I merely shrugged when Second Officer Volkonski told me, verbatim, of Pozdeev's statement. After all, these gentlemen were guests, and it behooved us to respect their beliefs. Besides, I thought, it would make the commissar feel better to have clean-shaven company with him, in view of his own inadequacy.

Sergei Nikolovich Mikhailoff, the navigator, blossomed forth after a period of time with a magnificent, full-grown, meticulously attended golden beard which reached half-way down his chest. His appearance was striking, and he looked every inch a Scandinavian or northern German freshly stepped out of a time machine from the Middle Ages. However, it was not long before his golden master-piece became slightly besmirched around the mouth. This was brought about by his constant addiction to hot, black coffee, which of course stained the blond whiskers quite appreciably. A wardroom joke was that Sergei had bet-ter desist from using so much vodka in his coffee, as it was certain that the alcoholic effects of the vodka and not the coffee was to blame for such tarnishing of his beard.

Glinka was able to sprout a handsome accumulation of jet black whiskers which he brushed tirelessly, as one might a favorite horse in preparation for a prize showing. Makar Rostopchin, too, grew a large beard which he also was careful to brush several times a day. Knowing his background, I often thought of him in terms of his ances-tors' gracing the royal palaces, huge beards establish-ing their lineage and stamping them as of the upper classes. The other beards were nondescript and mostly unimaginative.

My own beard was—fortunately—a flourishing one. It was streaked with silver, a curious situation because my hair is almost wholly dark brown. However, the silver and brown, I was told, added to the dashing appearance which my blue eyes suggested to the viewer. Rostopchin, scion of nobility and Russian high society in the days of the czars, used to tell me that I looked like his family's por-traits of Russia's last imperial Grand Duke. Grand Duke, I used to chide him, why only the Grand Duke? Well, then, the *Czar,* he would say. This would ostensibly ap-pease my vanity, and I would call to Rodion Trubetovski to bring me another Havana cigar. Fortunately for us, and thanks to Castro, there is no shortage of Havana cigars in Russia.

But it was not as "The Czar" or even as "The Grand Duke" that I became known to the crew. Other than being called The Captain, I had no idea that I was called anything else until one day Volkonski confided to me that I was widely referred to as "The Beard."

Somehow, such an appellation seemed to have unfavorable overtones; it was, I believed, slightly suggestive of something or someone unscrupulous, something fearsome, something awesome, and something unwholesomely dominant or dominating. I loathed the name and what it implied.

12

The Commissar's Little Red Schoolhouse

☐ FEBRUARY 4, 1962

The commissar sat at his usual place at the end of the wardroom table facing me, and began his customary daily indoctrination of the wardroom officers, usually carried out (as the cruise progressed) directly after the 11:15 P.M. meal. This normally resulted in the wardroom officers getting involved in serious discussions shortly after midnight—when, with their after-dinner brandies or choice liqueurs, they could reflect warmly on what the commissar had had to say in sparking off the discussion. This routine is widely carried out in most Soviet submarines, as it affords the officers a pleasant atmosphere in which to consider some of the material the commissar delivers throughout his indoctrinational lectures.

"Today," said Commissar Lvov, "we have just received some news by the wireless which points up our steadily increasing position of power and prestige in the world. In the next decade, certainly within the next fifteen years, most of the world will be under the direct influence of Communism. We will achieve this with or without force."

Lvov was giving the officers the routine dose of homespun propaganda. Now he got into specifics.

"One way the Soviet Union will dominate the globe will be through our exploration and exploitation of the remaining frontiers of the earth. For instance, we have today again reinforced our Arctic Fleet, and starting next spring, we will have five more research stations activated at the North Pole. At present, the two research expeditions we sent to the polar environs in 1960 are providing us with invaluable data and know-how in combating the problems of that region.

"We are primarily interested in controlling a new traffic route linking the Atlantic and Pacific, through the polar regions. Our station at Novosibirskiye Island has accumulated enough noteworthy information as to make control of the traffic routes there inviolately ours within the next seven years. We rely on fifteen automatic radio weather stations on ice floes in the Arctic basin, and have over a hundred polar weather and radio stations on firm moorings which are serviced by our Northern Fleet. What other country has the know-how that we do for true control of shipping in these latitudes? Only Soviet Russia!" The commissar beamed and, taking a quick swig of brandy from his glass, went on.

"While we of the Soviet Union are probing deeper and further into the mysteries of such frontiers as the Arctic and indeed, the oceans of the world and their bottoms, the United States still manages to contribute a little now and then. Today, Tass informs us that the Americans will this year inaugurate a five-day weather forecasting system to reduce shipping hazards. One of two centers operates on the east coast and the other on the west coast of North America. What the Americans plan on doing is plotting best courses for individual ships, so that they will avoid severe storms. We understand that the American centers are located at Norfolk, Virginia, and Alameda, California."

Glinka broke into the commissar's monologue.

"But if the Americans know so much about the weather, then why is it that they didn't know enough not to schedule this first spaceman they have, what's his name, Glenn, on a day when there would be good weather? The news bulletins I read a couple of nights before we left port said that their spaceman—what do they call him?—"

"You mean their astronaut," Lvov said in a superior tone.

"Yes, their astronaut, Colonel Glenn, I think that was his name, he sat on top of his booster rocket for a long time waiting to be blasted off, and he never was, either. All because of bad weather, and wouldn't you think if their weather predictor station on the east coast was any good, they would have known better?"

"That's the point I want to make, Lieutenant Glinka," said Commissar Lvov, looking every bit the wounded instructor, hurt because one of his pupils came up with a question that would have been answered anyway had not the pupil been so impatient. "Our reports have indicated that the Americans erringly planned to launch their first man into orbit on December 20, 1961, January 16, January 23, and January 27 of this year. But the weather was quite unpredictable for them. This means that their technology isn't what it ought to be. Now in *our* case, we have largely solved the weather problem, as you know. From our stations and system, we derive enough information to be able to plan ahead intelligently."

Ivan Baliuk spoke up.

"Commissar," he began, "has there been any further news that we may be unaware of, concerning when exactly the Americans now plan on launching their first man into orbit?"

"No," came back the quick reply, "but we have trawlers and other craft distributed across the expanses of the oceans—including in the Americans' own backyard—to intercept critical scientific data should the launch prove successful enough to get the capsule into space."

"Commissar," asked 'Devil' Dedusko, obviously having previously read the news bulletins of the day as they came in on the communications receiver, "I understand that the British aircraft carrier *Eagle* is now undergoing an intensive investigation to ascertain why or how electrical circuits in the ship's heating and lighting system were cut recently. Was this cable cutting some kind of sabotage for which our boys can claim credit?"

Lieutenant Commander Lvov smiled delightedly.

"Yes, I can now tell you, and with pleasure, without having to worry about undue disclosure of sensitive information, that the work on board the English ship in Devonport was in fact done by our boys. Of course, they were British, but they were oriented to our thinking in the larger scheme of things. And the Queen's detectives will never find out who did it, either. Not out of the thousands of workmen working on the refit job for that ship. No, but what our boys will continue to do will be to harass and hold up the repair and conversion work. With their exchequer in the shape it's in, if we keep up this sort of thing, they'll be bankrupt before long. Their economy really can't stand anything extra, you know."

"And that's where we move in?" Kulakov now talking.

"Not quite. But that's where the average English taxpayer moves in. That's how the regime will ultimately be overthrown, perhaps. Through discontent, inability to meet financial obligations, and all that . . ."

Mikhailoff intervened.

"But this sort of thing involving sabotage to one aircraft carrier seems rather minor in the over-all scheme of things, and I don't think there'll be any huge upheaval as a result," said the navigator with more sarcasm than anything else in his voice.

"Perhaps not. But don't you see," said the commissar, "the damage to the aircraft carrier is but a part of the whole. There are many other, and there will continue to be many other, even more telling blows struck at the British Establishment. The old Empire is no more, and what remains isn't long for this world! Each of these individual blows is nothing in itself, but collectively, they will unseat the capitalist masters!"

The commissar brought his fist down on the wardroom table, causing a thump which nearly upset his nearby glass of brandy. Then he brought up another subject, quite unrelated, but amazed even me by relating the two.

"The United States economy cannot stand an endless drain upon its reserves, isn't that right, Professor Pozdeev?" He didn't wait for an answer, but kept talking.

"Spain is now asking the U. S. Government for a fantastically huge naval buildup, at American expense, in return for the American privilege of maintaining strategic bases in Spain. It has already cost the American taxpayer over one hundred million dollars to buy and outfit the Spaniards with a halfway modern navy. If Franco gets his way, the Americans will pay another three hundred million dollars for the purpose of presenting a guided-missile warship navy to Spain. This will be quite a contribution, and one the United States taxpayers probably don't even know much about."

"You mean," said Volkonski incredulously, "that America is going to give Spain a whole new fleet of brand new warships just to get some missile bases on Spanish soil?"

"Well, bases, anyway, let's not say what *kind* of bases," smiled the commissar.

"Imagine that! How stupid of them," shot in Glinka, who then, suddenly flashing his white teeth in a big smile, said, "For that kind of money the Americans would do better to buy more of their Polaris submarines or maybe even concentrate on how to destroy our submarines!"

Volkonski looked at the clock.

"Well, gentlemen," he roared, "one last sip of your favorite beverage and we're off to our daily drills. By the way, no one has commented on the menu for this evening. Didn't anyone think the food unusually well prepared?"

"Well prepared, yes," offered Glinka, never at a loss for words, "but frankly, much as I enjoy some of your delicacies, I can't say as I enjoyed the tapioca pudding tonight."

Ivan Dedusko's eyes lit up.

"I'll second that, sir," he cried out almost spontaneously.

Volkonski threw up his hands in a defensive gesture.

"Tapioca! Who said anything about tapioca?" His tone of voice was incredulous.

"Well," I said, entering the conversation, "we are all aware of your skill in devising courses, Commander, but it *was* tapioca, wasn't it, that we had for dessert tonight?"

"No, Captain, as a matter of fact, it was not," said the Great Innovator, obviously relishing his role as a meal planner. "What else did it look like, gentlemen?"

"Do you really want to know, sir?" It was Glinka flashing his snow-white grin. Then, shrugging his shoulders, he said, "It was *really* fish eyes and pus, wasn't it?"

I looked quickly at Volkonski. He received the blow with magnificent aplomb.

"No, young man," said he, "but you might regard yourself as close." His eyes shot across the table to meet those of Professor Bogucharovo. "Professor," he continued, "you are a learned scholar of plant life. As such, you no doubt are well acquainted with certain forms of animal life which depend for their sustenance on your agrarian produce. Would you tell the others what type of metamorphosis is involved in the transition from one stage to the pupa or chrysalis stage?"

Bogucharovo knew full well what Volkonski was talking about. He decided to level with his interrogator and the others.

"What you refer to," he said icily, "is that life which is both immature, wingless, and often wormlike in form. It is colorless in most instances, and when cut up into pieces, retains life and forms in a globular shape. I believe what we are discussing are often called larva, or larvae; recent experiments in the biology department at Moscow University indicate that . . . that . . ."

Bogucharovo grimaced, haltingly managing somehow to proceed.

". . . that such form of life is very nutritional to human beings."

Volkonski stood up, smiling broadly.

"Yes, that is correct, Professor," he breathed, "but what else can you tell us?"

The professor sighed heavily.

"Some people," he said, swallowing hard, "call this form of life underdeveloped grubs. Others . . ." He raised his hand to his mouth, and said softly, "—others . . ."

"Yes, yes," interrupted Volkonski impatiently, "tell them!"

Lvov took another quick drink of his brandy, but kept his eyes glued to the professor, as if waiting for his lips to disgorge some kind of resoundingly horrible news. This they did.

The professorial nose twitched, and the lips parted.

"Maggots," he said.

13

The Drama Yet To Be Unfolded

Right after the navigator had given me the morning position report, I had sauntered up to the conning station and glanced down at the track on the chart. Leaning heavily on the chart desk, I studied the area. Trondheim, Kristiansund, Alesund, Bergen—these were the Norwegian seaports whose printed names on the chart seemed to drill themselves into my mind. We had left them all well to the eastward, and were about to transit between the Faeroes and the Shetlands.

"Don't forget," I said, turning around to face the watch officer, "the trawlers which have been with us will shortly depart, and we shall be alone. This places even greater responsibility on the watch to be carefully alert. I trust that all contact reports will be made to me promptly. If in doubt, I want to be called!"

The operations officer, Ivan Nicolai Kulakov, was the man to whom I addressed my remarks. He would be on watch for the next four hours, and it would be—presumably—bright daylight. Of course, at this time of year, there might well be snow or sleet or even rain.

The seas had been getting noticeably rougher, and some of the newer sailors in the crew, as well as our star passengers, Pozdeev and Bogucharovo, had decided they couldn't fight it. Thus, they had elected to withdraw to the confines of their bunks.

At about noontime, the escorting trawlers turned away to the southeast, heading for a point near the Orkneys. We sent them the wireless message, "Good fishing," to which they replied, "Good hunting." With the weather in this area becoming progressively worse, I decided to take a look through the periscope at the departing trawlers and anything else which might be in the vicinity. Intelligence reports coming to us had indicated that the British were getting touchy about all the Russian trawlers apparently congregating in their home waters, and I wanted to spot-check to see if there were any British eyes visible near us. All I saw through the periscope was rough water. Then, since one hundred feet was determined to be best for transiting, I took the boat down to that depth, though giving the watch officer instructions to come up to periscope depth at regular intervals to check everything in the surrounding area.

It was two o'clock in the afternoon when the watch officer called to me and said that he had just spotted a distant patrol aircraft crossing our path, heading in the direction of the trawler fleet which had left us. I ran up to the conning station and spun the periscope around to the approximate location of the aircraft. In a few moments, I could pick him up on the long-range glass. It was a British Shackleton patrol bomber—doubtless one of those they have running routine antisubmarine flights around their island kingdom, now that the power of Soviet underseas craft has been recognized in Great Britain. But in any event, I didn't care to wait around up there for him to spot us. We dived to a safe depth again.

However, within an hour, I received a chilling report from the conning station. It was Baliuk, now on watch. His message was clipped and to the point:

"Captain, are you there? This is watch officer Baliuk. Sighted ship contact bearing 180 degrees true, range three miles, on course 060 degrees true at ten knots. Evaluated as British destroyer type. Believed heading eastward to intercept trawlers."

"Good," I said, with what I am sure was no display of emotion, "they're off on a wild-goose chase."

Inwardly, I was intensely relieved that this combination of destroyer and aircraft had not somehow discovered the *F-689*. We were a big sub, some 1960 tons of steel, forged and molded into one of the most effective fighting instruments ever to ply the seas. With a bow-placed sonar hydrophone featured, the submarine was capable of about fifteen miles' worth of underwater detection capability (much more than most American ships are given credit for having). Under mild sea conditions, visibility through the periscope was attainable to about ten miles; we had approximately twenty conventionally powered torpedoes, which I was always prepared to fire on a moment's notice; we had three propellers, and three diesel engines and electric motors. Our center propeller generally was used for deep escape. The maximum depth to which I should have wanted to venture would have been about seven hundred feet, but this would have been more than enough to escape the then—and I think now—standard antisubmarine torpedoes carried by the United States and Allied navies.

Then, too, we were carrying a load of special electric homing torpedoes. Presumably, these had been provided to us for this cruise in order to secure a much higher capability for effectiveness over a wide range of belligerent actions.

By "breakfast" time, at seven-fifteen in the evening, our snorkeling sub had been pitching and rolling to such an extent, in what were becoming increasingly rough seas, that few officers showed up for anything to eat. Certainly, the two professors never even gave any consideration to getting up; the heaving and rolling boat made their self-imposed confinement to their bunks assured. As if things weren't depressing enough, Rodion Trubetovski tripped or slid in stepping over to the wardroom table, and dropped a large platter of soft Spanish omelet and salt mackerel, hot chocolate, freshly baked popovers and warmed syrup—most of it landing or splashing against Volkonski and Rostopchin.

Dazed, the Second Officer looked ruefully at the mess, and shrugged.

"Let us hope we don't get dashed up onto one of the Hebrides," he said dolefully. Then, he gave orders to cancel the engineering casualty drills we had planned for the ensuing four hours, and told me he intended to let the crew remain in their bunks as idlers until the seas abated. I had no objection. One thing I did not want, above all else, was a submarine full of sick, vomiting sailors.

I now went back up to the conning station, to the navigator's desk, and looked searchingly at the chart. Within the next twenty-four hours we would arrive at Point "C," where I would open up our red-enveloped sealed orders. It was difficult for me to wait. My impatience was getting nearly uncontrollable. Where would we be going? What was our mission?

Sergei Nikolovich Mikhailoff stepped up beside me.

"The coastal shipping would probably be heavier right now if it weren't for the heavy seas," he began. "Do you know, Captain, that those British still operate so much small stuff around these waters that actually, it's not too healthy for us to be coming down on this track . . ."

"Sergei Nikolovich," I remember replying, "you make the mistake of equating all their fishing craft and small coastal vessels with ours. As far as I know, Soviet Russia is the only country of any major importance which outfits not only its naval ships but many oceangoing types in the so-called merchant marine, too, with underwater sound and attack capabilities. I'm sure none of the Englishmen we come up against will have any sonar or depth charges in addition to their trawling nets or cargoes of coal."

Makhailoff raised his eyebrows and colored slightly.

"Captain," he said, "I wasn't referring to their underwater warfare capabilities. I was only thinking of the

movement down this track in the light of all the other ships
at sea in this area at the same time. Navigationally was
what I was concerned about . . ."

"Of course, Sergei, of course. As navigator, that is your
natural prime concern. And I concur. Think of it: Every
single day, there are over three thousand ships at sea every
minute of the day. Right here in the Atlantic sea lanes!"

"Yes sir, and as the commissar says, 99.8 per cent of
all materials must be moved by sea. Not by land or air. By
sea!"

"And our most solemn obligation is to deny the United
States and her allies the use of these seas. One day, perhaps not too far away—"

Mikhailoff's eyes sparkled.

"When that time arrives, let us hope I will have my
own submarine command. That is what I would like!"

"Sergei, I am sure you would do a most efficient job,
too," I said, lightly patting him on the shoulder.

"By the way, Captain," the navigator now said thoughtfully, "do you know, if we proceed the way we are going,
we will be in the commercial shipping lanes for the North
Atlantic runs to and from the Western Hemisphere."

"Yes," I said, "and believe me, there are really some
big ships we might intercept. There is nothing quite so
beautiful as watching a large ocean liner, her decks and
portholes ablaze with light, as she glides silently and ma-
jectically across the seas at night. Sergei, where are the
international shipping tables? You ought to look through
them once we find out where we are going, and then see
what shipping we should be most alert to intercept!"

Mikhailoff reached above the chart desk and pulled
down from one of the overhanging shelves a volume in
which were tabulated the timetables of the major international shipping firms on the North Atlantic runs.

The information which Sergei Nikolovich Mikhailoff
thus made available to us was subsequently used in my
watch instructions for the ensuing several days. It was, as

we shall later see, of considerable value to us in keeping informed about shipping in our immediate vicinity, while not divulging our own presence.

Although laid out in calendar sequence, Mikhailoff's researched listings of at least seven giant ocean liners which would pass through our then general area, bound to or from Europe, promised to be of value quite dependent upon where our secret orders would be taking us.

Perhaps sinking one of these goliaths of the deep would turn out to be our secret orders! After all the thought flashed through my mind, wasn't it known that America was bringing arms and munitions into England, into France and Germany? And why should the Soviet Union allow this buildup in supply to happen—*considering* that the ultimate use of such armaments would obviously be against the Russian people? We would shortly be in the same waters, or pretty close thereto, where the Germans in 1915 had sunk the Cunard liner *Lusitania,* as a result of *that* ship carrying ammunition to England; and weren't we in a war even today? Call it a "cold war" or anything else, it is still a pitting of one national power, one political concept, against another, and the struggle grows more taxing as each day passes.

Wasn't it Von Clausewitz, the famous German General Staff planner and military theoretician, who once wrote that armed hostilities (i.e., war) are a natural resort as an extension of diplomacy when negotiations themselves fail to deliver to the parties concerned their sought-after objectives? Right now, both America and the Soviet Union are desperately trying to outshine the other through every means short of armed hositilies, to achieve their nationalistic aims. Who is to say when one or the other side will believe that diplomacy can achieve no more in a given situation? That such a time could be immediate, or tomorrow, or the next day, or a month from now, is something all of us must consider. After listening to former American Secretary of State Dulles (a man who took the

U.S. to the brink of war all too many times, and who probably never fully realized just how close he came!) preach that America must *defeat* Communism, how could a Russian patriot think otherwise than that the Soviet Union and world Communism *must* ultimately *fight?* For that matter, how can the Americans think *other* than that Soviet Russia and her Communist-bloc nations will ultimately have to come to blows with the West? Hasn't Premier Khrushchev often said that the Soviets will some day "bury" America? And to carry this one step further, perhaps I should metion that the Voroshilov Naval Academy carries as required reading in its course on international relations a "white" paper written over one hundred years ago by the famous American naval officer, Commodore Matthew C. Perry, in which that prophetic gentleman said that he could see in the distance "the giants that are growing up for that fierce and final encounter; in the progress of events, that battle must sooner or later be fought." Commodore Perry was talking about the battle ultimately to be fought by the United States and Russia. The exact wording of his prophecy went something like this:

"It requires no sage to predict events so strongly foreshadowed to us all; still 'Westward' will 'the course of empire take its way.' But the last act of the drama is yet to be unfolded; and notwithstanding the reasoning of political empirics, Westward, Northward, and Southward, to me it seems that the people of America will, in some form or other extend their dominion and their power, until they have brought within their mighty embrace multitudes of the Islands of the great Pacific, and placed the Saxon race upon the eastern shores of Asia. And I think, too, that eastward and southward will her great rival in future aggrandizement [Russia] stretch forth her power to the coasts of China and Siam; and thus the Saxon and the Cossack will meet once more, in strife or in friendship, on another field. Will it be friendship? *I fear not.* The antagonistic exponents of freedom and absolutism must meet at

last, and then will be fought that mighty battle on which
the world will look with breathless interest; for on its issue will depend the freedom or the slavery of the world,—
despotism or rational liberty must be the fate of civilized
man . . ."

Thus, I thought, it might indeed be possible that the top
leaders in the Soviet had specified in my sealed orders
that I sink one, or even a number of large ocean liners or
even tankers, so that the West would have no means left
for ferrying large bodies of troops to a contemplated scene
of action. And if I were to sink one or more such liners,
who would be able to say that it was a Russian submarine
which did the foul deed? There are far too many independent countries today possessing submarines, to be able
to attribute such a belligerent action to *Soviet* submarine
operation! Perhaps this was to be the beginning of a war at
sea, a war of attrition in shipping, a war of starvation. Starvation, that is, for America and her allies. For, I recalled,
America relies entirely upon shipping to bring her the raw
materials and supplies she needs just for her very life in
peacetime—not to mention war.

But of course, I would not know until the following day,
when I opened those sealed orders, what our mission was
to be . . .

14

Sealed Orders—
and Bogucharovo's Own Devices

☐ FEBRUARY 6, 1962

The latitude was 56°30′ north, the longitude 12°30′ west. In a calmer sea and with all wardroom officers as well as our professorial guests present, I tore open the red envelope, rupturing with difficulty the wax seals and then placing the envelope down on the wardroom table before me.

Commissar Lvov leaned forward from the other end of the long rectangular table, expectantly waiting for me to read the MOST SECRET instructions which would disclose our primary mission. All eyes were fixed upon me and upon the thin binder which I now inspected. Lvov had a bottle of vodka on the table in front of him, and took a swig directly from the bottle itself.

"Gentlemen," I began, "at last we are at Point 'C.' I will read our MOST SECRET instructions."

Then, pausing momentarily to scan the material privately so that I could be the first to actually see the orders, I read aloud. The orders were as follows:

HEADQUARTERS NORTHERN FLEET
Kola Inlet
January 25, 1962
To: Commanding Officer, *F-689*
This is my Operation Order RED SAIL NINE.
From Point "C" proceed southward at 6 meters/ second speed of advance, passing through seas westward of the Azores, to Point "D," latitude 29 north, longitude

48-30 west. In this vicinity on February 15 in early morning hours, make rendezvous with Soviet tanker GRODNO, which will be headed for Havana from Vent-spils, Latvia, Soviet Union, at speed of advance of 6.5 meters/second.

Under cover of darkness, refuel and take on fresh provisions if required. Receive six Communist revolutionary workers from tanker, whom you will subsequently off-load by rubber boat (under cover of darkness again) in a cove to be designated by Señor Juan Marcos y Olivié, the leader of the special agents, somewhere along the northwestern coast of the Dominican Republic.

Thence proceed via direct route and Windward Passage, to area off U. S. Naval Base, Guantánamo Bay, Cuba, for general surveillance not to exceed ten days.

Upon departure from Guantánamo Bay proceed via Yucatan Channel to arrive Havana, Cuba, during darkness. You will be advised by February 16 of special instructions pertaining to this visit. Arrangements pending for transfer of Professors Bogucharovo and Pozdeev, and for extended period in port for minor repairs and military liaison conferences with local government.

On completion stay in Havana, proceed at discretion northward along the U.S. east coast for planting of 20 special beacons (instructions enclosed). Rendezvous with USSR trawler fleet in Grand Banks at latitude 45 north, longitude 50 west, for further instructions, if any, prior to return. Reprovision as necessary.

Priority of military missions assigned after disembarkation of revolutionary agents in Dominican Republic:

1. Lay special navigational beacons.
2. Test U. S. antisubmarine defenses and collect intelligence on U. S. fleet equipment and tactics.
3. Obtain photography of significant U. S. combatant ships and strategic coastal areas.
4. Impress Cuban Government with our joint mutual need for them to hasten completion of

submarine bases and ballistic missile complexes
for employment in case of a war with imperialistic
aggrandizers from the north.

Remain undetected at all times. Unless under unusual
circumstances, do not approach U. S. mainland
closer than the three-mile territorial limit. Strike
only if attacked. Return Kola Inlet no later than
May 30, 1962. Amplifying instructions will follow periodically.

(Signed)
CHABANENKO

"That," I said in conclusion, "is what we will be doing!"

Lvov took another drink and passed the bottle down the
table to Volkonski, who had extended his right arm in
anticipation. Professor Bogucharovo was the first to speak.

"Captain, Commander Lvov, gentlemen," he began,
somewhat pompously, "the time has come to tell you precisely what *our* mission is, beyond the sketchy information
that has just been revealed to you. Professor Pozdeev and
I are embarked on a crusade, a veritable crusade. One
that would have made the expeditions of the early Christian knights look pale and insignificant by comparison."

His dark black eyes darted from officer to officer. He
was obviously relishing his role now as orator. At long last,
he had an opportunity to lecture to us. Once more, he was
back in form, with a captive audience. And besides, the
submarine was cruising in mild seas, and the conditions
for human comfort were good—at least for the moment.

"Now that Señor Castro has announced his fullest devotion to the Marxist ideology, Soviet Russia is going to
embrace him to the very fullest. We can ill afford not to
do so. We are going to exploit this Red nest in the Caribbean for every single ruble it's worth. Or maybe I should
say, we are going to exploit this relationship right down
to the last Cuban peso. With our resources, our machinery,
our industrial and engineering know-how, we are

going to bolster Señor Castro's regime until it is a most awesome monument to Communism in the Western Hemisphere. It will be a Cuba fresh from the bonds of corrupt capitalist exploitation, fresh from the bonds and shackles of American dominance, eager to take her place in the vanguard of nations which increasingly will stand to profit from breaking away from North American thralldom. Cuba will henceforth be a nation among nations, the very hub of Communist organization and enterprise in the Western Hemisphere against the Wall Street connivers. Mr. Volkonski, let me have a bit of that French brandy Rodion just brought you. Althought I hate to say it—" (yet it was so obvious he didn't hate to at all) "I regard myself somewhat of a connoisseur, too."

He took a nip; then, raising his left hand to wipe his lips, he continued.

"Professor Pozdeev and I are going to Cuba as Special Advisers to the Cuban Government. As you may know, their farm problems are almost as bad as one would find in the United States. It will be my job to reorganize their farms into collective blocs which will yield massive produce for the betterment of the peoples. And when I have finished there in Cuba, I may be assigned elsewhere, to some other ripe South American country, to deliver it from the chains of economic servitude to the United States and the capitalist interests which have made these countries 'Banana countries.' Professor Pozdeev is going to offer his services as economic brains behind the Castro regime. Together, we will pull up the country by its bootstraps. We will have a strong Red bastion there before long, one which will be so powerful that the more belligerent of the avaricious North Americans would even themselves have to think twice before advocating action under cover of their old Monroe Doctrine in an effort to overthrow Castro."

"Monroe Doctrine?" It was Lvov, sensing that the conversation had developed into one of international politics, which was *his* field.

"Monroe Doctrine!" he repeated. "Let me tell you all that the era of potency for that doctrine has long since gone by the board. The American State Department, I have heard it said, is well-enough saturated with some of our admirers, and is, in fact, so fortunately riddled with what they call real liberals, that any kind of unilateral action by the United States against Castro, or any other South American nation going our way, would be quite unlikely. No, we won't have to worry about the Americans' Monroe Doctrine. The day of presidents like Theodore Roosevelt is over and done with. It would be horrible to think what we would be up against if a man like *that* were in power today!"

Glinka, a grin on his face, interrupted the commissar.

"Theodore Roosevelt!" His voice was incredulous. "But wasn't he the American president who won the Nobel Peace Prize?"

Volkonski joined in, his jowls flapping as he twisted his head quickly to look over at Glinka.

"Peace Prize? Nobel? I don't even think there *was* any Peace Prize back in *those* days! But I always thought Roosevelt was the big cowboy fighter who ran up that fortified hill in Cuba back around 1898! !"

Glinka continued, unabated.

"Yes, he did, but he was also the American president, as I recall, who was the arbitrator for us at the height of our unsuccessful war with Japan back in 1906."

The commissar poured himself a glass of brandy, and Volkonski, noticing it, asked, "Say, don't you think it wiser to stick to vodka?"

"Don't you think you might better stick to your own business?" replied Lvov tartly, as he raised the glass to his lips and downed the brandy. Then, realizing the caustic tone of his reply, he added, pleasantly, "For alcoholic consumption, I am my own best chooser. For superior delicacies on the daily bill of fare, however, I shall ever be in your debt for masterful cuisine!"

The compliment, backhanded or not, was a salve for Volkonski. He loved it. And the look of consternation on his face quickly disappeared.

"What we have to worry about," the comissar went on, "is not the American State Department, for they are now dominated by a new kind of thinking, one which in effect says, 'Go slow, Mr. President, and let's not *exacerbate* the Soviets.' "

"Exacerbate? What does that mean?" It was Volkonski.

"That," responded Lvov, "is an English word, peculiar to our times. It is frequently used by the underlings in the U. S. State Department to indicate their determined desire not to irritate us, not to do anything which we wouldn't like, sort of like appeasing us, in fact."

Glinka now re-entered the conversation.

"But the American presidents don't seem to be soft like that," he said quizzically. "Eisenhower certainly was tough on Communism, and Truman before *him* sent troops into Korea, didn't he? And President Kennedy we must admit is a rabid anti-Communist, a fighter, and a private capitalist to boot. Look how he talks about possibly moving U. S. troops into Laos. That man's no cream puff, no pushover for us. Even their old Vice President under General Eisenhower came over to our country and argued with Premier Khrushchev. Don't you remember?"

The commissar looked at Glinka condescendingly.

"Lieutenant Glinka," he said slowly, "you miss the point. Of course the Chiefs of State are opposed to our inroads. But it is some of their aides who help us. Stop a minute and think! Back in 1961 when the attempt to invade Castro's Cuba was pulled off, why do you suppose the American president didn't use the naval air power available on that carrier they had down off the Bay of Pigs? I'll tell you. He was advised against it by some of these aides! Good thing for us, too, because if those aircraft had been

used, Castro probably wouldn't be in power today . . .
Now my point was that Theodore Roosevelt would never
have listened to some of those advisers whom Kennedy listened to. He would have doubtless wanted to be on the
scene himself, right on that carrier, maybe even in one of
the airplanes . . ."

I listened to this diatribe with reservations. To my
mind, Kennedy was a tough customer; a former combat
naval officer, and one who knew how to fight and whose
war record as a younger man spoke convincingly of his
strong character and will to win. But what the commissar
was saying about some of the American presidential aides
or advisers seemed only too plausible. Not all of them, of
course. But, some of them . . . and not just in Kennedy's administration, either!

Lvov now raised the vodka bottle to his lips, first waving
it freely and with a smile toward Volkonski.

"Well, anyway," Professor Bogucharovo observed, "we
are on our way to the Caribbean! How delightful! And
while I am enjoying the sunshine and basking on the
beaches are the palm trees overhead, you people will still
be sweating along in this thing, down with all the fishes
and the seaweed!"

He sat back in his chair, obviously dreaming of sunshine, sand, and palm trees.

"But Professor," the commissar asked, "how do you
know you won't be out in the cactus wastelands somewhere, with just the arid, sun-baked, sun-scorched, friz-
zling heat and sand and nowhere near the beaches? That
to me sounds more like what you are going to be in for.
Ha!"

And with a derisive slap on the table with his right hand,
he again eyed the vodka bottle. This was much to the enjoyment of the other officers who, looking at Bogucharovo,
burst out laughing.

"One thing, Professor," said Glinka devilishly, "if you
do happen to get lost on some Cuban wasteland, with all

that sand and dry earth and everything, if you get caught with your pants down, let me tell you how best to handle the situation. After all, there might not be any toilet paper there for you!"

"Young man," the professor responded hastily, "let me tell you right now that although I am sure you are an expert in these matters on board a submarine, I would prefer to be left to my own devices when ashore!"

Instantaneous laughter, in which Bogucharovo himself joined heartily, resounded through the officers' country.

15

For Drill: Intercepting a Fast "Carrier"

☐ FEBRUARY 7, 1962

Navigator Sergei Nikolovich Mikhailoff, his blond hair together with his blossoming beard now growing into a true "new look," was working over his chart table at the conning station. The quartermaster of the watch had just taken his evening position report to me, and Sergei had appended a note to the slip, advising that tonight we might well be alerted to encounter our first large ocean liner in a transatlantic run. His research listing designated all the major leviathans of the seas which might normally be expected in the waters around the British Isles during the present two-week period.

I left my berth and went up to join the navigator. I found him poring through the *Soviet Merchant Marine Manual of International Shipping,* a large and comprehensive volume adorned with the photographs and characteristics of all the world's registered merchant ships. As he thumbed through the pages, I caught glimpses of everything from old pre-World War I freighters and colliers (still plying the seas, of course) to the *Queen Mary.* But the glimpses of these were short. Mikhailoff was searching for a specific ship. Finally, he found it.

Turning to me, as I eased up to the chart table, the Teutonic-looking officer smiled and declared that by his best calculations, we might well have a chance to sight the large American passenger liner SS *America* this night. His best figuring put an interception somewhere before midnight.

The *America,* one of the world's most famous Atlantic

Ocean transports, and a luxurious floating palace, would be westward-bound from Bremerhaven, Le Havre, and Southampton. Her destination: New York. This huge 26,000-gross ton ship of the United States Lines would probably be making about thirty knots and, due to her size, would present a large trace on a radarscope. Furthermore, she herself would be using a surface-search radar, and doubtless would be active in sending out wireless messages. Thus she would offer a good target for passive listening by our electronics operators. It would be interesting to alert the watch to this ship, and perhaps, on the basis of our own intelligence, endeavor to make the interception, rather than to leave it to chance. As a matter of fact, this could serve as an excellent war training drill in ferreting out and intercepting an enemy ship of comparable size.

"Sergei," I said, resting my hand on his shoulder, "you have done a good piece of work here. Tell me, what *other* kind of ship, for the purposes of an interception drill, might we assume to have similar size and speed characteristics to this big ocean liner? Eh?"

Mikhailoff's lips parted in a handsome grin.

Glancing quickly at the quartermaster, and winking (which I observed), he went into a bit of histrionic mimicry to answer my question. "Captain," he said, "on what kind of ship would you be most likely to hear something like this . . ."

And, imitating a boatswain's mate piping a short, shrill blast on his sea whistle (bosun's pipe), he sounded off:

"TWWWeeeeeeeeeeWWWWTTTTT! Now hear this! All pilots lay to the ready room for briefing, all pilots lay to the ready room for briefing, on the double, on the double, I say again, all pilots lay to the ready room for briefing!"

Mikhailoff's performance was handled with just the right amount of nasal quality to make it seem identifiable with the sounds a man's voice would make over a public address system. It was a masterful imitation.

"Captain," our newly discovered vaudevillian concluded, "tell us, do you think I answered your question?"

The humor of the reply appealed to me, and I laughed. It never occurred to me at the time that perhaps Mikhailoff's answer was not really in good taste, considering that I was the captain. But, as I have said before, I wanted a "happy" ship, and above all, I wanted true camaraderie in the wardroom.

"Sergei, your comparison of the characteristics of the passenger liner *America* with an aircraft carrier remind me that we should consider ourselves peculiarly fortunate in not having encountered that newly formed American antisubmarine group which has been operating in these waters lately. You know, the ASW outfit that is supposed to block the passage of Soviet subs from the Northern and Baltic Fleet bases?"

"Yes, Captain," the navigator responded, "I know. The carrier they have with them is supposed to be the *Wasp*, isn't it?"

"Don't know for sure, Sergei, it may be the *Essex*."

My information was that the Americans had decided to place a submarine hunter-killer group in the waters between Iceland and Britain. The purpose in peacetime could be considered one of training; in event of sudden hostilities, the forces would already be on the scene and ready for action. Actually, when the Soviet High Command learned of this deployment of American naval strength to these waters, there was mixed feeling. The more belligerent of the hierarchy demanded counteraction, advocating a public show of Soviet submarine strength off New York Harbor. The Chief of Staff to Admiral Chabanenko, as a matter of fact, urged his chief to persuade Premier Khrushchev to let a Soviet wolf pack of submarines put on a target practice demonstration just outside the three-mile limit at New York City, in full view of transiting ocean liners—Preferably the SS *United States* or the *Queen Mary* or *Queen Elizabeth*. The other, and prevailing group, felt that we should bide our time, and with our modern equipment not even worry about the Americans, with their World War II techniques and equpment.

In any event, I felt that this possibility for an interception would be good to capitalize upon. With a messenger sent off to get the Second Officer, I walked over to the watch officer, at the time on the sound-powered interior telephone to the forward torpedo room. It was Kulakov, the operations officer, who was calling to speak to Glinka. Ever alert for all eventualities, the former explorer of Boston Harbor wanted to make sure that our torpedoes were all ready for action.

When he had finished his call, I told him to watch for signs of the huge liner, which I wanted to observe personally at close range. Meanwhile, the navigator had called the electronics officer and advised him of the situation. This subsequently brought Dedusko running up to the electronics spaces, where he quickly inaugurated steps to insure our detection of the *America* at the earliest possible time. One of the things Dedusko did was orient the passive electronics operator to the presumed bearing limits in which we would probably find the liner, together with the presumed frequencies that that ship might be using as it employed its radar and sent its wireless messages.

On my approval, also, the submarine was brought up to such shallow depth that not only the whip and loop-antennas were able to be flipped up for use above the surface, but also, the surface-search radar antenna was raised now for periodic sweeps to try and find the quarry.

At about ten o'clock in the evening, the electronics listening station reported intercepting signals evaluated as possibly those likely to come from the *America*. The frequency of the signals intercepted were identical to those issued by that ship. For confirmation, I ordered the radar antenna raised higher and asked for two full sweeps over a thirty-mile radius. The results were good. A large blotch appeared on the radarscope, about twenty-two miles to the south-southeast. Presently, Lieutenant Ivan Baliuk, in the underwater sound room, came up with a report establishing loud, heavy propeller noises, presumably those of a large, fast ship, coming from the same direction as our directional antenna and radar target.

"That's her, then," I said to the watch officer. "Let's take a good look through the periscope in the right direction. Do this every three minutes from now on."

Navigator Mikhailoff had started plotting the contact on a relative-motion circle sheet. "For best interception, assuming that contact is making thirty knots—"

"Good show, there, Sergei," I exclaimed. "Let's try her at thirty knots and see what course we should come to at best underwater speed to come within a mile of her!"

Mikhailoff's pencil and parallel rulers worked quickly across the paper. Hmmm. He bit his lip.

"What's the matter?"

"Well, Captain, we'll have to change course fifteen degrees to the right . . ."

"Good enough. Make it so," I interrupted.

The watch officer responded with alacrity. Within seconds, the long-range Soviet attack submarine F-689 was shifted to a course at highest underwater speed, in order to make the interception.

There were still about ten miles separating the Soviet and American sailors when I first saw the maze of glittering lights identifying the America through the periscope. Huge ocean liners always are visible from afar, especially at night, when their massive configuration, all ablaze with electric lights, provides a unique relief from an otherwise dark and vacant oceanic scene.

With continued maneuvering, we were able finally to position ourselves such that the great passenger ship did indeed pass across our bow—directly in line with six bristling torpedo tubes—and as a training exercise, I had each officer in turn come up and peer through the periscope at the wonderful sight.

"Think of the champagne that's being guzzled on that tub tonight," I remember Lieutenant Glinka saying with a loud sigh.

"Yes," I told him, "but you know, I think most of them would be switching to whiskey-on-the-rocks if they knew *we* were here, less than a mile away, looking down their throats with six ready-to-go torpedoes pointed at them!"

The navigator smiled.

"Captain," he said, "do you know, I'd bet most of them would rather switch to vodka than face those torpedoes!"

"Yes," the commissar added, as he, the last man to look through the periscope, gave the handle braces over to the watch officer again, "but don't forget—there might still be some who'd stick by their beliefs. There's that crazy group who keep telling people they'd 'rather be dead than Red.' That kind, we've got to liquidate, if for no other reason, just that they would rather have it that way . . ."

16

A Curtain of Repugnance

It was on the early morning watch that we got the message. I was at the conning station, looking again at Mikhailoff's list of large ships which were due to cross our track sometime within the next few days. My eyes scanned the names of these huge vessels.

There was the *Queen Mary,* westward-bound, which probably would pass the track line about the tenth. Then there was the *Sylvania,* also westward-bound, and probably nearest to us on the thirteenth of the month. Other ships I recall were the *Saturnia, Carinthia, Constitution,* and *France.* However, I doubted that we would actually pass close enough, at any given time to see any of these ships.

This was what I was thinking when the operations officer came swiftly up to relay an order from Admiral Gorshkov himself. For we had just received an encrypted message. Decoded, it was unique in its cold, apathetic tone and in the broad scope of possibilities which it opened up to us. So sweeping were its possibilities and ultimate lines of action that I wondered whether there had been an omission or mistake in the transmission or receipt of the message. But my sober consideration of the situation made me realize that the communication was written with a chilling determination.

The dispatch indicated clear-cut determination and concern on the parts of the Communist hierarchy in Moscow. It ordered me to move at best speed into the anticipated oceanic recovery area wherein the American astronaut Glenn would be expected to land; if possible to do so, I was to observe and record pertinent technical data associated with the re-entry and recovery of the capsule; if the opportunity presented itself, I was to utilize whatever means available to me to recover scientific data otherwise exclusively the gain of the United States! Additionally, I was authorized to take such measures as I deemed necessary, to deny to the Americans what telemetry I could without being detected, and to insure my own safety. However, we were to embark on this project only after effecting the previously scheduled rendezvous with the tanker *Grodno*.

I shall never forget the first few words of that urgent message as it appeared on the tape:

MOST SECRET . . . EXTRAORDINARILY IMPORTANT . . . COMMANDING OFFICER F-689 FROM SUPREME NAVAL HEADQUARTERS . . . UPON COMPLETION YOUR RENDEZVOUS WITH GRODNO PROCEED BEST SPEED TO EXPECTED RE-ENTRY AREA U. S. ORBITAL FLIGHT OF MANNED CAPSULE . . .

And then, in detail, the message told me my job:

YOU WILL AUGMENT SOVIET SUBMARINES F-700 AND Z-521 ALREADY ON STATION POSITIONED IN OVAL SHAPED AREA APPROX 200 MILES LONG AND 50 MILES WIDE, CENTER OF AREA 900 MILES DUE SOUTHEAST OF CAPE CANAVERAL FLORIDA USA AND 250 MILES DUE NORTHWEST OF SAN JUAN PUERTO RICO. SPACE FLIGHT DELAYS IN LAUNCHING EXPECTED TO CONTINUE UNTIL AFTER FEBRUARY 19 DUE TO ADVERSE WEATHER. UPON ARRIVAL TAKE STATION WESTERN SECTOR ABOVE DESCRIBED OVAL AREA. EXERT EVERY EFFORT TO LOG TECHNICAL RE-ENTRY DATA AND OBSERVE OPERATION. WHERE POSSIBLE, DENY TO U.S. SUCH GAINFUL DATA OTHERWISE EXCLUSIVELY AMERICAN. INITIATE SUCH MEASURES AS

NECESSARY TO DENY TELEMETRY TO U.S. AND TO INSURE YOUR OWN SAFETY. REMAIN UNDETECTED. INTELLIGENCE INDICATES AMERICANS WILL TRY FOR THREE ORBITS WHICH IF SO WILL RESULT IN CAPSULE LANDING IN ABOVE DESCRIBED AREA. BE ALERT FOR U. S. RECOVERY FORCES AS FOLLOWS: CARRIER RANDOLPH, DESTROYERS SEVERAL IN NUMBER, POSSIBLY AIDED BY CARRIER ANTIETAM AND CONSTELLATION. U. S. AERIAL RECOVERY FORCES EXPECTED TO NUMBER IN EXCESS 60 PLANES AND HELICOPTERS. GOOD HUNTING FROM GORSHKOV.

I must confess that my studied reaction was one of perplexity. It was obvious that I was being accorded a wide berth of freedom in carrying out my mission, and as a matter of fact, that I was being given several missions, some of which, though not wholly named, might be implied. Commissar Lvov was the first to openly impress this upon me.

"Captain," Lvov said, "our mission is clear, at least to me. How do you expect to 'deny to America such gainful data otherwise exclusively American'? How *do* you propose to deny all that invaluable technical data to the United States? And with all those ships in the recovery area, how do you propose to 'insure your own safety'?"

By a raise of my eyebrows and a canting of my head I signaled him to answer his own question for me. This he did.

"If the American is successful in completing an orbital flight around the world, we must either claim him ourselves, or . . ." and with a wave of his hand, Lvov signified an extension of intent. Slowly, his voice projected a curtain of repugnance around the whole operation.

"Or, Captain," he concluded, "we must destroy him."

This callous statement was made with no show of emotion. It was simply another illustration of Lvov's fundamental lack of concern for morals, ethics, and human life.

"You will have no choice, Captain," continued the commissar, aware, probably, of the shock he had succeeded in inducing by his cold-blooded opinion, and now willfully desirous of making the most of it. My controlled response was an expression of disbelief that Supreme Headquarters could have meant me to do what Lvov now suggested.

After all, here was a bold man, this Colonel Glenn. He, along with Gagarin and the other Soviet cosmonauts, was among the bravest of the brave, and I was repelled by the thought of destroying him. The suggestion was indeed so repugnant to me that I began, even then, to feel like a coward. A bemedaled coward, to be sure, but still—a coward. What Lvov said I must do did not seem honorable. And I had been schooled to think that the profession of arms was honorable! This would be murdering a helpless man, a space explorer who had risen high above into the heavens and joined with the realm of the infinite universe. He would be one who might even have come closer to a Divinity, if by chance such exists.

I shuddered, for to abide by the commissar's interpretation of my new orders would be inherently repulsive to me. To make war on a strong enemy, to sink an American admiral in his bunk some night while he might be sleeping in his flagship—yes! That would be within the rules of my own private ethics. But *this* man, this American space explorer, would be a man of science; perhaps a man whose exploit if successful might serve to advance all mankind further along the road to understanding our larger universe. I recoiled from the idea that I was to hunt for this brave man's space capsule and then destroy him in it. I didn't agree with the commissar that my orders meant that I should commit this crime.

I made the mistake of expressing my qualms about this mission to young Makar Rostopchin. Not that he did not agree with me, in fact quite the contrary. His vows to his God included the ancient Hebrew commandment, "Thou shalt not kill." And Lieutenant Commander Rostopchin took his religion seriously.

One night it was his misfortune to discuss openly this new mission assigned us, and he did so by questioning our moral rectitude in obeying the order as interpreted by the commissar. Unfortunately, Lvov was present, and from this moment, the two became bitterly resentful each of the other. Worse for me, this was the start of my own real difficulty with the commissar. The climax of the conversation went something like this . . .

ROSTOPCHIN: Commissar, if we destroyed Glenn, the wrath of Jehovah would be upon our heads. It would be murder! I am opposed to killing a defenseless human being. After all, we're not at war.

COMMISSAR: Not at war! Apparently, you haven't listened very carefully to my lectures. We're up to our necks in war with the capitalist society. We have to prevent them from catching up to us in our conquest of space. Don't forget, whoever captures space captures a unique way to control the rest of the world! Soviet Russia is ahead, and we must keep it that way.

ROSTOPCHIN: But not at the expense of losing our sense of values.

COMMISSAR: Values? The important thing is not values, but only a matter of whether we are finally effective. Are we contributing to the ultimate triumph of the People over the moneylenders and the international bankers?

ROSTOPCHIN: You can say all this, Commissar, because you're the representative of the Party. But I'm first a Russian, then a Jew, and I have to live according to my conscience. I have God to fear.

COMMISSAR: What a pity that such a fine specimen of manhood as you is a Jew. No, Makar Rostopchin, you are not truly a Russian. You are a Jew, yes. But Jews are international people, they are a race and they live wherever they are. You nor your people cannot claim to have roots in Russia any more than you could claim it in Germany under the Nazis. It is a good thing that we are closing down the synagogues.

ROSTOPCHIN: I won't hear any more such abuse from you.

COMMISSAR: Hush, or we may start the *pogroms* again.

ROSTOPCHIN: You forget to whom you talk. Remember, Commissar, that my family were important in Holy Russia, when your ancestors were nonentities.

COMMISSAR: Ah, but that is all changed now. The Czars have passed into oblivion, as you will, too, Makar Rostopchin, unless you desist from arguing with me about what you call your cherished morality!

ROSTOPCHIN: I'm not the only one who thinks that we'd be wrong to do as you suggest. The Captain himself has told me he views the order with consternation.

COMMISSAR: The Captain? He *does,* does he? That, my friend, is very, very interesting . . . [and then, turning to face me] Is this true, Captain?"

We were sitting at the wardroom table, and several of the officers were present. Most were embarrassed by the commissar's words with Makar, who was well liked. My first reaction was to dismiss the subject, yet I knew that this I could not do. I had told Makar my sentiments, and this was the time I would be bound to back him up. I swallowed hard, for I could sense that this would be the beginning of a rift between me and another representative of that insidious political administrator, Vice Admiral Grishanov. I had hoped that my scrape with Sverdlov would be chalked up to a personality conflict, and I was certainly not at all eager to have myself regarded as a chronic antagonist of commissars. But my convictions were stronger than my desire for professional self-preservation.

"Yes, Commissar," I said slowly, fingers tapping the table in front of me, "what the chief engineer says is true. I am loath to believe this order implies that I am to destroy the American space-explorer. I agree it would be murder.

Yet I can understand our need to prevent the Americans from gaining the information the capsule will contain . . ."

"Captain," Lvov hissed, "forget your morals. This is not a children's game of good or evil or anything like that. This is our chance to help insure our dominance in the world."

Good or evil! the words struck home.

My mind recalled the associated words in the Christian hymn. Shaken, I rose and went to my berth. But I could not clear the words from my mind.

. . . And the submarine continued on course as planned.

17

The Greatest Gift

☐ It was early morning on February 14, the traditional St. Valentine's Day of the Christian Churches. The *F-689* was cruising at 16.5 knots on the surface, en route to the rendezvous with the tanker. We were passing through what is sometimes called the Sargasso Sea—a massive area of seaweed in the middle of the Atlantic Ocean.

I came up on the bridge just before morning twilight to get a bit of fresh air before diving. Most of our daily drills had been completed and the preceding hours of darkness, wherein we had been up and about with considerable activity, had as usual resulted in an accumulation of stale air sufficient to give me a slight headache. Lieutenant Mikhailoff, who was navigating in the conning station when I came up to the bridge, was now standing at the foot of the ladder connecting the bridge to the conning station.

Through cupped hands, he yelled up to me, "Captain, it's just about morning twilight—it should be getting light pretty quickly now!"

Looking then instinctively to the east, I could see faint ribbons of daylight beginning to reflect on an unusually glassy-calm sea. It was a beautifully refreshing sight. The air was moist and salty, but, I thought, so fresh. Fresh! I took several deep breaths and then gazed transfixed at the faintly breaking dawn and the sea. For me it was exhilarating, and I am sure it has stirred in other men a like love of this expansive environment.

Presently, I was aware that the veil of darkness had indeed all but evaporated—the full light of a new day had suddenly come from the east. I sighted 360 degrees around and then quickly scanned the sky above. The dark shape of the magnificent *F-689* might be accidentally spotted, I thought, by an intruding aircraft. It was time to dive.

Before going below to the conning station, I turned to Lieutenant Glinka, the bridge watch officer, and said, "Dive her to periscope depth for a trim. Then we'll take her down to four hundred feet for a bathythermograph reading to see how the water temperature looks."

Glinka's white teeth flashed in his customary grin. "Aye, aye, Captain," he called out after me as I disappeared down the manhole to the conning station.

The next orders I heard came from Glinka, who shouted, "Dive, dive," and immediately I heard the heavy but rapid scurrying of feet of the trained crewmen executing his command. In quick succession they jumped down the ladder into the conning station, thence to the control station to man the wheels which control the diving evolution. The conning station hatch leading to the bridge was slammed shut and dogged tightly as Glinka, en route to the control station to take over the task of diving officer, excitedly shouted to me, "Conning hatch shut and secured, sir."

I nodded my acknowledgment.

It was a routine dive, but as always, I felt a bit squeamish.

I watched the depth gauge and inclinometer.

—Passing 35 feet; down angle 5 degrees.

I ordered the boat slowed.

—Passing 45 feet; down angle 10 degrees.

The negative, or heavy ballast water, was blown out as usual. This would help the submarine to level off at desired depth with a neutral state of buoyancy. Everything seemed normal.

—Passing 57 feet, now at periscope depth . . .

—Down angle 15 degrees and *increasing!*

. . . 16 . . . 17 . . . 18 degrees, and *still* increasing! Something was wrong!

Just then, Glinka shouted up, yelling frantically to me, "I think the stern planes are jammed on full dive! I've lost all control! !"

The urgency and obvious fear in his voice were contagious. I glanced at the navigator, Mikhailoff, whose face also registered disbelief mixed with trepidation.

But why hadn't Glinka caught this malfunction before this, I wondered. He should have. But there was no time to reprimand him now. His incompetency would have to be dealt with later.

My eyes looked up again at the depth gauge and inclinometer, as I roared, "Blow all ballast tanks! Emergency astern!"

—Depth 125 feet; down angle 28 degrees.

I could hardly hold on to the railing which partially extended around the hatch to the control station. The noises of the assorted equipment breaking loose from their moorings, and the sounds of unfixed gear crashing forward to the deck, was deafening. And then, there came loud screams from men in the galley. Could it be too late, I thought?

The momentum of this huge sinking craft was tremendous, I knew.

—Depth 350 feet; down angle 35 degrees.

Still going down, and *fast*.

I remember the yell of the quartermaster as he slipped and flew headlong past me, crashing finally into the forward end of the conning station.

Too late! Too late! The words were etched in my thoughts . . .

For a brief instant, a thought now flashed through my mind of that Sunday back in 1959 when I sat in the Washington, D.C. Cathedral and listened to the words of that haunting hymn. Was there a God for me, and was he standing near within the shadows, keeping watch over us? *God! ! DO SOMETHING! !* Was it a prayer? It was not; the time it took to think these things was but momentary. But, I later reflected, how strange to have had such thoughts pass through my mind at such a time of anxiety and impending disaster.

—Depth 500 feet; down angle 40 degrees, still dropping!

The bow of the *F-689* was now almost hanging at test depth, beyond which the hull would crush. Perhaps it was too late. Too late . . . too late . . . too late . . . too late . . . the words rang out so clearly in my mind.

In the wardroom, Professor Bogucharovo had been sipping a cup of coffee when suddenly he was thrown backward out of his seat, against the wardroom lockers. Books fell out of the high cabinets and bombarded him almost into unconsciousness. Unfortunately, the coffee urn broke loose and dumped its fresh contents over his right upper chest and right forearm. Already in a near state of shock, his cries of anguish and pain were heard only by Rodion Trubetovski and by his fellow professor, Pozdeev, who had simultaneously been catapulted out of the toilet compartment where he had been sitting, clear across the passageway and into the bulkhead.

Bogucharovo was badly scalded, and, save for his clothing protection, would have been burned severely.

In the galley, the cooks had been preparing dinner. The crew's tables had been set with plates and cups, forks, knives, and spoons. The canned peas and carrots had just been slipped into a cauldron of hot water; the boiling potatoes were just about done, and the Polish ham was ready for the pineapple sauce dressing. What happened in this compartment is indescribable. I saw the aftermath. That aftermath was also seen in all compartments and spaces throughout the submarine, except for the conning station which is one deck above the others.

Food and debris was sloshed and thrown throughout the boat. Hot potatoes, peas and carrots, sizzling Polish ham and bits and pieces of earthenware plates and cups, knives, forks, and spoons, all hopelessly mixed with spare engine and electrical parts broken loose from other compartments, lube oil, hot coffee, and human bodies all made up a massively incredible sight.

I gave the order, "Stop all propellers!"

This was in an effort to help control the perilous angle of the submarine.

I waited, tense, perspiring.

I guess I finally did pray, quickly, after a sort.

And then, suddenly, the down angle lessened to 35 degrees again. I looked at the depth gauge. It read 640 feet, but the bow was far below that. Several more feet might mean our being physically crushed. The dials were now stopped.

"We caught it," I shouted. "Thank God!"

I breathed easier.

But we were still not out of danger. I ordered "Ahead speed" as the F-689 now quickly leveled off to zero degrees angle, then started slowly upward.

—Passing 550 feet. Up angle 10 degrees . . .

We were still out of control, only now we were rising, and with increasing rapidity. The F-689 was grossly light due to the blowing, earlier, of all ballast tanks. My next command was almost coincidental with the thought itself going through my head about the ballast.

"Flood all ballast tanks, flood all ballast tanks!"

This action would slow down the ascent. Already, all the loose gear and rubber were beginning to fly back in the opposite direction, toward the stern. I could hear the onrushing seas now pouring into the ballast tanks. It was a frightening roar, but most welcome.

—Depth 475 feet. Up angle 15 degrees and increasing . . .

—Depth 400 feet. Up angle 20 degrees . . .

The ship's upward momentum now was too great—we would crash through to the surface, I was positive. The explosive burst of the submarine up through the water into daylight would be almost at a 45-degree angle—enough to perhaps break the ship's back upon the bow's return to the water! The thought was terrifying.

In the forward torpedo room, the compartment nearest the bow, a torpedo which was lashed to a loading rack broke loose from its holding clamps and slammed backwards with a crash against the sound room. I could hear the tremendous impact, and hoped that no men were in its path. They would surely be crushed by its sheer force of collision with the stationary impediment, man or matériel . . .

—Passing 200 feet. Up angle 30 degrees and increasing!

—Passing 125 feet! Up angle now 35 degrees!

I yelled, "Blow all ballast tanks! !"

If I did not do this now, I feared we would sink again— still out of control. At best, I could expect the *F-689*, after breaking through the surface, to sink back down again by its sheer momentum, to a deep depth. By making the boat light once more, at least I could prevent us from returning to dangerously deep depths out of control.

Passing 50 feet . . . Up angle 35 degrees . . .

The bow was probably just breaking the water's surface.

It *could* be worse, I imagined . . .

At least, we were still alive—most of us, anyway, I thought.

And then, the ship went dark.

We had lost all lighting. Automatically, however, the battery-powered emergency lights were turned on by trained and alert sailors. Daily training in the event of such a casualty had paid great dividends.

And now, with a roar and a rumbling swoosh of tons of salt water, we exploded to the surface at the horrible up angle of 39 degrees. I recall glancing at the depth gauge. It read "0." The *F-689* must have porpoised half a length into the atmosphere. Then, with a terrific bang, the forward section slapped back against the water's surface. For a moment I imagined the ship had broken its back. The Soviet ship designers certainly are to be commended for a sturdily built ship, I reflected a few minutes later, for miraculously, the submarine escaped unscathed.

Once again, the *F-689* slipped back beneath the sea. It was sternways this time, but with the bow at a 20 degree up angle. The situation was still not in hand, but at least my morale was improving. And my composure had returned. I ordered the propellers stopped.

At 125 feet depth again, with the propellers now going ahead, the up angle decreased and the ship began to rise slowly to the surface. At 50 feet, rising moderately due to the lightness of the boat, it began to level off. I knew now that the submarine was at last under control. We popped to the surface for the final time. And now it was a glorious feeling, for we stayed there. Stayed there, that is, until order, confidence, and morale could be restored throughout the submarine.

Luckily, for the next one and a half hours that we were on the surface effecting repairs, our presence was not detected. But the "routine" dive had taken its toll—and made me realize fully that casualties do occur, often when most unexpected.

Examination of the stern planes by our underwater diver revealed that a block of wood, entangled in heavy seaweed, had lodged between the port plane and the hull. Eventually, through superb workmanship by seamen under the watchful eye of Chief Petty Officer Igor Novikov, the wooden block and entwined seaweed were extricated.

As for Lieutenant Glinka, I felt that his failure to take prompt corrective action in blowing the ballast tanks and reversing the propellers soon enough was unforgivable. His error, therefore, was duly noted in my patrol report covering the individual efficiency of each officer assigned to my command.

But more important, perhaps, the casualty list was disheartening. In the case of my Second Officer, Volkonski, the injury sustained was a direct result of his efforts to correct the initial damage done by the torpedo which had crashed loose. Shortly after the sub had surfaced for repairs, Volkonski, as a trained officer-artilleryman, had gone forward to help reposition the heavy torpedo now awkwardly resting diagonally across the forward torpedo room. On one of the attempts to lift it into place, the rig slipped and Volkonski, pushing his own body weight against the tremendous onslaught of the heavy torpedo, was smashed down to the deck, bruised and bleeding. Worse, the strenuous physical effort on his part produced a pronounced rupture of his abdominal wall, and he lay in agonizing pain while the medical corpsman administered morphine and first aid. It was obvious that he would be of no further use to us on this cruise, and I realized that when we rendezvoused with the *Grodno,* we would have to transfer him for appropriate medical care.

Professor Bogucharovo's scalding was not too serious, but one of the cooks, a commissary petty officer named Ivan K. Isachenkov, and a seaman named Peter Gehgrenko, were burned raw by scalding water in the galley. The latter, to make matters worse, had also suffered a compound fracture of the right forearm when a cauldron overturned on him, pinning him beneath it.

A torpedoman, named Golovkoff, had slipped from a ladder and broken an ankle. And then a drawer full of electronics spare parts had come crashing into him, tearing his face into a pulp on the left-hand side. The navigator, Mikhailoff, was accidentally stabbed by a loose and flying pair of navigational dividers. They punctured the fleshy part of his throat; a quartermaster had had to withdraw the spiked prong from his neck, and the medical corpsman had immediately administered an injection of tetanus antitoxin. Besides these injured men, there were seventeen others suffering varying degrees of bruises, cuts, sprains, and minor ailments resulting from the episode.

This had been St. Valentine's Day, 1962!

I shall never forget it—for on this day, we had received the greatest gift of all: our lives.

18

Pink Champagne and Red Revolutionaries

☐ FEBRUARY 14, 1962

This was the day that Second Officer Volkonski began to show signs of deterioration physically in the area of his abdominal rupture. There now appeared great bluish coloration of the outer suface of the abdominal wall, and Volkonski lay writhing on his bunk. The medical corpsman did what he could by placing ice packs on the sore regions, and by attempting to console the injured man with the oft-stated observation that he was sure he wouldn't have to operate. Unfortunately, this made Volkonski feel even worse, as he had not too much confidence in the surgical competency of a naval hospital attendant. Furthermore, what insignificant degree of confidence he did have was additionally undermined when the corpsman, on taking Volkonski's temperature about midday, said matter-of-factly, "Well, I guess I'd better read up on what I might have to do, just in case I have to do it, you know . . ."

And then, an hour or so later, poor Volkonski was nearly terrified when the corpsman approached him, stroking a freshly shaved face completely devoid of the heavy beard which he had had but a short time before.

"How come the shave, corpsman?"

"The whiskers might get in the way when . . . er . . . if I have to operate, sir," came back the informative reply of the man upon whom devolved the responsibility for deciding the actual necessity of undertaking such surgery, as well as the operation labor itself.

Volkonski's little eyes stared vacantly in abject horror,

and then closed as if in deathlike resignation to the ghastly inevitable.

But the surgical knife never penetrated his skin aboard the *F-689*. The ice packs brought about an improvement in the condition, so that no action was necessary until after he had been transferred to the tanker the next day.

The "midday" meal (served close to midnight) was a time of great anticipation. Although writhing in agony with what had developed as a double hernia, acute, Volkonski had managed to alter the menu as his last contribution to the sumptuous fare served in the wardroom. From his bunk, he had ordered the commissary-porter, Rodion Trubetovski, to write down his dictated ideas as to what this "last supper" (so to speak) would consist of. Rodion was sworn to secrecy, so that none of the officers knew what the menu would be prior to actually sitting down to the meal. However, care was taken to advertise the fact that for this last occasion, Volkonski was outdoing himself. For the Final Meal, he had himself brought in, flat on his back, and put down that way on the wardroom couch. He wanted to be present during the consuming of this, his ultimate dietary triumph.

When I got the word that this last meal was to be a flourish, I myself got into the act and sent for Rodion Trubetovski.

"Rodion, please see to it that the special wine cabinet is utilized tonight," I said, passing the key to this liquid treasure chest to him.

"And by the way, I shall want to make a toast tonight to the Second Officer," I went on. "So, for the occasion— and I shall make it directly after the first toast following the main course—I will want to have pink champagne."

"Aye, aye, Captain, so then I shall have two champagne glasses at each place," observed the thoughtful Rodion, whose efficient service I am convinced at least equaled that of his father in the household of the Cantacuzenes.

Thus was set up the stage for the Monumental Tribute to Gastronomical Indulgers.

With soft chamber music piped in over the recording system, the wardroom officers sat down at last to truly one of the finest dinners ever served beneath the surface of the seas. It was masterful. We even had time for Alexei Kryzhanovski, the clerk, to type up written menus which were handed out to the diners immediately upon their seating themselves.

To start with, there was the appetizer. We had had it before once or twice, but due to a limited supply of basic ingredients, were not able to satisfy the demand for more frequent servings of this delicacy. Commissar Lvov loved it; between swallows, he observed that we ought to have had this dish more often, because although absolutely delicious, it required more frequent consumption in order for people to cultivate a "taste" for the course. It was simply small Italian tomatoes scalloped out, with caviar filler, and each individual dish carried four or five of these stuffed tomatoes well ensconced in sour cream.

The next course, served with white wine, which Volkonski assured everyone through painfully clenched teeth (he was still in agony) was the best Chablis from the Yonne wine country, was swordfish steak wrapped in lettuce, and sprinkled with fresh lemon juice.

When this had been consumed, Rodion, assisted by two other commissaries brought to the function from the crew's galley, brought on antipastos for us to dabble with until the main course could be served. When it was brought in, together with chilled rose wine from the Moselle, there was a roar of approval. There they were—sea crayfish on one platter, surrounded by various kinds of sauce and parsley, celery and herbs, and on the other platter, sizzling rare steaks adorned with juicy truffles.

With these went baked potatoes accompanied by a delicious paste of cream cheese mixed with salted olive oil and mayonnaise, assorted vegetables, freshly baked breads of several kinds (including pumpernickel), pickles and olives, cucumbers, sliced cabbage, avocado salad, Polish ham steaks floating in apple vinegar, sardines covered with melted cheese, baked apples floating in brandy, and a cup of borsch. Then came side trays of assorted nuts, shrimp, prunes stuffed with carp eyes, sour mash milk cheese, and spiced fruits.

Naturally, with the steaks came the added attraction of sherried, pulped chicken and duck gizzards bathed in an egg soufflé.

Finally, 'Devil' Dedusko rose to make the first toast of the evening. It was correct that he should do so, as the junior member of the wardroom mess. Protocol dictated this. Pushing back from his vantage point close to the still heavily laden platter of succulent beefsteaks, Dedusko stood up and, rashly discarding naval tradition, instead of toasting the Head of State, blurted out, "Where else but in the People's Navy could anyone stuff himself with such eats?"

The commissar seemed to be the only one approving of this rather crude outburst. He himself arose and, hoisting his own glass of golden champagne, said firmly, "Indeed, where else?"

And from the sidelines, shelved henceforth perhaps but nonetheless still aware of his seniority, Volkonski piped up with the saving toast, "To the President, the Premier, and the Supreme Soviet!"

All arose and sparkling, bubbling French champagne passed between lips already moist with anticipation.

And now in came Rodion with the other two commissary-porters—all armed with uncorked bottles of cold pink champagne. Within moments, the loud pops of the flying corks were followed by the effervescent pouring of samples to be imbibed by the three commissaries, each quickly voicing the standard declaration of beverage purity in conformance with the chief naval commissar's edict.

Of course, the porters had been thus sampling all fresh bottles of wine throughout the meal, but it is mentioned here only because Makar Rostopchin, at this point, as he watched the ridiculous little ritual being performed, protested, "For God's sake, now, easy there on the amount you people sample. There isn't too much of this kind of champagne on board and it's my favorite. Captain, I move this rigmarole be dispensed with."

Commissar Lvov, who had been guzzling the last drop of golden champagne from his other glass, now looked up quickly at Rostopchin. It was obvious that fireworks were in the offing. For Makar Rostopchin had again offended the commissar, this time by assailing a directive authored by his (Lvov's) immediate chief and head boss man, Vice Admiral Grishanov.

"Are you questioning the judgment of Admiral Grishanov, Mr. Rostopchin?"

The words were slow and deliberate, and it was as though the prosecutor were moving in for the kill.

I moved—and none too soon. Makar Rostopchin was already on his feet, a blush of anger coming across his features, already well flushed by the fermented grapes of France and Germany. In that second, I too was standing, newly filled glass of bubbling pink champagne held outstretched in a steady hand. My toast was predetermined, of course, but it also now came up at a fortunate time, when it would serve to forestall any new outbreak between the commissar and the engineer officer.

"Gentlemen, gentlemen! Arise all! and let us toast that intrepid, fearless experimenter in the exploitation of international cuisine, that master of exciting and ravishing new delicacies, he that has diligently sought our gastronomical satisfaction, the man behind the menu this evening, our own Lieutenant Commander Nikolai Volkonski, perhaps the most rare of epicurean masters in all of Soviet Russia! And while we toast this shipmate of ours, let us express our sorrow at his most unfortunate plight. To you, Nikolai Volkonski, who have been so efficient a Second Officer, and for whom the entire boat has felt a true respect, may I offer this toast in sadness at your having to leave us tomorrow, but with the hope that soon, you will be with us again!"

Volkonski smiled happily, pain or no. And the glasses were drained. The rest of the dinner was anticlimactic.

FEBRUARY 15, 1962

It was no more than three hours later when Sergei Nikolovich Mikhailoff reported to me that we were, as close as he could determine, on station for the ordered rendezvous with the tanker *Grodno*. Coming up to periscope depth, the watch officer searched the area. The electronic direction-finding antenna was raised, and we exerted all efforts to find our friends. But due to our lack of success visually, via electronics listening, or by underwater sound —at first—I decided to take a brief moment to look at the surrounding scene on a radarscope.

The reward was there. Some twenty miles to the northeast, there loomed the radar splotch which must surely be the tanker. The navigator worked out a maneuvering solution, and in short order, we were committed to a course at best speed for interception.

It was in the murky gray-black of early morning, not much before morning twilight, when we surfaced, bow pointed at the large shape no more than a thousand yards away. We had already established that she was the *Grodno*; first by identification of her propeller noises at a good distance before actually closing in at close quarters; then by observing her send off some mast head-light signals of positive identification, interceptable and understandable by anyone able to read Morse code in the immediate area.

The sea was mild and black; the air warm and damp.

Up on the open bridge, I looked painstakingly through my binoculars at the large ship, searching for some signs of deck activity. The tanker had stopped dead in the water, and was lying to. Presently, a bridge signal lamp was pointed in our direction, and a signalman on the tanker banged away on his shutter lever—a noise easily heard on the sub bridge, a thousand yards away—transmitting a query. Simply put, it was whether we were ready to receive designated passengers. My reply, affirmative, also alerted the tanker to take on board for medical attention my erstwhile Second Officer and the other men who had sustained serious injuries.

A boat from the tanker made three trips over to the starboard side of the *F-689*. The first unloading disgorged three revolutionary agents, headed by Señor Juan Marcos y Olivié, a Latin-American type with considerable property in storaged firearms for his mission. The second load brought three more. All were dressed in campesino style; all were armed. The third trip brought fresh provisions, including lemons.

And on the final return trip of the boat, Lieutenant Commander Nikolai Volkonski was transferred from the submarine to the tanker, along with the other three seriously injured men, Isachenkov, Gehgrenko, and Golovkoff.

The *F-689* had lost an effective Second Officer and three well-trained submarine crewmen. In their place had come, for however short a time, six dark and swarthy Latins—forerunners of Communist revolution in the Caribbean islands near Cuba.

19

My Own Moment to Decide

☐ FEBRUARY 16, 1962

The *Grodno*, following the transfers of personnel and provisions, had churned away on a divergent course from our own, heading her directly toward Havana. Her expected time of arrival there would be February 22. Our rendezvous with her, according to Navigator Mikhailoff, had been at 29°10′ north, 49°55′ west. In view of his "feat" of successful navigational positioning of the *F-689* in mid-ocean for the rendezvous, Lieutenant Glinka, still unabashed despite his recent slovenly, unprofessional performance in diving the sub, wrote up a citation (in jest) which he posted on the wardroom bulletin board. It read as follows:

From: Peter, Father of the Russian Navy and Chief of Staff to Father Neptune, Admiral of the Ocean Seas
To : Lieutenant Sergei Mikhailoff
Topic: Citation for Extraordinary Performance
1. Lieutenant Mikhailoff, you have demonstrated a devotion to duty and a professional ability beyond the call of submarine navigation. Despite a severe head cold, a warped zhooeyovich and a crooked quartermaster assistant, you have daily, in fact hourly, overcome the above-mentioned obstacles and have known down to a palm's breadth, the position of the Soviet submarine *F-689*. Never in all the history of submarining have men owed so much as to you, he that has left us in so dire a state of medical need. That specific feat for which you

deserve such credit must be alluded to, but in conjunction with it, you are to be commended for the entire
operation, to wit:

 (a) Getting underway from Kola Inlet before you
      knew which chart to use, and still not ground-
      ing us all.

 (b) Entering the North Atlantic Ocean with no
      mishaps, without ever actually knowing it at
      the time.

 (c) Passing successfully between the Faeroes and
      the Shetlands without realizing it.

 (d) Causing your position reports to coincide daily
      with the dead-reckoned positions previously
      laid out on your charts.

 (e) And finally, in bringing this submarine to the
      predetermined rendezvous with the GRODNO,
      a feat of true Soviet expertise.

2.   In view of these feats, you are hereby awarded the
Pendant of Peter the Great, with Ribbon and Rubies,
and are to be accorded the full privileges attendant to
the Gold and Red Order of the Three-Point-Fix.

(*Signed*)
PETER
By Order of the Admiral

. . . And the *F-689* plunged southwestward, at maximum sustained cruising speed, her objective the anticipated sea recovery area for the space capsule of America's
first orbiting astronaut. A message received from the
Grodno indicated that intelligence estimates placed Lieutenant Colonel Glenn in the space capsule almost contin-
uously at this time, awaiting good weather. But, according to Soviet weather predictors (much further advanced
than the Americans) the earliest probable time for the
launch would be about February 19. By then, we ought
to be on station.

 Also of interest was another message received. It came

in during the snorkeling hours of darkness on the six-teenth, and was from Admiral Gorshkov. It suggested that the six passengers bound for Santo Domingo (their ulti-mate destination) not be made aware of the effort to ren-dezvous with the space capsule; it went on to give some specific information on the United States men-of-war be-lieved to be operating in the Caribbean Sea, and espe-cially those temporarily based at the training station at Guantánamo Bay.

Then, Gorshkov laid out the project we were to accom-plish in Havana. He specified that I was to prompt Señor Castro to move immediately in expediting the construction of the Soviet submarine pens in certain Cuban ports and inlets, that I was to visit the ballistic missile sites that Cas-tro was building, to bring back a detailed report on their progress, and to see generally that Soviet objectives were being met in Cuba. In particular, Gorshkov wanted to make sure that at least one wing of missiles was pointed at the American naval base at Charleston, South Caro-lina, where it is known that the U. S. Navy is basing its Polaris stockpile.

Of course, the Americans normally would not think that our missiles sent to Cuba were capable of hitting such U. S. coastal cities as Charleston. But the truth is that they would be capable of bringing destruction and annihila-tion to such other cities as Miami, Jacksonville, St. Petersburg, Tallahassee, New Orleans, Mobile, Columbus, Georgia (where the U. S. Army has its most effective training post), and of course other cities within compar-able range. Furthermore, within a short period of time, even longer range missiles may be sent from Russia to Cuba. As a matter of fact, this has amused most Russian leaders, because America seems so excited about what happens in Laos and South Vietnam, but hasn't appeared too much concerned, at least until now, with what goes on right under her nose!

In any event, the *F-689* received up-to-the-minute in-

structions pertaining to the Cuban visit, and I was warned
not to let the Latin-American Communists on board know
what we were going to be doing prior to their own landing
on the shores of the Dominican Republic.

This last matter was rather difficult to do, because
Señor Juan Marcos y Olivié was a shrewd customer. He
was, perhaps more accurately, plain nosey. However, to
insure that he find out as little as possible, I arranged to
have his five subordinates eat and live in the crew's spaces,
and assigned him to a bunk directly above Commissar
Lvov, the while asking that gentleman to take Olivié under
tow and keep him from learning too much about our most
secret missions. In this instance, the commissar was masterful. Mostly, Olivié, whenever he could gain an audience, talked about the growing unrest and need for social
as well as economic upheaval in the Latin-American countries. His greatest hate was what he called the *norteamericano* "banana country" policies which gave to the U. S.
neighbors to the south an inferiority complex, completely
undeserved. He ranted and raved about the forthcoming
violent change which he and other revolutionary sons
would bring about for the people (in his own words, *los
peóns*).

Thus it was that neither the mustachioed and swarthy
Olivié nor his cohorts knew what was happening when
on February 20, at 2:38 P.M., Eastern Standard Time, I
lined up the American space capsule *Friendship 7* in the
cross hairs of my periscope. They were unaware that I,
watching that vehicle as it bobbed helplessly in the sea, was
inwardly wrestling in agony over what further action I
should take.

Other Soviet submarines had previously observed space
capsules and rocket nosecones float down or go crashing
into the ocean reaches. Also, Soviet scientific and research
ships and submarines had gained invaluable information
about the American flights during orbital or other spacial
flying time.

We ourselves, together with the other two submarines in the Glenn recovery area, had received up-to-the-minute dispatches from Soviet "trawlers" (hydrometeorological ships) and through these messages were able to know most of the critical information concerning Colonel Glenn's flight as he was actually making it. This, together with Soviet scientific conclusions about the probable recovery point itself (always changing), was information which we used to maximum advantage. Hence our maneuvering discreetly and unobserved into what turned out to be a fantastically accurate position for visual observance of the Glenn capsule as it drifted into the Atlantic Ocean after its three orbits about the world.

Return with me now to the scene.

Envision yourself in the conning station of one of the most powerful attack submarines in the world—a highly maneuverable, powerfully aggressive instrument for the pursuance of national objectives. An instrument which if wielded properly, with skill and professional brilliance, could bring about otherwise improbably if not impossible attainments. As I stood there in the cramped conning station, hands clenched about the handles of the periscope, watching Lieutenant Colonel John H. Glenn, Jr. descend into the Atlantic, I knew we were the only ones in the immediate vicinity—several complete sweeps of the area had failed to produce any signs of nearby shipping or aircraft. It was obvious that the Americans, with their extensive surface ship recovery flotilla, had not been kept as accurately informed as were we three, the Soviet subs *F-689*, *Z-521*, and *F-700*.

The cryptic messages from our nearest Soviet hydrometeorological ship (disguised, of course, as a fishing trawler) had provided us with the best possible maneuvering and positioning recommendations. Of these things, I was well aware as I stood there looking through the periscope, drops of salt water splashing down irritatingly upon my head and neck, from the never watertight periscope shaftings above.

Opposite me was Commissar Lvov; this was a great moment for him, too, and he was there to insure that everything was well under control. For the occasion, he had detailed 'Devil' Dedusko to keep the inquisitive Señor Juan Marcos y Olivié busy, far from the conning station. So Dedusko had taken Olivié into the wardroom, closed the watertight doors, and tried to interest his Latin-American guest in a small new transistor-type radio which he had bought just before the cruise in the popular department store on Moscow's Red Square. Although largely unsuccessful in awakening any particular interest in his involuntary pupil along the lines of radio, Dedusko nonetheless did manage to keep his man there throughout the critical period of action against the American space effort.

Sergei Mikhailoff's voice thundered through the cramped conning station with the navigational position.

"One hundred fifty miles east of Grand Turk Island," came the voice of the man Glinka had decided was eligible for the Pendant of Peter the Great.

"Make a notation in your log," I yelled out. "American space vehicle descending on bearing 020 degrees. Range five thousand yards. Horizon clear. Making all speed to close."

Then I shouted out, "Give me all the propeller turns you can for this shallow depth!"

To the commissar opposite me, in a more subdued tone, I said, "I want to get in there before any rescue aircraft comes near."

Baliuk now moved in quickly to take a photograph of the descending capsule.

Then, to the watch officer nearby, I heard the commissar say, "Make ready a forward torpedo tube for firing; we shall want the special electric homing torpedo. Set it on *fast* speed."

My mind whirred, not in confusion, but in a steady

sifting of information, facts, orders, apprehensions, possible actions, and final judgments concerning the action taking place. The capsule had just landed in the water, and I could see it, bobbing gently in a wavy but mild sea. Underwater sound now announced that they had just picked up very fast, light propeller noises off our starboard bow.

In a split second, I had wheeled the periscope around to the danger bearing. The sight I saw nearly terrorized me. It was incredible! Bearing down upon us at full speed was a U. S. destroyer. I recognized her immediately as an old one, hence nothing to worry about under normal conditions. But these weren't normal conditions. The commissar still wanted to unleash a torpedo at the space capsule, now about thirty-five hundred yards away; there was an American destroyer bearing down on us rapidly; and I was under strict orders to avoid detection! Caught in a similar circumstance in a shooting war, there would have been no problem.

But this wasn't war—at least not to *my* mind. Not yet, anyway. And here was an American man-of-war bearing down upon us at what looked like hydrofoil speed . . . the range to her was but 4½ miles at the most! Possibly less . . .

"My God!" I said, loud enough for those around me to hear. Lvov's ears caught the indiscreet utterance.

"God?" he snarled, hissing his contempt for my exclamation.

"You hear too well, Commander," I shot back, "this is no time for niceties of the Party line." And, continuing to peer into the periscope, I said, "Do you know what I'm looking at?"

There was no instant rejoinder, and I didn't prolong the moment of silence.

"We've got a United States destroyer charging down our throat!" Then, loud enough for the quartermaster to hear for a log entry, I shouted, "American destroyer, bearing

140, range eight thousand yards, target angle zero. Speed fast."

"Sink the bastard!" It was the commissar, his voice excited, his tone high.

My immediate order to the watch officer was to make all torpedo tubes ready for firing, and to advise the diving officer that we might have to go down to deep depth fast.

"We must *sink* them!" It was Commissar Lvov again.

"Impossible!" My answer was loud and prompt. "Our orders are cut and dried. We are to observe and take data only, and don't forget, we are to avoid being detected."

"Captain," roared Lvov, "you have been charged with denying that same data to the Americans! Most of it is recorded in film strips and instruments within the capsule itself. How do you propose to deprive the Americans of it if you don't either take it yourself or sink the capsule?"

Baliuk now moved up with his 35-mm camera and I let him slide in to take another quick photograph of the tossing space vehicle.

"I tell you, Captain, we have no choice but to fire at both the capsule and the oncoming destroyer," Lvov persisted, his face becoming colored in what must have been a combination of anger and frustration.

I raised my hand in a gesture of restraint.

"Commissar," I yelled back at him, "if we are attacked, yes! Then I shall shoot! Why else do you suppose I'm taking the precaution of making ready all torpedo tubes for firing?"

My voice had risen to parade-ground volume: I desired all others who had been listening to Lvov's exhortations to also hear my reaction. It made no impression on Lvov, however. He continued his argument.

"Captain, if that destroyer picks us up, we may be dead geese within the hour! I demand that you not ruin the whole situation! We can sink that destroyer before they ever know what's happening! And then we can deal with the capsule!!"

The commissar's voice was loud, belligerent, and derisive. I seethed. Who was he, anyway, to tell the captain of a Soviet submarine what his business was? After all, Lvov was a *political* officer!

"You will kindly confine your remarks to other than the decision I have made," I blurted out. Actually, I had made no decision. At that point, I had only a foggy idea of what I would do. Basically, of course, it was that I would close the range a bit more to the capsule in order to see firsthand its immediate reentry state. I was, naturally, very much aware that the Soviet High Command was interested in obtaining specific data recorded by the capsule's instruments. But I had been unable to determine how, precisely, I could succeed in this mission while maintaining secrecy relative to our presence in the area.

"The decision you have made?" It was Lvov, his voice abusive. "*What* decision, Captain?" His eyes, flashing with contempt, were riveted on me.

"Tell me," he went on, pressing the attack, "is your decision to repeat your failure in Beirut Harbor?"

The words stung like a dagger thrust into my side and twisted for ultimate agony. I could not let this commissar get away with such talk any more than I could have let Sverdlov talk back to me on the old *W-7* in the Mediterranean, back in 1958.

I trained the periscope around to the submarine's heading. We were pointed directly at the tilting, gently rocking space vehicle. I could read the lettering on the side—UNITED STATES. The words were vertically stacked, and it was only now and again that I could make out the word "STATES"—but they were there, and seeing them sent a chill through me. Was I wrong in hesitating to do what the commissar was urging me to do? Should I undertake the precipitate action that might possibly lead to a third world war? But were we not already *in* World War III—at least, in the *cold* war phase? Wasn't it my duty to think only of my country, and to serve her without thought of anything else? Shouldn't the United States quite properly be denied the secrets of space flight, at least until the USSR had put a man on the moon? The commissar might be right. I began to hedge.

"Now is the time! Now is the time! Now or never!" It was Lvov, bellowing infuriatingly.

Surely this *was* the moment to decide. I couldn't wait much longer. A hostile, or at least potentially hostile, submarine-killer—the destroyer—was bearing down on us fast. I looked over at Lvov. His cold eyes blazed in anger; his mouth was twisted into a vicious, petulant contortion. I glanced at my watch. It was 2:43 P.M., Eastern Standard Time.

The watch officer sang out word relayed from the forward torpedo room. "Special torpedo ready, speed setting fast. All other tubes ready."

I am sure my forehead was sweating. But I couldn't be sure. The salt water, mingled with hydraulic oil droplets, had been dripping down upon my head. I peered through the periscope again. The cross hairs were lined up precisely on the bouncing capsule. This, I thought, was a sight I would carry with me to my grave . . . and I was repulsed by the thought of the impending liquidation of America's first globe-encircling astronaut.

Again the voice of the commissar:

"What are you waiting for? We won't have this chance again!!"

And then, the thought suddenly flashed through my mind that indeed, the chance would *not* come again. Spontaneously, there came before me the words of the Anglican Church's hymn:

> "*Once* to every man and nation
>   Comes the moment to decide . . ."

My heart was beating so violently that I was sure everyone in the submarine could hear it. Cold sweat dampened the palms of my hands, making it slippery holding onto the periscope handle braces.

"What are you waiting for?" It was Lvov, his impatience beyond control, his voice a disparaging mockery of my competence.

"Shut up, you fool! Shut up!" My retort was instantaneous, and it was thunderous.

I took my eyes away from the lenses and glanced at my wrist watch again. It was 2:44 P.M.

Another look through the scope . . .

There it was . . . a dark little can, sort of like an oddly shaped bell, bobbing idly, and dead-centered in the cross hairs of my periscope.

The sight froze me momentarily in an illusion. In my mind's throbbing backdrop, where the hypnosis of compelling thought often sires visions, I was carried away trance-like to live a grim and grueling experience . . .

Hollowly, as if sounded in a cavern and reverberated through endless mountain gorges, I could hear myself give the command . . .

"Fire!"

I heard the watch officer too, in this moment of unreality, relay the word through the intercommunications system, and I watched the bright blue water, the azure, cloudless sky, and the helpless capsule of the intrepid American colonel.

"Kphoomph!"

It was the torpedo being launched. I had heard that sound many, many times before. But I had never felt so high-keyed, so unsure of myself, as at this moment of firing. And, in my mind's eye, I could see the bubbly wake of the torpedo, as the weapon ran hot and straight toward the capsule.

My illusion was suddenly terminated by a report from underwater sound: "Surface ship propeller noises increasing. Contact very close. Bearing 140. Course believed steady."

And then the voice of the commissar, riding hard on the heels of the information from underwater sound:

"Captain!" Lvov was shouting at the top of his voice. "That bastard is coming right at us and if you don't do something right away, it's going to be all over. For the *last time,* let's get this thing turned around and give that damned destroyer the works, before he runs us down! We can wait for the capsule until later."

The onrushing destroyer now demanded my immediate attention. To the watch officer, opposite me, I said in an undertone, "Train me around to bearing 140. I shall have a look."

As the periscope was brought around speedily to the desired direction of sight, the voice of Lvov mumbled something about "those bloody stinking sons-of-bitches," and then he screamed, "Let's blow them to eternity, but now, *now,* Captain!"

The American destroyer was fully visible now, and no more than two miles away, plowing through the sea at great speed. A spread of torpedoes would in all probability finish her off. And then, *then* I could take care of the space capsule! I stepped back to peer over at the commissar. He took full advantage of the opportunity to throw another barrage of inducement my way.

"Captain," he said, "for your own future, you have but one choice to make! We *must* sink that destroyer before we do anything else, and *then* we can take care of that capsule. Do you know what it will mean if the United States recovers that space vehicle? Think of the data they'll have! I tell you, in the interests of the Soviet Union, you dare not lose this opportunity! I charge you, Captain, with taking immediate action!"

I glared at Lvov. I was deeply antagonized by his publicly "charging" me with anything. Instinctively, I linked him with an oppressive evil force. The words of the hymn, *"For the good or evil side,"* somehow flashed across my mind's eye. In that flick of an instant, I think, I made my decision.

"Commissar," I remember saying, "the responsibility is mine, not yours. I know my duty. That duty is primarily to remain undetected on this cruise and to carry out the original orders upon which we were committed."

Then, in a voice ringing with authority and no doubt bolstered by my subconscious realization that I had just reasserted my own rights as commanding officer, I called out, "Down periscope!"

To the watch officer I said, "Take us down to two hundred feet."

The periscope handle braces were slapped up vertically and the chain reaction was set in motion. I moved out from the spot to which I had been almost fastened for the past forty-five minutes or so, and came face to face at close quarters with Commissar Lvov. His countenance was a study in unmanageable rage. His beardless face was almost livid, contrasting remarkably with the bewhiskered appearances of all others in his vicinity.

Mikhailoff and Kulakov were standing by, looking somewhat helpless and embarrassed in the face of the tension between their commanding officer and the commissar, with whom they both had been most friendly. It was indeed an awkward position. Fortunately, Lvov decided to leave the scene and go to his bunk.

For all intents and purposes, this was the end of the Glenn episode. The *F-689* was able to move away undetected by the destroyer (later to become world-famous as the U.S.S. *Noa,* recovery ship of America's first orbital flight astronaut). Silently, we headed for the northwestern shores of the Dominican Republic.

Glenn was safe. Glenn was a hero. Glenn deserved to be a hero. But Glenn had been in more danger than even he,

I am sure, ever imagined. In fact, I have come to feel that for this man who had seen the Universe—*indeed, beyond the dim unknown*—"*God must have stood within the shadows,*" keeping him safe from harm.

I shall never forget, of course, the oppression and the burden of this incident, this "moment to decide, in the strife of truth with falsehood, for the good or evil side."

20

The Affair at the Midwinter Resort

☐ MIDAFTERNOON, FEBRUARY 20, 1962

For the past hour, the submarine had been cruising submerged and rigged for silent running, heading generally southward from the Glenn recovery area. Our depth was four hundred feet, our speed perhaps three knots. I was now certain that we were in no danger of detection. After its fast approach on the capsule, we heard the *Noa's* propellers stop and then go full-speed astern (or so it sounded). We listened to the noises of those propellers as they maneuvered the ship gently in the proximity of the capsule, and it was not long before the underwater listening equipment picked up the accelerating propeller turn counts which to us indicated that the destroyer had made the actual capsule recovery and was now headed back to join the rest of the American units or, at least, the aircraft carrier with which she had been operating.

Satisfied now, in my own mind, that we were in a position to move out from the general area with no attendant risks, I leaned over the navigator's chart and surveyed the cartographer's interpretation of this section of the world in which we found ourselves. To the southeast was the Brownson Deep, an incredibly fathomless area of the ocean and a favorite locale for deep-sea oceanographers.

To our south lay the eastern edge of Hispaniola; and, between us and that island, coral reefs and jagged, abruptly rising sea mounts to make submerged navigation hazardous save through one of the many "passages" which struck my eye. Which one would we take? Until now, I had not discussed the matter with anyone, and did not

197

even know exactly where Señor Juan Marcos y Olivié desired to be cast ashore. It was time to find out.

"Come, Sergei Nikolovich," I said, my right hand coming down with a slap on the chart, "let's go find the Latin and find out where he wants us to take him."

The navigator untaped the area chart, picked up a pencil and pair of dividers, and nodded for me to precede him to the wardroom.

Señor Juan Marcos y Olivié was seated at the wardroom table with 'Devil' Dedusko and Commissar Lvov when we entered the compartment. Fascinated by what he was doing, Lvov and Olivié were intently watching Dedusko as he violently shook a small bottle of Italian dressing preparatory to spreading some on a small salad which Rodion apparently had just prepared for all of them. What fascinated them was the method which Dedusko used. At a glance, I could see why they sat looking at him the way they did. On the table was the top to the salad dressing bottle. What, then, was being used to seal the bottle as Dedusko shook it violently back and forth to insure his homogenization of the contents? It was at once obvious. Dedusko's right hand sported only four and a half fingers. Somewhere, quite a while ago, doubtless while dabbling with some mechanical device, the fourth finger of his right hand had been amputated. Only a small stub remained; it was this stub which, inserted in the bottle opening, now sealed the salad dressing in the bottle as Dedusko shook it back and forth.

Apparently, both Lvov and Olivié were too gentlemanly to comment on this boorishness; they said nothing, but merely continued to watch in speechless shock. It therefore fell upon me to end this disgusting act. I did so by calling out, "Very well, gentlemen, shall we put away the victuals and get down to business? Rodion! Bring on some fresh hot coffee, if you please. I will take my usual small cup."

As though lightning had struck, the dexterous manipulation of the bottle suddenly ceased, the finger stub was extricated, and the table made clear for Sergei Nikolovich to set down his navigational chart in front of the Latin.

Drawing up a chair opposite Olivié, I asked Dedusko if he would mind letting the navigator sit in his place next to the leader of the revolutionary agents. The seat was instantly made available to Sergei, who sat down and proceeded to tape the four corners of the chart to the flat surface of the table. Lvov, on Olivié's left, watched the proceedings in silence. It was clear that he was still angry over our having aborted what he considered was our mission—sinking the Glenn space capsule.

Rodion brought in the coffee on a tray. Steaming and delicious in its aroma, it was, I thought, even more satisfying in the anticipatory moments of inhaling its vapors than in actually drinking it.

Olivié's black eyes focused on my small cup—a demitasse—and then glanced furtively at the large Navy mugs with which the others had been served. I could detect a slight frown on his brow.

The navigator was now smoothing out the chart and studying it. Presently, he nudged Olivié and said, "Where do you want to be taken to?"

Olivié's dancing dark eyes switched from my demitasse cup to the chart before him. Quickly, they scanned the areas denoting the large island of Hispaniola and its surrounding waters to the north. I could see his interest in the various northern approaches to the island. Finally, his right index finger moved over the chart until it stopped at a point between the promontories of Monte Cristo and Cape Isabella.

"On this northern coastline, I think probably right here, we will choose to make our landing," he said slowly, looking up to ascertain any reaction from his listeners. Seeing none, he continued, "The one hundred fathom curve approaches the mainland of Hispaniola within three-quarters of a mile at this point here."

His finger tapped a point midway between Rucia Point and Brimball Point, a place well inside Isabella Bay. I reached over, took a pencil and ruler which the navigator had put down on the table, and drew a track which would take us from our present position to the desired location.

From the Glenn recovery area, it was 110 miles on a generally west-southwest course to Silver Bank Passage, a natural channel of very deep water (averaging twenty-one hundred fathoms) lying between the Mouchoir and Silver Banks. (The Silver Bank Passage is but one of several navigationally acceptable approaches from the north to Hispaniola, through an area of endless coral reefs and small islands.)

Mikhailoff now took his dividers and measured the length of the two principal directional legs which I had laid out for the voyage to Isabella Bay. To Silver Bank Passage it was 110 miles; from there to the disembarkation point three-quarters of a mile off the Dominican shore, it was seventy-five miles.

"At a speed of advance of 2.6 meters per second," the navigator said crisply, "we would be able to land you by 4 A.M. two days hence. Right where you want to be." He turned to look at Olivié, who was entranced. "This would give you about 2½ hours at least until daylight. You want to have it early morning light shortly after your arrival on the beach, don't you?"

The Latin looked at his Swiss Rolex watch.

"Hmmmmm. By tomorrow around noon, where will we be?" His dark eyes skirted the faces of the others and came to rest on mine. I again leaned over, examining the chart. I would indeed want to transit the Silver Bank Passage in broad daylight—navigationally, it would be easier. My answer to Olivié was directed to the navigator.

"I should like you to get us to the Silver Bank Passage by around noontime tomorrow, and then, as you have suggested, we can arrive where the señor desires by no later than 4 A.M. the day after tomorrow."

Then, addressing Olivié, I said, "But why did you want to know where we would be tomorrow at *noon?*"

Olivié's lips parted in a wide smile.

"Because this is the last noontime at sea that I may ever spend, and I have been fascinated by reading in sea stories and reports of how seamen like the Englishman Captain Bligh always took their high noon sun lines to find out where they were. I should like to have someone show me how to do it, and it will be interesting for me to know in advance where you think we will be."

I am sure I must have frowned. Who could be certain that it would be possible, in the light of shipping which might be in that area at that time, to surface sufficiently to take such a reading? I smiled at the salt-water enthusiast and promised to provide him with a lesson in navigation.

"Lieutenant Dedusko," I called out, turning to the electronics brain now seated on the wardroom couch behind me, "I should like you to give Señor Olivié a lesson in nautical navigation. Get a sextant and explain to him exactly what we do . . . no, no, not just now, later, whenever convenient . . ."

Dedusko probably needed a day's work in navigation— at least, celestial navigation. I was sure that all he knew about navigation centered on his knowledge of the operating characteristics of our electronics navigational equipment. It was therefore not surprising to note his face take on a look of near despair.

I faced Olivié again, smiling, and reached for my demitasse. It was empty. Pressing the wardroom pantry buzzer, I summoned Rodion to the table from his waiting station behind the sliding panel shielding the wardroom from the food preparation area. He refilled the cup.

"Now, gentlemen," I remarked with a broad smile, "let me teach you a lesson. Look into your big coffee mugs. All of you have at least a half a cup left, don't you?"

Señor Olivié looked down warily into his once steaming,

three-quarters-full cup of choice Brazilian coffee. He nodded, perplexed. Lvov shrugged his shoulders. "So?"

And the navigator, looking into his cup, merely frowned.

"Gentlemen," I went on, "the secret I pass on to you is this: If you like good hot coffee, never take it in big cups. For you will never be able to drink more than half before the rest becomes tepid—or worse, plain cold."

The commissar looked pensively at me.

"I agree with you, Captain, but this demitasse habit you have is not one representative of the traditional habits of the People. To me it smacks of a society gone by, never to return! It's something Rostopchin's old man might have used back in the days of the Czar!"

There was a loud cough to my rear and I turned to find the engineer officer there. Anger and disgust were clearly registered on his face. Lips curled in a near snarl, Makar Rostopchin queried, "Did I hear my name mentioned?"

As Lvov squirmed slightly, preparatory to replying, his interrogator reached into a shirt pocket and, withdrawing his silver snuff packet, now tossed it alternately from one hand to the other. The rhythmic sound of his hands snatching it in mid-air was punctuated by the commissar's answer.

"Yes, my dear Makar Rostopchin," he roared, "you did, that is a fact! But it is of no significance. Old habits and customs—such as your snuff addiction—are dying out. There is no place for them in the modern world. Today and tomorrow, we can have only those things which *all* of the people can benefit from or use. There must be nothing available to *some,* but not to others. And all of us must conform to the custom and to the will of the majority." He glanced at me. I managed to laugh.

"Hah! My friend," I said, "do you mean to tell me you object to my choice of cups?"

"Not at all, Captain. But you must admit you are pursuing an old custom of the hated nobility, of the so-called 'upper classes'. You must surely see the incongruity of a Soviet commander in such a ridiculous situation?"

"Commissar, I equate my choice of a demitasse to one's individual choice of shoes, or cigars, or anything personal. I think you are making a lot out of nothing."

Lvov's face flushed; then he relaxed into a smile. His words still pressed home his point.

"Behind my argument is the belief, Captain, that before we can bring Communism to all peoples, we ourselves must set the example of a society free from the small manifestations of privileged minorities, free from the stigmas of—"

"Wait a minute, wait a minute!" It was Rostopchin, chiming in. "To my mind, your bringing up such personal habits as my use of snuff, or the Captain's personal preference for a demitasse, and your condemnation of them, on the grounds that they remind you of the eccentricities of a social class dead or dying, is quite farfetched!"

Commissar Lvov turned crimson again. One thing he loathed was being criticized, especially before others. After all, he was the direct representative of Vice Admiral Grishanov! Surely, he thought, *that* was sufficient reason to immunize him from the counterarguments of others!

But in any event, I was beginning to find the session in the wardroom to be in increasingly bad taste, and consequently ended the discussion with, for Lvov, cruel finality. To him and the others, I merely said, "Gentlemen, as far as I am concerned, pressing this particular discussion could serve no useful purpose. Therefore, I will thank you to consider it at an end."

The reaction of Commissar Lvov was priceless to watch. Obviously, I had just cut him off when he was about to launch into another one of his incessant political-social-economic harangues. Face now scarlet, he arose, went over to the wine cabinet, opened it, and drew forth a bottle of vodka. Without comment, he poured himself a small glassful and in one uninterrupted motion tilted the contents into his upturned mouth. Then, with a loud clearing of the throat, he waved and stepped out of the ward-room.

Meanwhile, paying him no heed, Señor Olivié had reached into a pocket and produced a silver pocket-type humidor, from which he removed two Cuban cigars.

"To think that we are within almost shouting distance of Cuba," he murmured. "To get these cigars I had to buy them in the G U M Department Store in Moscow, and now they're being brought practically halfway around the world again!"

He smiled his widest possible gold-revealing smile. One could not help noticing the row on row—or so it seemed—of gold fillings planted around the perimeter of his gum lines. He offered me one of the cigars, and I took it.

"Señor," said Rostopchin, who had moved around and seated himself in Lvov's former chair, "where do you come from?"

Olivié turned his dark, leathery face toward the man on his left. "My blood," he said, "is the good blood of old Spanish nobility, exquisitely mixed with Haitian French and offered in my flesh and humble person as the best common denominator for leadership in the Latin America of the future. For what could be more representative of the stock of these countries than one in whose veins flows the blood of the mingled masses? Indian? Spaniard? French-man? African? In my forebears, in what some might call baseness, is the very base itself of human culture from a true blend of many cultures. I am the product of the races of man. And in the forthcoming world of joint ownership by each man and his neighbor, in the common possession of all property by all peoples in a controlled State, where the State is the People, who could better serve all people than one such as myself? I *am* the People!"

I could think only of the French King Louis XIV, the Sun King, whose words, *"L'état, c'est moi,"* seemed no worse than Olivié's interpretation of himself.

"But where do you come from señor?"

"On the Isle of Hispaniola, near the little village of San Pedro de Macoris, I was born," Olivié said reflectively. "My father and his father before him were planters, and they had done well. The fascist Trujillo assassinated him many years ago—my father, that is. I have known poverty, but I should never have had to know it. I have seen the greedy *norteamericanos* come down and exploit my homeland, as they have most of the countries in *la América Latina*. Thanks to the training and to the understanding of the great Russian people, however, we may still save our lands for our own peoples."

"And what of the other five in your party?" It was Dedusko, opening up after a long silence.

"They are all hand-picked, former neighbors and associates of mine; two were former foremen on sugar cane plantations in Haiti. I got to know them when the Party sent me on a good-will trip throughout the island last year."

"But how could you go on a good-will trip when Trujillo was in power?"

"Well, naturally, it had to be done in secrecy. What happened was that ostensibly, I had the papers purporting to make me a field supervisor for an American farm equipment company. Supposedly, I was going around speaking to the workers about the efficiency of their farm equipment, and the like. As a matter of fact, it was so well handled that even big fruit companies welcomed me and my 'delegation' to their plantations."

"And no one in the government knew you were really talking Communism to all those workers?"

"No, señor. They would never think so, because, in true *norteamericano* tradition, I always was careful to leave big tips—you know, gold-lined gratuities—in the hands of the people I thought could do us the most good. They all naturally supposed that here was just another vulgar display of American business bribery. And they took it, as usual."

"What then?"

"Well," said Olivié, puffing on his Havana cigar, "that is how I got the invitation to go to the Soviet Union and learn how to become truly efficient. For ten months, I have been in Moscow, learning all there is to know about how to organize a successful revolution. That is our mission here in the Dominican Republic to which you take us. And," Olivié chomped down unmercifully on his cigar, "I have at my disposal enough weapons, enough munitions, enough bayonets, to make my quest for upheaval more than a mere success. It will be like a volcanic eruption, changing the complexion of everything that these peoples have ever known. Yes, they will need a leader. And it shall be I who will point the way for them. You know . . . I am no longer a man of no means!"

Makar Rostopchin drew him forth even more.

"You have an independent fortune?"

"The successful champion of the people cannot be a pauper, surely you will agree?"

"But how did you get money? I thought Trujillo killed your father," broke in Dedusko.

"*Sí,* señor. But even the leader of the Common Man must have a wherewithal to impress that same Common Man. By nature, a human being likes to follow one who looks commanding, one who is successful, one who lives as all others would themselves like to live. Do you not agree? So, *mis amigos,* your most understanding government has seen to it that I have the monetary means to properly impress the masses. They now will look at me as the example of what they themselves might become, under Communism. Of course, some of my personal fortune is tied up in guns and munitions. But that is all right. It has been provided to me, in my name, and is available to me on request from independent shippers in the Caribbean. What I will do is sell each of the rising freemen his own weapon, as well as his own ammunition. So I will gain two-fold. I will have money and I will have an army."

"How soon will you take over in the Dominican Republic?" It was my question this time, and I asked it through dense clouds of brown Cuban tobacco smoke.

The Moscow-trained revolutionary smiled slyly.

"Who is to say? *Amigo mío,* it could be any day that I am ready," he said foxily.

FEBRUARY 22, 1962

It was the birthday of the Father of the American Revolution—230 years later! And so befitting for such an action to occur as now took place slightly more than half a mile from the beaches of a Caribbean island. There, at ten minutes before the hour of 4 A.M., the Soviet submarine *F-689* lay to and prepared to disembark six Russian-trained Latin-American revolutionaries, in the quiet waters of Isabella Bay, Dominican Republic.

George Washington, as the leader of the New World's first great social revolution—in which the common man stood up against the tyranny of a remote propertied minority—would surely have been pleased had he been able to survey this scene: six revolutionaries stepping gingerly from the stern deck-walk of the submarine into the three rubber, air-inflated paddle boats assigned to land them and their equipment on the beach. That the Trujillo family no longer reigned made little difference; the word from Olivié had been that last year's insurrectionist movement, carried out by some of his followers, had miscarried because of insufficient funds from the USSR. Under the cover of democratic reform, the "banana" companies of the United States still dominated the scene—or so Olivié believed.

In any event, the small band of Communist agents (one of whom was himself certain of some day ruling perhaps all of the Caribbean) shoved off from alongside not much past 4 A.M. The revolutionaries carried emergency provisions, weapons, and ammunition in each paddle boat. Not even a faint glimmer of dawn could as yet be seen in the eastern sky. This was good. But the night was not totally black. On the shore, there were occasional lights, set apart each from the other in many places, but in one place, near a telegraph station, we could see several red lights together with the white. Probably marking high tension wires. It was a starkly fearful moment, watching the small rubber rafts being paddled quickly away from the submarine, away into the blackness of the water toward shore; the water itself half covered with a noticeable early morning mist; the black shapes of the coastline mountains etched against the somewhat lighter but purple-hued skies above; the stars still blinking across the heavens, and here or there a black splotch where clouds barred the eye from a view to that vast expanse. No moon. A perfect night for the introduction of these espionage agents upon whose success—or failure—local history might depend.

Professor Bogucharovo, himself on deck to watch the landing operation, remarked happily that he was glad *he* was going to make *his* landing ashore via a gangplank; he would just as soon leave this type of episode to the cloak-and-dagger crowd.

"Give me *Dignity*, every time," he blabbed, apparently for the moment forgetting his own one-time nudity in that commodity.

Pozdeev, too, had come up for air. The last three miles of the way in toward shore had been with the submarine fully surfaced. The opening of the submarine proved tantalizing. Crewmen swore up and down that they could recognize land nearby just from the offshore smell. Perhaps they could. Certainly, most mariners will agree that to the salt-air sensitive nostrils of the average mariner, there *is* a definite change in odor, a specific alteration in the smell, even a strong offensiveness, to the proximity of land as a seaman might become acquainted with it, through the sense of smell. For the odors of land from off shore bring to the pure nostrils of the seaman all the smoke, the burned residues, the rotting seaweed and tidal flotsam, the stinks of dead fish thrashed ashore upon the beaches; and the stench of river outflows into the sea itself. The amusing part about it all is that most landlubbers, when they stand on the shore near the sea, take sizable breaths and gasp their pleasure at the opportunity to stand there and breathe in "fresh salt air."

There is, in truth, no opportunity for a land inhabitant to smell true "fresh salt air," unless he takes himself at least ten miles to sea!

And now, no later than four-thirty in the morning, the Soviet submarine *F-689* twisted around and nosed seaward once more. Our course was west-northwest; our destination the United States Naval Operating Base at Guantanamo Bay, Cuba. It would be 115 miles to the Windward Passage, and then 135 miles down to the southwestward into the American Navy's training grounds. The thoughts of tangling once more with U. S. Navy warships was invigorating. It was an excitement not unlike that which I experienced back in 1958, on operations against the famous U. S. Sixth Fleet.

It was still George Washington's birthday, February 22, 1962. But it was now four o'clock in the afternoon, just twelve hours after we had left Señor Olivié to his own devices. We had been pushing generally westward at 5.2 knots, at varying depths, dependent upon the best underwater levels to move in for success in avoiding detection. Every hour, the watch officer would move through a range of depths to ascertain the temperatures; this information led to the cruising level for the ensuing hour. Actually, the track I had laid out with the navigator was planned for a bare minimum of meeting with coastal shipping. Most of this commerce would be conducted well inshore of us, I felt sure.

Thus, by 4 P.M., we had not come in contact with any other shipping; our navigational position, as determined by radio direction-finding and radar observations, was thirty miles due north of Cap Haitien. Looking at the chart, I recalled a past cruise, many years ago, when I went into that harbor aboard a Soviet freighter, and in the overlay there in port had taken the traditional touristic donkey ride up the tortuous and precipitous mountain trail leading to the Napoleonic-era brick and mortar fortress of that mad, black Haitien Emperor, Jacques I (Jean Jacques Dessalines), who for more than a decade defied the troops of Imperial France. One who has ridden up that winding, dangerous, incredibly steep mountain trail to the castle-fortress high atop the loftiest peak on the cloud-level ridge-line never can forget the experience. And so, my own thoughts reverted to that day long ago when I made my buttocks so sore on a jolting, wobbling, cavorting old four-legged donkey that carried me on that adventurous visit.

Tortuga Island lay some thirty-five miles to the southwest; neither our electronics snooper equipment nor our underwater sound gear indicated strangers anywhere near us. The watch officer reported that visual sweeps through the periscope determined the horizons and the skies above us to be uniformly clear. I went up to the conning station and looked through the periscope at the wonderfully blue water. Not since my cruise in the Mediterranean had I seen such thoroughly enticing blue water through the periscope. And the sun was there, bright and golden. The sea was gently choppy, with little wavelets and occasional whitecaps—but nothing more than a foot in height.

"Beautiful sight, isn't it, Captain?" It was the watch officer, Ivan Nicolai Kulakov. He continued.

"Captain, you know, when I was on board the trawlers, we used to take advantage sometimes of the sunshine and warm water, and go swimming over the side. I don't suppose you might consider us lying-to up on the surface for about a twenty-minute swim call, would you?"

The thought gave impetus to my own private consideration of just such a move. Why not? Turning to the watch officer, I said with deliberate slowness, as though for the first time pondering the question, "Well, Lieutenant, you are the operations officer. Tell me, how much danger is there that we might be seen if we surfaced for thirty minutes?"

A look of delighted surprise came over the features of the swimming enthusiast. "Not thirty minutes, Captain. That might indeed be too risky. But twenty minutes . . . that would probably be all right. I might suggest that since the Americans don't expect foreign submarines in this area, it might be all right for us to guard against the possible surprise flight of a commerical aircraft over us by activating our air-search radar. Then we could insure ourselves against being inadvertently seen."

"What, though," I said, "might the Americans think if one of their ships spots our radar beacons from this location?"

"I'd say unlikely, Captain. Most of them are so delirious over the successful recovery of that damned space capsule that they aren't even thinking about Soviet submarines at this time," responded the man who had set foot ashore in the United States not too many months before, as a "sick" Soviet seaman. I was compelled to believe him. Not the least of my reasons for accepting his counsel was my own inclination to give the crew an opportunity for pleasant recreation.

"Mr. Officer of the Watch," I intoned, "you may pass the word that we will have a swimming party over the side in about ten minutes. In preparation, please see to it that before fully surfacing, we have a complete intelligence roundup from all electronics aids, regarding any contacts, surface or aerial, within detection distance of us. If the coast is clear after this last-minute intelligence collection, then you may surface. Of course, do not forget to take a 360-degree look through the periscope, too, as a last-minute precaution. Any questions?"

The watch officer beamed. "No, sir," he answered cheerfully. And then I went to the wardroom, where I knew Professors Bogucharovo and Pozdeev would proba-

bly be seated at the wardroom table, seriously engaged in
a fight-to-the-finish game of chess.

To leave the surfacing operation to the watch officer by
himself, without my being physically on the spot near the
control station, was something I felt I really had to do—
especially in view of what I considered was a need to have
me show positive confidence in other watch officers after
Glinka's fiasco.

True to my expectations, the Soviet educators were indeed to be found in the wardroom, and it was Pozdeev
who seemed most exhilarated. At a glance, I could see
why. He was winning.

"Gentlemen," I began, "the time has come to sample
the sea. Within the next few minutes, we shall be surfacing for a swim party. The nearest land—"

"Land? Land?" Bogucharovo could hardly contain himself. "Are we close to land?"

"Professor, hurry; get into your swimming suit. If you
have none, your birthday suit will be fine. The nearest
land is about two miles away."

"Ahhhhh! Oh, Pozdeev, isn't that nice?" Bogucharovo
chortled merrily.

"Swimming, eh?" The economist spoke up now. "Well,
good! By the beard of the Turk, I am ready! But I say,
how thoughtful of you, Captain. Waiting two more days
until I can get my 'Saturday night' shower for this week
would be tough on me. Of course, I understand the problem, what with the difficulty in keeping fresh water in the
submarine. But as Peter was a prophet, may I say I will
indeed take advantage of—"

"Captain!" Bogucharovo broke in rudely, "there is just
one thing bothering me."

"Yes?"

"I thought we were going out to seaward from Hispaniola, far enough so that there wouldn't be any danger of
anyone accidentally seeing us."

"Yes, Professor, that is correct. That's what we did

after we left the agents ashore at Cape Isabella. We headed far out beyond the limits of the coastal traders and fishermen."

The agrarian professor's eyes widened. Slowly, furrows rolled up across his forehead. Pozdeev, opposite him, looked up at me quizzically.

"But," Bogucharovo said, "how come we have land only two miles away?"

"Simple, Professor," I grinned. "It's straight down."

The vertical movement, up and then down, of Bogucharovo's Adam's apple, did not go unnoticed. But I did not capitalize on the man's discomfiture. Just then, the word was passed on the public address system, "Stand by to surface, stand by to surface," and within a moment I could hear the ballast tanks being blown, followed by sensing the up-angle resulting therefrom.

Commissar Lvov entered the wardroom.

"Captain," he began, "I am surprised that you are doing this. What if we are spotted? What if something goes wrong?"

"Nothing to really worry about, my dear Lvov," I replied. "Better hasten into your swimsuit, or you will be the last man to avail himself of the new tropical resort which I have just opened for your midwinter pleasure!"

Lvov persisted. "Captain, I hope you know what you are doing."

His warning irritated me; as the master of this submarine, his pursuance of this line of questioning was offensive. It wouldn't have been so bad had he been a real naval officer, but that is what submarine-assigned commissars universally are not; he, of course, was no exception.

"Well, Commissar," I answered, "I don't know about you, but as for me, I am going up topside to see how the crew enjoys this little outing."

So saying, I proceeded up to the conning station and thence to the bridge. The sunshine was brilliant, and it blinded me. The sun, warm and delightful, was truly a tonic. Now, with increasing numbers of the crew climbing up topside and moving back to the after main deck, I turned to the watch officer and said, "Lieutenant Kulakov, you may pass the word to jump in as soon as I see some extra lifelines and at least one heaving light-line up here."

Rapid orders shot forth from the watch officer to the other members of his watch, and within a few seconds, my request had been complied with. The quartermaster of the watch was ordered to sound the bell for swim call and, with the submarine lying-to in a leisurely slow roll with the gentle ocean swells, the now crawling deck suddenly cleared as bodies—most of them marbly white and nude—jumped, dived, or fell over the side.

I had decided not to abandon my ship, but to remain topside on the open bridge where the crew could see me. There would be plenty of time for me to enjoy the blue waters of the Antilles after I had made port safely in Havana.

The milling about of the swimmers, and the skylarking which the crew engaged in, could not have been going on for more than five minutes before the thought suddenly struck me that it might be wise to have a rifleman or two up on the open bridge, for protection against possible shark attack.

Seeing the gunnery officer about to climb down to the lower deck from the starboard side of the bridge, I reached over and grabbed him by the shoulder.

"Going in for a swim, eh, Glinka?"

"Oh, why, yes, sir. Why, sir, isn't it all right?"

"Quite all right, Lieutenant. But it might be a good idea if you had a couple of your men come up here with some rifles, just in case we get caught short here by a shark or two . . ."

Glinka's jaw dropped noticeably.

"Sharks?"

"Why, yes. We are in the southern part of the North

Atlantic, you know . . . or had you forgotten this is where the old Spanish pirates made the Englishmen walk the plank into the schools of waiting maneaters?"

Glinka gulped.

"Better get a couple of riflemen up here on the double," I said, slapping him nonchalantly on the back as he turned to go down into the submarine again.

But it was too late.

Above the normally loud skylarking and gay laughter, the boisterous shouts of playful sailors indulging in good sport, and the raucous yells of cooped-up men giving vent to their pent-up emotions by extraordinary heights of noisy roughhouse, both on the weather deck and in the water, there suddenly came a blood-curdling shriek of agonized terror and pain. Following hard on the heels of the horrifying scream came the shout which froze me on the bridge.

"Sharks! !"

The cry was repeated, wildly and in terror. It came now as a chorus of anguished, frightened, fearful voices. The chant was punctuated by more shrieks and cries of "Help!" The scene in the water by the sides of the submarine was a sight never to be forgotten. There was a tremendous wild thrashing of human arms and legs, as men tried desperately to heave, catapult, drag, climb, or be pulled back on board the boat—back to safety. The great splashing in the water prevented me from finding out where the shark or sharks were attacking. The shouts not only continued—they rose in volume and in pitch. It was the nearest thing to bedlam that one might imagine. Then I saw it—just off the port quarter, a momentary view, but I saw it. A sudden swish, a dark, blade-like dorsal fin, and, among the splashing, thrashing human arms and legs hell-bent on removing their owners from the sea, a swirl of crimson. Not much, but definitely the bright red scarlet color of blood.

Where was the gunnery officer? GodDAMN that man, where were the riflemen? Rifles, RIFLES! I was shouting, desperate. My arms were flailing in great circular sweeps of unavailing enticement to the men to get back on board. It was useless. I was absolutely powerless to help them. I shouted down to them, "Get up, get up, GET OUT OF THE WATER, GET OUT OF THE WATER, QUICKLY, GET OUT OF THE WATER!!!"

And topping it all off, the quartermaster was standing up there on the open bridge also, shouting stridently to the men down below in the submarine that what we needed was rifles, rifles, RIFLES, DID YOU HEAR ME, RIFLES! THERE ARE SHARKS UP HERE!!! The watch officer himself was adding to the commotion by blowing his shrill, warbling-like constabulary whistle to get the attention of the swimmers still in the water.

And when at length the crying and the shrieking were over, when the last thrashing sailor was recovered from the sea, and the senior chief petty officer had conducted his muster of all the crew, the grim and terrible tally was dealt to me as an everlasting nightmare.

Missing was Rodion Trubetovski.

Missing also was young Alexei Kryzhanovski, the commissar's clerk, and favored young sailor-protégé.

His right forearm gored and horribly mutilated, his right side ripped open over a fourteen-inch scissor-bite, supply and commissary Lieutenant Georgy Rodzianko had been hauled back on board by his swimming companion, Ivan Dedusko, himself bleeding from an eight-inch slash above his left knee.

After the injured had been taken below, I turned to the watch officer and quietly said, "Take her down to two hundred feet; make your course 285 degrees true; I will want only a slow speed as I do not wish to arrive at the northern end of Windward Passage until about eight o'clock tomorrow morning. Please check for details from the navigator."

Then, with a last sad look at the clear blue sky and the bright, sunny weather, I slid heavily down the manhole into the conning station below, and walked slowly to my quarters.

Collapsing into a chair, I held my head in my hands. My God, oh, my God! what had happened to me? Almighty God! Why had this happened? Why? *why? why?*

As though listening to an echo from the past, or from another world, I heard the word passed over the public address system, "Now stand by to dive, stand by to dive," and listened hollowly as the Atlantic Ocean flooded into the ballast tanks with the customary roar associated with diving.

Faithful, conscientious Rodion Trubetovski would never hear that word passed again. Nor would handsome young Alexei. And the horror of what had happened to my two officers! *God!* I cried aloud, Oh, GOD!

There was a sudden swish of my stateroom curtains, and I knew someone had stepped inside my quarters.

The voice was cold and unfriendly. The words I heard were pointed. I looked up, slowly, and turned to see the silhouette of a heavy-set man blocking the entrance to my room, his body between my line of sight and the electric light bulb in the passageway.

"What did you say? Who is that?"

The phlegmatic voice repeated slowly the same unmistakable but almost unbelievable words.

"This, today, Captain, you will pay for, believe me," I heard the commissar say bitterly . . .

21

Then Came the Shocker

□ Commissar Lvov turned and swept out past the still swinging dark green curtains, hanging somewhat bunched-up now to the side of the rack over the entrance to my cabin. The unshielded light bulb from the passageway was blinding. I rubbed my eyes, and looked down at the deck. The whole business was so freshly imprinted in my mind, the actions that had occurred were so irrevocable, there was so little I felt I could do.

I just sat there, slumped, unbelieving. A glance at my bulkhead clock—it was only five-twenty in the afternoon—it was only about an hour before that my crew had been intact, lively, fun-loving! And now the blight; now, the cloud. Presently, rapid strides coming down the passageway alerted me to receive another visitor . . .

A figure loomed once more at the entrance to my room.

"Yes, who is it?"

"Why, it is I, sir, Lieutenant Kulakov."

"Yes?"

"Captain, the watch has been relieved properly, we are at desired depth on course 285 degrees true and are making three knots. The navigator informs me that we shall be at the northern end of Windward Passage at the time you desire . . ."

Kulakov made no move to depart, nor to say anything else . . .

I broke an extended silence.

"What else, Lieutenant?"

"Well, sir, I wanted to apologize to you for my lack of foresight in taking precautionary measures."

"The responsibility was mine, Lieutenant."

"But Captain," persisted the operations officer, "I should have had those riflemen up there long before—"

"Of course you should have, Kulakov! And of course I should have seen to it that you did, too, before the men jumped over the side. But we muffed it, and there's not too damned much we can do about it now, is there . . . except remember it, eh?"

Kulakov shuffled his feet.

"How are the injured, are they all right?"

My question brought a welcome response, now, as he ran his fingers through his hair and said, "Yes, sir. The corpsman had thought, at first, from all the blood, that we might lose another man, but he's given a lot of drugs to the man and is sewing them up right now. Would you care to come see?"

I didn't, but I really had no choice. It was a matter of presenting myself to the wounded officers and, if I couldn't cheer them up, at least make them realize I felt sorry that we hadn't been able to do something to avert their being attacked. As I arose and went over to the small washbasin to look in the mirror for guidance in combing my hair, Kulakov broke some more news.

"Captain . . . the commissar walked into the radio-wireless room a few minutes ago and began drafting up a coded message to Vice Admiral Grishanov."

Grishanov! So he was to get into this little episode too, I thought.

There wasn't much doubt in my mind that Lvov had written the message in private and that no one else knew what it said, but I asked Kulakov anyway whether he knew.

"No, sir," came back his reply, "but I have an idea that he is reporting an unfriendly version of what happened this afternoon."

I swallowed hard. So Lvov was reporting me to Moscow! It was suggestive of Sverdlov. I grimaced, and expelled the water from my comb with a gusto that must have made Kulakov realize how angry I was.

"Captain," Kulakov continued, "I would like, as your operations officer, to recommend that we comply with basic directives for emergencies at sea, and send a dispatch both to Admiral Gorshkov and to the Northern Fleet Commander, advising in general terms of our casualties; also I recommend that we seek assistance from the Cuban authorities just as soon as we can get over there in Cuban waters. I'd say we ought to ask them to take both Rodzianko and Dedusko ashore for hospitalization just as soon as we arrive at a convenient place off the coast."

He was right, and what he was recommending, I had known we must do. I had just been deferring such a decision, knowing that however necessary it would be to unleash the bad news, as long as I avoided the ugly task, I was immune to outside criticism and retribution, if any might be forthcoming. However, Lvov's writing up his own personal report changed things somewhat. It would now be mandatory that I use the wireless first, to get my own version into Headquarters before his arrived to discredit me. I faced Kulakov, and gave him his orders.

He was to go to the radio-wireless room and insure that no messages were transmitted from the ship before I had sent my own official dispatches. Meanwhile, he, Kulakov, was to draw up recommended messages for me to send, both to higher naval headquarters and to the Cuban authorities.

With Kulakov thus occupied, I proceeded to the wardroom, where the commissary officer was lying on the wardroom table, resting his bleeding and bandaged body on crimson-smeared sheets. The medical corpsman was there, hovering over him, and, with a needle and catgut, seemed to be well along in mending the man. Mikhailoff, assisting the corpsman, looked over at me and said, "He's out. We've given him some ether and a lot of morphine.

Pulse is weak, but that's understandable, considering his gouges."

Ugly was the only word to describe the scene. And over on the couch, Dedusko lay, sweating and half-covered with blood-stained sheets. I glanced at Mikhailoff.

"He's already been sewed up," he volunteered. "Real good job, too, Captain. Don't think he ever felt it. Of course, he was out, too. Ether . . . that's what we gave him. Some sulfa, too. Same for this one—" he nodded to Rodzianko.

"Well," I said, clearing my throat, "we will be putting them both ashore within the next twenty-four hours. I am sending a message to get assistance."

I walked past the pantry. It was empty. Rodion had left it, and he would never be back. My feelings of guilt were overwhelming. But there was little I could do. I returned to my own room, and, sinking into a chair by my desk, grabbed a Japanese ball-point pen, a piece of paper, and a stray cigar I saw lying atop the desk. Placing the cigar in my mouth without lighting it, I chomped down viciously as with the pen I now drafted my own ideas for the messages that I would shortly send out by wireless.

By six o'clock, I had sent one encoded message to Northern Fleet Headquarters, the same to Supreme Headquarters, and another one via specified short-wave frequency, and also in code, to the Soviet consulate in Havana. The former reported the two missing sailors, and attributed their loss to shark attack while engaged in aquatic recreation; also, the injuries to the officers were duly recorded, but the dispatches made plain that the incident in no way affected the capability of the submarine to pursue its mission. The dispatch to the Soviet consulate in Havana merely requested instructions for the covert transfer of two critically injured officers, victims of shark bites, and stipulated that the transfers to Cuban medical auth-

orities must be made within the next twenty-four hours. I
asked for the exercise of extreme secrecy in handling the
matter.

And, when this had all been done, the commissar sent
out his lengthy encoded message. However curious I was
concerning its contents, as a mere line naval officer I was
not privileged to know what he released to his higher
headquarters. But I could guess.

I walked up to the conning station, to look at the navigational chart. Taking dividers, I measured off the distance to Windward Passage. It was about forty miles. Did
I really want to wait until eight o'clock the next morning
before arriving there? If I increased our speed to ten knots,
we could be there in four hours. That would mean a midnight transit of the passage . . . but perhaps this would
be even better! Yes, I thought, that's what we would do.
There certainly were ample navigational lights and
beacons on shore to pilot by. And if the messages from
the consulate and higher headquarters came back this
night, I would be able to proceed, if necessary, at perhaps
seventeen knots on the surface to move prior to daylight
into whatever east Cuban port was designated.

The orders were written down for the watch. We would
increase speed to ten knots and proceed toward the Passage. I would want to pick up replies to those messages we
had sent, and this meant that we'd have to leave the whip-
antenna raised while snorkeling along at high speed.
These instructions were also written into my orders for the
next few hours.

Having thus changed our plans, I went back to the wardroom, where I found Makar Rostopchin had taken over
and, after the sewing jobs on Rodzianko and Dedusko,
had caused both those officers to be carried to their bunks.
He had also supervised the cleaning up of the wardroom,
and had seen to it that one of the crew's commissaries
now reported to the wardroom for duty in Rodion's stead.

The new man's name was Usoupoff. Casually, Makar in an aside informed me that prior to the Revolution, Usoupoff's family had been extremely high on the social ladder of old Czarist Russia. "And now," he sighed, "look what has happened to him."

By ten o'clock that evening no messages had been received. There was little to do, in this event, other than to continue the voyage as previously planned. Hence, we turned to the southwestward, entering the Windward Passage for transit between Haiti and Cuba, into the Caribbean.

It was while we were snorkeling at ten knots, proceeding on course as planned, and at nearly 2 A.M on February 23, that the wireless operator jumped up from his chair in the radio-wireless room and shouted out the fact that he was receiving encoded dispatches from Supreme Naval Headquarters. The watch notified me and I rushed into the radio-wireless room. Mikhailoff, alerted, reported that we were now about ten miles westward of Cape St. Nicholas, on the western tip of Haiti. It still would not be too late to turn back to the northward and head under cover of darkness and at high speed for some place on the northeastern coast of Cuba.

But we were lucky. Admiral Gorshkov's staff operations officer, who signed the message for the admiral, merely directed that we head for Santiago de Cuba at best speed and, while remaining undetected, contact the Soviet consul directly for local instructions. The dispatch ended on the curious note, "Do nothing to reveal your presence in locality to unfriendly sources. Continue on mission assigned." I noted that a copy of this message was also addressed to Northern Fleet Headquarters. This no doubt accounted for the fact that we never received a direct reply from that headquarters to the message sent there some hours earlier.

With Mikhailoff, I went over the chart of the approaches

to Santiago. However I did it, I would have first to skirt the U. S. fleet operating area just south of the Naval Base at Guantanamo Bay. I did not know what or how many U. S. warships would be cruising around down there during this period, in daylight or in darkness, and thus I was compelled to draw out a track which would take us far to the south of Guantanamo, by at least sixty miles. Then, we could swing back to the northwest and make it to Santiago de Cuba with less chance of detection by U. S. surface or subsurface craft. As a matter of fact, it was the subsurface craft which I frankly feared the most. And, although I knew, of course, that American men-of-war of all types train in those waters, I still did not know how many or what types of submarines the United States would have operating down there. The thought of running into one of them, unsuspectingly, chilled me thoroughly.

Mikhailoff calculated the distance over the tracks I had laid out. He frowned, and, turning to me, said, "Captain, if we proceed at best speed, we will be there in the bright sunny daylight. What an unfortunate time! Know what? I recommend we just decide on what time we want to get there off Santiago, and then adjust our speed accordingly."

"Right as far as I'm concerned. We just can't afford to go along at best speed. That's out. It'll have to be a damned slow speed, I'm afraid. What do you recommend?"

The navigator took his dividers and, elongating the arc from the first leg, added the remainder of the distance to the first arc formed. It came out to be about 170 miles. The bulkhead clock said 2:45 A.M.

"I'd say let's try to get them to receive us when practically everyone who shouldn't be up *isn't* up," Mikhailoff suggested. Seeing me nod, he asked, "How about us being there at midnight tomorrow night? I don't think that either Rodzianko or Dedusko will *die* if we don't get them ashore before then. And we certainly don't want to reveal ourselves, do we? Let's see, now, Captain . . . that would be . . . ummm . . . ohh, about 4.5 meters per second speed of advance for us to use . . . say, perhaps, eight knots or so?"

I stroked my neatly trimmed Castroite beard, and replied firmly after a moment's hesitation, "Very well, make it so." Thus decided, I slapped the navigator on the back and turned around to the watch officer. It was Glinka.

"Lieutenant," I said, "I guess you've heard the plan. Now, let's kick up no American destroyers in our wake or anything like that! I'd like to make about eight knots now. Keep a sharp lookout, and be sure we stop snorkeling before morning twil'ght. Notify me, of course, of any contacts which may be critical. You understand."

I wasn't so sure he did understand, but I had no alternative except to try to make him believe I had continued confidence in him, despite his previous fiasco. In truth, I must admit, it was gratifying to see his response was no longer one of lighthearted indifference, washed along by an all-too-present grin. From him, I now got a smile, but a more military "Aye, aye, Captain."

Returning to my stateroom, I collapsed once more into my armchair. What to do now? With a sigh and a heavy heart, I knew what must be done. The accident with Volkonski, and now this most recent mishap, had wrought havoc with the internal administration of the submarine. Key people were out of the picture. I had to have a reorganization. The ship's routine must continue, and now, as never before, perhaps, since we were entering the stamping grounds of American fleet units, I would have to demand complete and abiding loyalty and extra effort from all hands to insure our success.

My ultimate plan was to give to Makar Rostopchin the new Second Officer's hat; that is, I decided to devolve upon him all the duties of the Second Officer. Since he was the only officer well enough acquainted with the engineering plant, he would, of course, have to continue to supervise the engineering personnel. To take Dedusko's place as electronics officer, I decided to assign Ivan Baliuk his post as an additional responsibility. After all, Baliuk was already the intelligence and underwater sound officer; he could easily enough take on the responsibility for the other electronics equipment.

Finding another clerk for the commissar would be something else again, however. Alexei had been, in truth, a fair-haired boy with him; a young, blossoming, pink-cheeked lad of handsome features and pleasant disposition—one whom I think Lvov wanted ultimately to channel into the commissioned officer training programs for political administration. One could never be sure, however. I recall overhearing one of the crew, beyond sight of me across a galley range, once intimate to another that Lvov's unabashed fondness for Alexei had more to it than just the paternal interest of a teacher or political leader toward a protégé. The remark stuck with me, and the more I thought about it, the more it mollified my feelings. If Lvov were now out to ruin me, as Sverdlov had been . . . then, to fight fire with fire might be the best solution. And I sat there, continuing to think of every little last glance, every smile, every demonstrative action I had ever observed from Lvov in his dealings with the young lad who had passed now forever out of his reach. And I preferred to think of that reach as a lecherous one.

Not much before the morning twilight, Makar Rostopchin chose to stop by my room. I motioned for him to be seated on my bunk; when he had done so, I wheeled around in my chair and, tilting back and yawning (for I had only caught small bits of dozing rest in my chair during the preceding few hours), said casually, "What is it, Mr. Second Officer?"

Rostopchin's blue eyes sparkled, and his face flushed. Throwing his head back spontaneously, he erupted into his usual boisterous laughter. "Captain," he managed to say finally, "that's what we need, a good joke!" And then he shook his head slowly in an amused manner. "I just left the conning station," he went on, "and do you know what? The commissar is up there, for the first time checking the navigational charts and all as though he were responsible for our safety or something. Can you imagine?"

"That is his privilege," I countered, but then, seeing Rostopchin shrug wondrously at my seeming unconcern, I ventured further.

"Makar," I said, hesitatingly, "you are in fact now Second Officer. As such, I will have to depend upon you, starting now, for additional information to aid me in keeping a tight rein on this command. You understand that, of course. At the same time, I shall expect you, and not me, to run the internal administration of this submarine. You may count on my unqualified support, for I have every confidence in your capability."

Rostopchin leaned back on the bunk, and propped himself up on a crooked elbow jutting into the foam rubber mattress, over which the red bedspread was draped.

"I shall tell you frankly," I now admitted, "that the commissar and I are finding life quite difficult together. I am quite sure he would rather have had me lost over the side than young Alexei."

I watched Makar's facial expressions most carefully, for any clue as to some kind of intimate knowledge about Lvov which he was aware of but which normally he might not bring into a discussion. But Rostopchin's features remained unmoved.

Then came the shocker. "Captain," the newly designated Second Officer asked, "do you have any idea at all why Lvov has been promoted?"

"Promoted?" I nearly jumped out of my chair.

"Why, yes sir, haven't you seen the message? Why, by the beard of Ivan, if you haven't I'll bet it's because the operations officer thought you'd better get a little sleep before you found out about it. After all, there's not much that can be done about it, one way or the other . . ."

"My God! Did you say *promoted?* Makar, for a golden ruble! You're jesting, man. I'm afraid I can't find it amusing, though."

"No, Captain, I mean it. About a half hour ago, an encoded message was received and Baliuk broke it. It was addressed to Lvov, and it just said, 'your message received, good work,' etc., and then it said, 'effective immediately' he was to be a post-captain in the Office of Political Administration in the Navy."

"Hell! Who the devil wrote that damned message to him?"

"Why, Grishanov, who else?"

"Yes, of course. Before he reported here, he was the old boy's aide."

Rostopchin bit his lip, then said, "But Captain, his elevation surely won't make any difference in his position on board *here,* will it?"

I knew, naturally, that although officially it would not, nonetheless, commanders in the Soviet Navy are indeed inferior in grade to post-captains, and the thought of Lvov being jumped two whole ranks at this time, to a grade senior to me, was quite maddening. It was so infuriating that I got up and kicked my chair over. Whatever he had sent in that message of his, I was certain he had said something important enough, or damaging enough to me, anyway, to have Grishanov feel it worth the new rank for the man.

"Well," I said, finally, "I'm exhausted. Makar, take over and run the show for a while. If you don't mind, I'm going to hit that bunk for a few minutes."

Sleep I did. The stress and the tension of the past day had been too taxing, and I slept soundly for a good uninterrupted eight hours. Makar Rostopchin had taken me at my word. He had reorganized the wardroom officers in their duties, had for the time acted as a buffer to preclude my getting non-critical reports and calls when I needed some heavy sleep, and perhaps more than anything else, had started his tour as my new Second Officer by seizing the initiative just as I wanted him to. Much later, I found out that he had politely congratulated the commissar on his promotion, and then had courteously but firmly announced that henceforth, he, Rostopchin, would act as intermediary between *all* other officers on board this submarine, and the commanding officer. Lvov did not press the point.

22

What Guantánamo Could Become

☐ In view of the message from Supreme Headquarters directing me to Santiago de Cuba, and at the same time telling me to make the final arrangements locally through the Havana consulate, it was necessary for the *F-689* to cruise for several hours during the evening of the twenty-third of February with the whip-antenna protruding above the water. Since the Soviet consul in Cuba had already been sent a message request for assistance, it now remained for him to respond. Naturally, I grew more and more anxious as the hours went by. We had done our part fully, including sending an amplifying report to the consulate, advising that midnight on the night of February 23-24 would be convenient as an expected time of arrival off the entrance to Santiago.

Finally, around eight o'clock in the evening, we received a short-wave wireless encoded message from the Soviet consul, stating that all shore arrangements had been made for our arrival at the time specified. The dispatch went on to state that when all was clear for surfacing, a red blinker light would flash alternately at seven-second intervals from the top of the old Spanish fortress which stands atop the cliffs rising up vertically from the outer harbor entrance. A motor launch would then come out to us, once we returned the signal by aiming an infrared signal lamp at the fortress blinker light.

The message concluded by saying that two high-ranking Cuban officials would embark in the launch for transportation to the submarine, and that if possible, I was to take

them on board for the remainder of the trip around Cuba
to Havana.

Shortly after midnight, the *F-689* surfaced one-half mile
off Santiago de Cuba's harbor entrance. For the forty-five
to fifty minutes immediately preceding the surfacing, I had
been intently spying through the periscope to detect the
anticipated signal. Everything had been readied and the
two shark-injured officers were waiting patiently but in
great pain for their disembarkation. Rodzianko's right
forearm had begun to fester, and his whole body had been
overtaken by chills and fever, despite the antibiotics which
the corpsman had administered. Both officers now lay on
stretchers in the forward torpedo room.

Now, with the submarine in position, it was a matter of
just waiting for the signals . . . and then I saw them. It
could have been just a blinking red aerial warning light
indicating a high-positioned menace to air navigation. But
it wasn't. It was the signal to surface and reveal our presence. This we did.

Lying-to there on the surface, so close to the shore, and
within a few minutes' flying time from the big U. S. naval
base to the eastward, was most unnerving. It was therefore
a definite relief when I spotted the launch plowing through
the water toward us.

Twenty minutes later, Rodzianko and Dedusko had
been transferred, and we had taken on board two slovenly
attired, long-haired, greasy-looking Latins (one with a
black beard), as well as a staff officer from the Soviet military mission to Cuba, Soviet Air Force Colonel Ourusov.
This Soviet representative was dressed in lightweight
sports clothes, with a Panama hat topping off his nearly
bald head; I did not know him, but relied on his identification papers for the necessary verification. Although I shook
hands with each of the Cubans as they alighted on the
deck of the open bridge, I did not recognize them or realize
who they actually were until the submarine had been again

submerged. They merely came on board with the colonel, were rather quickly hustled down the manhold to the confines of the submarine below the bridge, and did not register one way or the other with me until I myself jumped down from the outside, slammed the hatch shut, and let the watch officer take us down to 150 feet.

Post-Captain Commissar Lvov had met them at the foot of the ladder connecting the bridge with the conning station, and had taken them to the wardroom. That is where I found them, as the watch officer obeyed my instructions and headed due south at slow speed.

At the table, waited on by the new commissary-porter, Usoupoff, sat a delicately small, mustachioed, youngish man whose lips curled back in what appeared to be a rather sardonic smile. The other Cuban, a very heavily bearded one, was fingering a glass of dark rum which Usoupoff had planted before him. Opposite him sat Lvov, and to the commissar's right hunched Ivan Baliuk, the intelligence officer. Lvov looked well in command of the situation. Raising his eyebrows, he boomed, "Captain, *los señores* Raul Castro and the Cuban Communist Party Chief, if I may call him that, Ché Guevara."

Neither of these two Cubans inpressed me very favorably, either then or later. I nodded, walked over, and shook their hands again, and apologized for having been so brusque when they had come aboard.

Castro flipped a king-size cigarette into his mouth, having drawn it from a gold pocket humidor concealed in the left front shirt pocket of his Army-like green fatigues. (The "fatigues" looked like, on closer inspection, anything but Army general issue, however. They appeared to be made of lightweight nylon or silk.) His compatriot quickly produced a lighter and, leaning forward, flicked the flint-wheel. The diminutive brother of the big Head of the Cuban State puffed contentedly and with a wave, chirped, "*Gracias,* Ché."

Lvov began to dominate the conversation.

"This is certainly a great honor for us, señores. You, Señor Castro," he purred, "as the head of the Cuban Armed Forces . . ."

Raul Castro dropped his eyes and took a long puff on his cigarette; Guevara looked up at the overhead and stroked his beard. And then, the momentary silence was broken by a new voice.

"Ah, well, gentlemen, so! It is good to be here!!" It was the colonel, stepping into the wardroom, escorted by Mikhailoff. "I have been looking for a moment at the navigational chart, and wondering where we are going next. I have some information for you on the Yankee ships in the area . . ."

"Yes, Colonel," went on Lvov, "that is good, would you not think so, Captain?" and then, turning to Castro once more, he continued where he had been cut off.

"Señor Castro—"

"Please, just say, 'Raul.' "

The commissar smiled unctuously, and, acknowledging this bid for informal relations, said, "Thank you, Raul. Everyone calls me 'Commissar,' but my name is Georgy. Georgy Mikhailovich Lvov, and you would honor me by just addressing me by my first name if you desire."

Castro glanced at Guevara, who fidgeted and then spoke up.

"We would really prefer to simply address you as 'Commissar,' if you don't mind. I say this because it is important that those who are with us later on in your visit to Cuba —and you will be our guests, I hope, for several weeks— should learn to associate you more fully with the work you do in political orientation. To be less formal might damage the image which we want to project, of one of the Soviet Union's top-notch commissars being here with us. You understand, I am sure."

Lvov beamed. He was in his glory.

"Well, anyway, you may call me just plain Raul, if you want to," said Castro indifferently. "Of course," he went on, cigarette now dangling from the corner of his lips, "everyone knows who I am anyway, and that I am the over-all Commander in Chief in substance of the Cuban Armed Forces. But I really need not be talked of by title every time someone talks with or about me."

The Soviet colonel, well acquainted with Castro and Guevara, interposed and settled what might have degenerated into an unpleasant series of continued remarks.

"It is so, *es verdad, es verdad,*" he soothed. *"Caballeros grandes no desean las palabras bonitas o las referencias a los grados."* Though his Spanish may have been doubtful in its grammatical perfection, it did nonetheless have the soothing effect needed at the time.

I now spoke up, and asked whether Castro and Guevara particularly wanted to do or see anything specifically. They replied that they had never before been on a Soviet submarine—any kind of submarine, as a matter of fact—and that when they had learned of our proximity, and that we would shortly be coming into Havana itself, they sought the necessary approval from Fidel. He had given them his blessings in their request to go aboard and sail around the western tip of Cuba.

"One thing we would like," said Castro, "would be to go up off Guantánamo and surface right in the center of the Naval Base Bay. What else would better teach those *norte-americanos* that the land and waters of Cuba are ours to do with as we see fit?"

It was then necessary to tell Castro and Guevara that our mission was really so sensitive that we could never do anything of the sort—at least, not on *this* cruise. Perhaps at some later time. But, I told them, we still had to move up into the waters south of Guantánamo, perhaps move in quite close to the base itself, and observe the American fleet units at close quarters. They—Castro and Guevara—could then have a pride of accomplishment, in the realization that they were on board a submarine hostile to the United States which they so thoroughly loathed, and that

that submarine was able to encroach upon the training grounds of the U. S. Navy!

The idea appealed to both Cubans, and gave Colonel Ourusov the opportunity to again bring up the matter of information concerning U. S. ships in the Guantánamo area.

Ourusov reached into one of his pockets and drew forth a black notebook. From it, he began reading the names of U. S. ships which he said our best intelligence revealed were either in Guantánamo, would be there soon, or were in nearby waters. From this list, it was evident that the Americans would have plenty of naval strength in the area during the next few days, and that our mission in spying on them would probably be most successful.

"This weekend," said the colonel, "we have cause to think that many of the ships normally in training at the Guantánamo Base will be visiting in various ports in the Caribbean. Most of them will return to the Guantánamo training waters early Monday morning. For instance, the *Forrestal*—"

"Yes, that's one of their biggest aircraft carriers, isn't it?" It was Raul Castro, interrupting.

"Well, if you don't include the nuclear-powered carrier *Enterprise*," I said.

The colonel didn't wait. He kept right on.

"The *Forrestal* is supposed to be visiting in Port-au-Prince, Haiti, this weekend. She should be back off Guantánamo, or at least in the area, early Monday morning."

"The *Forrestal*," I interjected, "is quite a ship. I'm happy to say that this won't be the first time I've looked at her through a periscope."

Guevara was astounded.

"You mean, señor, that you have been in a position to sink that big ship before? And you didn't do it? *Santa María*!"

Post-Captain Commissar Lvov's icy words punctuated the astonishment of the number one Cuban Communist.

"Tut-tut, *mís amigos*," he intoned. "Not only that, but our good captain of this most powerful submarine has looked through his periscope at *many* objects which he could easily have damaged or sunk!" Lvov glanced at me with a penetrating, hateful gaze.

I chose to ignore him.

"What other ships will the Americans have in Guantánamo for tra`ning next week?" I asked.

The Air Force colonel smiled. He was beginning to feel like a Very Important Person, perhaps someone on whom the success of the submarine's mission might fatefully depend. He was about to open his mouth to read more from his little black book when I decided to put an end to his fanciful delusions of naval importance.

"Of course, you know that the *Forrestal* is but *one* of the many ships of the Americans which we *already* know to be in these waters, and although we didn't know she'd be in Haiti this weekend, we aren't at all surprised. Northern Fleet Headquarters have already apprised us that the *Enterprise*, the *Forrestal*, the new American destroyers *Dewey*, *Decatur*, *Sampson*, and some others will probably be operating down here in a training status." I was rattling off from memory the names of the ships which our previous intelligence had supplied.

Colonel Ourusov blinked. He hadn't expected, I am sure, that a submarine nearly a month out of the remote port of Murmansk would have such up-to-the-minute appreciation of what was going on in the world—especially in his own immediate military world right there in Cuba. But, I reflected quickly, it probably wasn't at all unusual for an Air Force type to have little if any true appreciation of sea power or naval capabilities.

Colonel Ourusov's eyes looked down into his little black book once again, and he recommended reading from his notes:

"The big new American destroyer *Sampson*, which

you have mentioned, Captain, will be due in these waters Monday morning from a visit to Montego Bay. They're probably going there to pitch a good Jamaican rum party."

Guevara threw back his black-haired head and downed the remnants of dark rum in his glass, then gasped, "Ahhh!" as the new commissary-porter, Usoupoff, glided unobtrusively over and refilled the glass.

The Soviet Air Force colonel went on with his reading, speaking somewhat louder now.

"The American submarine *Sennet* will be at Ocho Rios this weekend, but will be back off Guantánamo late in the afternoon of the twenty-sixth—Monday—and, say! Captain," he asked slowly, "is there any danger you might get discovered by this American sub?"

I replied quickly that of course there was always that chance, that submarines have the greatest of fear about interception from an enemy submarine; however, I told him, perhaps the American submarine and not the Soviet sub should be the one to worry! This produced a chuckle from everyone in the wardroom.

My intelligence officer, Lieutenant Baliuk, pushed ahead with this thought that I had engendered. Said he, "The *Sennet* is an old World War II American submarine of about fifteen hundred tons. She isn't even a true 'Guppy' type . . . what I mean is, although she has a snorkel device, she can't operate as well or as efficiently as subs which have been designed from the keel up as true submersibles. Not that this sub, the *F-689*, is a 'true submersible.' We aren't, because almost daily we have to come up to snorkel for recharging the batteries and for fresh air. Only a nuclear boat can stay submerged indefinitely. But this American sub we're talking about, the *Sennet*, is really an old type from the last war. Nothing to worry about, I'd say. After all, we're almost five hundred tons heavier, a hell of a lot faster, and *we're* the ones with the real good homing torpedoes and—"

"Of course," I interrupted, "we can never d'scount *any* enemy submarine, but what the lieutenant is saying is simply that we are better equipped than she is!"

I could see Guevara relax noticeably. And the Air Force colonel, also, seemed somewhat relieved. The answers to his question satisfied him. He continued with his reading.

"We may expect the Yankee submarines *Chivo* and *Picuda* to be down in this area next week. I hear the *Picuda* is coming from Key West. The *Chivo* is going to be in Haiti, probably Port-au-Prince, sometime within the next two weeks." The colonel looked at my intelligence officer. "Tell me, Lieutenant, are these subs anything for us to worry about, more than the first one I mentioned?"

Baliuk got up and walked over to the wardroom book cabinet. "Wait a moment, Colonel," he said, drawing out a 1961-62 copy of *Jane's Fighting Ships*. Castro now beckoned to Usoupoff to give him, also, a drink of rum.

Lvov's voice entered into the conversation again.

"The important thing, of course," he said, "is that if we ever think we're going to be in a tough scrape, we'll take appropriate action to alleviate the situation."

"What do you mean, *alleviate* the situation?" spoke up Castro, nodding appreciatively to Usoupoff for the fresh glass of rum which the latter had brought to him.

"He means," I interceded, "that whenever in my opinion, as commanding officer, I bel'eve it necessary to do so in order to avoid being detected and having subsequent embarrassment brought upon the Soviet Union, I will take offensive action against the aggressor."

Raul Castro's beady eyes blazed with astonishment and wonder. "*¡Por dios!*" he murmured.

"That is the answer I think the commissar wanted," I said, "but in truth, I feel that before that time comes, I would resort to other, more stealthy, more fox-like techniques to insure our withdrawal from the scene unscathed and still unexposed."

Mikhailoff now spoke up. "We might just go down to

maximum depth and sit there. Way down there below the depth the American subs of this vintage can move to!" He referred to the U. S. subs previously mentioned by name. "And way down there, we'd be able to slowly, s-l-o-w-l-y, creep out . . ." His right hand moved horizontally across his front, fingers purposefully wavering. Guevara's eyes focused on the wavering fingers and he looked quite transfixed. Perhaps the rum he had imbibed had something to do with it.

The Air Force colonel now pulled up a chair opposite me and, clearing his throat, proceeded to announce that there were many more ships on his list. But Baliuk had now found what he was searching for, and cut him off.

"These subs, the *Chivo* and the *Picuda*," he said, reading from the large blue volume which he now spread out atop the wardroom table, "are Balao class submarines." Looking up at the colonel, he said simply, "They're like the *Sennet* after a fashion but are somewhat better. Same class, practically. Better refitted and they call them 'Guppys.' If it seems confusing, let me just say that this sub in which you now ride is much more advanced."

Ourusov's face registered delight. He then again cleared his throat and read from his notes:

"Several auxiliaries will be in Guantánamo this next week. You may expect the ammunition ship *Mazama*, the refrigerator ship *Arcturus*, the attack transport *Alcor*, the oiler *Kaskaskia*, the landing ship, dock, now that's a funny name for it, isn't it? The landing ship, dock, *Spiegel Grove*, and I have information saying that the tanker *Sabine* will be departing the area. The tanker *Aucilla* is due to arrive in Guantánamo from Norfolk, Virginia, about the fifth of March. The destroyer *John Paul Jones* will be here during the next two weeks, along with several others."

Raul Castro's eyes flashed. "I'm all for sinking some of these ships," he said firmly, in his staccato Spanish, which I could, nonetheless, understand.

Downing the rest of his rum, Fidel Castro's small

brother launched into another line of thought. Bringing the now empty glass down upon the wardroom table with a bang, he asked, "Where have you looked through your periscope at the *Forrestal* before?"

"The Mediterranean Sea," I answered succinctly.

"Way over there?" Castro seemed incredulous. "But, Captain," he said, "that's where the Americans have that powerful Sixth Fleet of theirs. How did you ever get that *close* to the *Forrestal*? I always thought the Yankees really protected those big carriers when they were operating as fleet units—you know, as differentiated from down here where they all train more or less independently."

"American naval authorities, and I'm sure the American public," answered Lvov quickly, "seem to think that their Sixth Fleet is the ruler of the Mediterranean. Little do they really know!"

For their enlightenment I took Castro and his swarthy friend, Guevara, on a short trip of narration through the Mediterranean. I told how although the Americans think they "own" that ancient sea—and this, surely, is the view of not only the American Navy but also the American tourists—the projection of Russian submarine power is indeed capable of making "molten coffins" of large U. S. fleet units in those waters. Perhaps the commissar explained the situation more graphically. Said he, "U. S. *turistas y marineros* think the Mediterranean is their own private playground. The English think they 'discovered' it. Now of course, here, I'm talking of the Riviera ports where you can always find big American aircraft carriers, guided missile cruisers, destroyers and auxiliaries, as well as those big ocean liner tourist ships which bring all that American gold to the Côte d'Azur.

"Well," he said firmly, "it wasn't the English, and it isn't the Americans who have their foot in the Mediterranean the most strongly."

Lvov went on to tell the Cubans that the present director of the Monte Carlo Casino was General Polosov, the last living Russian gambler of the *Belle Epoque* back in the "Gay Nineties." The first Russian settlement on the shores of the Riviera took place in 1770—long before the English ever "discovered" Cannes.

"Why, back before the turn of the past century," Lvov confided, "do you know that Russian princes and Grand Dukes used to go to the French Riviera in droves? Did you know that it was Prince Cherasky who built a palace above Cannes, where he kept over a hundred servants? Fifty of these servants were there just for gardening! Imagine! And another famous Russian had a villa where he had cellists playing music for him day and night! Right there near Cannes, where the Englishman, Lord Brougham, was supposed to have 'discovered' the Riviera!"

Guevara was interested. "But I never knew you Russians got out of the *Baltic,* until recent years!"

"Humph," exclaimed Lvov. "Let me tell you something more. All you have to do is ask the French themselves. I tell you, by 1900, the Riviera was actually speaking with a Russian accent! Our Grand Dukes Vladimir, Michael, and Boris were all the acknowledged leaders of the Côte d'Azur society of that period. Why," he went on bragging, "we Russians had the famous ballets of Diaghilev, staring Nijinsky, performed right there in Nice. Monaco, too. In fact, we made Monaco the Capital of the Dance. And what's more, Russia almost bought Monaco! Now what do you think of *that?*"

"So?" It was Castro.

"So?" The commissar's face reddened.

I entered the conversation by merely saying that what the commissar was trying to do was show that we Russians had a good, strong claim on the Mediterranean life, even more so than the Americans and the English. And I topped it off with the remark that if the Kremlin wanted to do so, and our submarines were deployed there in strength, we probably could send to the bottom all the warships sent into Mussolini's old *Mare Nostrum* by any government hostile to Soviet Russia. I did not, however, elucidate upon my own experiences there tracking the Sixth Fleet all over their supposed unchallenged stamping grounds.

"Well," said Castro, "at least, you have more influence, more friendly acknowledgment of your existence, here in Cuba than you might imagine. Of course, Colonel Ourusov knows how grateful we are to you for helping us in our fight for a true revolution here. You know, we have the Red flag, with gold hammer and sickle, sharing the breeze in Cuba with the Cuban national ensign. And when you take us into Havana Harbor, you will see a huge sign on one of the longest piers. It is a greeting to all Soviet sailors entering the city. It's in Russian lettering, too. It says, 'Peace and Friendship.' Above it, in Spanish, are the words, 'Fidel—Khrushchev.' "

"Yes," the commissar intervened, "and that's the way it should be, too. We in Soviet Russia are glad to take all the exports you have from Cuba. As I recall, we are now receiving about 80 per cent of your total national produce, are we not?"

Guevara answered affirmatively, and noted that before Castro came to power, Soviet Russia took only 2.6 per cent of the Cuban exports. He expressed pleasure at the twelve-year credit agreement signed by Cuba and the USSR, and said he was delighted with the machinery and equipment Russia was sending into Cuba.

I was particularly interested in the comments of both Raul Castro and Ché Guevara concerning the value of the USSR technical training offered to Cubans. Both these Cuban officials stated that they were more than pleased at the reciprocal agreements concerning workers, students, and technicians. Well over fifteen hundred young Cubans are currently studying in universities in the Soviet Union; others are enrolled in Polish, East German, and other Communist countries. Nearly a thousand young Cubans are learning about agriculture from advanced farming experts in agricultural technical centers in Soviet Russia. Nearly two thousand Czech, Polish, Russian, and Chinese technicians are working in Cuba itself.

But of equal importance is the fact that Soviet military power has been planted right under the noses of not only the big Guantánamo Naval Base of the American fleet, but it has been planted—and *pointed*—from its Cuban soil sites, directly at specific targets in the United States.

Castro reverted to our discussion of the Mediterranean. Bringing up the matter of sea power in that area, he said he had heard that the Italians had recently been exerting themselves in the field of antisubmarine warfare. He wanted to know whether we were afraid of the Italians. Practically everyone else present laughed uproariously, including myself. After all, the Italians fought two world wars within a span of twenty-five years, and although they weren't whipped in the first, they came very close to it; in the second, their Army, Navy, and Air Forces did nothing of any consequence except go down to defeat.

Nonetheless, I was compelled to tell Raul Castro and his companion that Soviet intelligence does acknowledge the resurgence of the Italian Navy after nearly two decades of neglect. I mentioned, in particular, one Italian naval commander named Francesco Castracane degli Antelminelli, whom Soviet agents believe is spearheading the present drive to modernize the Italian Navy through efforts in the antisubmarine field. I told the Cubans that the Italians, thanks probably to this Antelminelli, are now developing small, sixteen-man submarines for antisubmarine work. They aren't ocean-going types, but are designed to get close to enemy sub pens and harbors, where they could conceivably be effective against larger submarines. Right now, Italy has six submarines. Of these, three are old U. S. subs, and one is a new one built by Italy. The other two are old World War II subs salvaged from the Navy of *Il Duce*.

"Pues," sighed Raul Castro sleepily, for it was nearly two o'clock in the morning, "so why worry about those damned spaghetti suckers?"

And on this note, the conversation ended. Raul Castro was nearly dozing; Lvov was having obvious difficulty keeping his eyelids open; Baliuk was curled up on the wardroom couch, still looking through *Jane's Fighting Ships,* but with heavy eyelids.

I nudged Baliuk and suggested he might like to show the señores to their bunks. The last thing I said, as all arose to find their sleeping berths, was that we might have to spend as much as the next ten days collecting intelligence in the Guantánamo area.

That is what we did—and it was not until the fifth of March (with our Cuban friends still on board) that I felt we had exhausted the possibilities for further intelligence gathering in the Guantánamo area.

By then, we had spied on the inner harbor of Guantánamo Bay, where the larger ships usually anchor; I had maneuvered far enough into the outer harbor, between Windward Point and the opposite shore, that I could plainly see the American admiral's luxurious tropical palace atop a small bluff called "Deer Point" on the navigational chart. We took several periscope photographs of the installation and ships within the harbor, as well as some photographs of ships of the U. S. fleet as they emerged from or entered the sheltered confines of Guantánamo Bay. It was interesting to note how devoid of submarine defenses the big naval base was. Or maybe we were just lucky.

Some of the American warships which we observed while operating off the southeastern end of Cuba included the *Enterprise,* the *Forrestal,* the *Dewey,* the *Decatur,* the *Sampson,* and literally a dozen other ships. In fact, not very many of the ships that Colonel Ourusov had in his little black book managed to escape our detailed observation. Of particular interest in such close scrutiny, of course, were any new electronics gear on board, as might be evidenced by new antenna arrangements; new tactics possibly being devised in antisubmarine warfare (there were none!); and witnessing the fast power runs of the ships.

Some of the other ships which I looked at off Guantánamo, always through the cross hairs of my periscope, were the U. S. men-of-war *Mazama, Arcturus, Alcor, Kaskaskia, Loeser, Spiegel Grove, Sabine, Aucilla, John Paul Jones, Harwood, Power* (which I had spied upon in the Mediteranean back in 1958, when she was operating with the *Abbot*), the *Sullivans* (named for five U. S. brothers who were lost in World War II), the *Gary*, and several others. Of course, many of these were auxiliaries for the support of combatant ships. But the fighting ships there fared no better than the dull-looking tankers or oilers. We watched them all with the same degree of covert adriotness that would be demanded in time of a shooting war.

Finally, on taking our departure from the Guantánamo Bay area, we headed westward along the southern Cuban coast, bound for Havana. My last reflection was that Guantánamo could become another Pearl Harbor.

23

We Cannot Coexist Eternally

☐ Moving westward along the southern coast of sunny Cuba was so indescribably different from our movement, the previous month, along the northern shores of Russia and Norway, around North Cape into the Norwegian Sea. Here along the shores of this so-called "Pearl of the Antilles," there were nothing but blue skies and golden sunshine. What a contrast to the sight of the low, white dunes of the Russian tundra near Kola Inlet. What a contrast to the world, so vastly different, of Murmansk, where in summer there is sunshine, but where in winter it is almost perpetually dark. I thought of the treeless plains we had left up there in northern Russia for this glorious sunshine and rugged coastline of southern Cuba! Alas! That we could not enjoy that sunshine . . . for it was only by coming to periscope depth occasionally that we were even aware of the outside weather conditions.

Professor Bogucharovo and his friend, Pozdeev, met the two Cuban "dignitaries" the day they had come aboard; though, granted, it had been some eight hours after the Cubans' first setting foot on board that the two Soviet professors actually made their introductions. They had, in these waters, become great bunk artists—they had come to love sleep as only the mythical Morpheus could have. Of course, both of them found in Guevara an intellect of comparable level. The three of them soon spent their waking hours hovering over the wardroom table, discussing everything from Marxist theory to various plans of world order predicated upon creeping socialism. It was obvious at the outset that the trio had a common denominator—that degree of intellectual brilliance which precluded their understanding the immediate realities of everyday situations.

Commissar Lvov managed to sit in on some of their sessions, but, being basically of a rather limited mentality, he avoided the really deep conversations into which the trio often moved. He was blessed with no proclivity for intelligent reasoning, as I had long before decided.

On the seventh of March, in the early morning hours, we passed well to the southward of the now-famous Bay of Pigs. Since we were still on our regular patrol cruising hours, all hands were up and about when the navigator walked into the wardroom and announced to those present —including the trio alluded to previously—that the submarine was due generally south, now, of that portion of the Cuban coast where the Americans had aborted last year with their ill-advised assault on Castro's Cuba.

This produced immediate reactions from Raul Castro as well as Guevara. They both joined in a tirade at the United States as Lvov looked on approvingly. Then Guevara ended the discussion by saying that of course, Castro and he had known all along that the U.S. wouldn't truly, wouldn't really, use open, armed U. S. support in such an invasion attempt as the anti-Castro forces put on. After all, they explained, as long as the extreme liberal bloc controls the U. S. State Department, no concrete overt action against Cuba could be foreseen.

"As nominal Commander in Chief of the Cuban Armed Forces," said Raul Castro, "I was right there on the beach protecting us from invasion. I was in a command car, directing the entire defense operation. I guess you *marineros* didn't know *that,* did you?"

We had not known it, of course. But it was an interesting sidelight, firsthand, of the affair which doubtless has gone down in history as one of the worst possible invasion schemes of modern times.

Raul Castro, elated, went on to reveal that his forces—

troops under his direct command—had captured 1179 insurgents, all enemies of Cuba and invaders for whom awaited but one fate—the firing squad. He was vitriolic when he spoke of the American destroyers which came close to the beaches and tried to pick up the invaders' survivors.

Why had the Americans not used their ships and planes to pave the way for the invasion? In Guevara's opinion, it was because several of the American president's closest personal advisers and State Department aides felt that for him to commit U. S. power would be a step toward general war. Of course, even the commissar views general war as a distinctly remote possibility. At least, he told Castro and Guevara that he doubted Soviet Russia would have entered into the situation in any event, other than to file strong protests in the UN.

"Some American officials," I recall Commissar Lvov saying, "really believe that Communism is beginning to fade from the world arena. They actually think it is a moribund suprapolitical force.

"Therefore, I'd say that as long as men like that are in positions where they can influence U. S. foreign policy, our efforts are made that much easier."

When Baliuk told Lvov that we had previously discussed this same subject, Lvov answered by saying all the better, for he had found repetition to be the most effective means for getting points across to people. "And the reason I want to get this point across, about such dreamers," Lvov said, "is because in addition to the belligerent activities of which we are guilty, if you can call it 'guilt,' we do have people helping us in America, even though they may not even realize it."

One of the things most pleasing to Soviet leaders, of course, is the position taken by many "do-gooders" in America: They who would embark on a program of massive foreign aid, without concern about the political faith of the recipients, or their positions or leanings in the cold war.

"You mean," Baliuk said, "that these Americans—these socialist types in the higher echelons of the American Government—are sort of looking forward to a day when Communism has moderated into democratic-socialism and capitalism has deteriorated into democratic-socialism, and that they think this will finally be the day when the entire world can live blissfully forever?"

"Right," said the commissar. "They look forward to what they consider the inevitable day when the new world order will be one of universal socialism."

But what neither the commissar nor Baliuk mentioned in that conversation was that ultimate world socialism is precisely what Marx and Lenin were always talking about. Communism, after all, is only a means for achieving socialism on a huge and widespread scale.

Now Guevara was talking about the final objectives of worldwide Communism. There was no doubt in my mind that he identified himself and Cuba with the universal Communist movement which has its headquarters in the Kremlin.

In my own mind, I have often wondered, frankly, how anyone in the West could ever think that the Soviet Union will stop at less than world dominion, world thralldom, under a super-socialist state headquarters? Apparently, various high officials in America choose to forget the words said by Premier Khrushchev in April 1955, in Warsaw, Poland:

"We must realize that we cannot coexist eternally for a long time. One of us must go to the grave. They—the West —do not want to go to the grave either. So what can be done? We must push them to their grave."

Even though I had grown to have tremendous prejudices when it came to Commissar Lvov, in that I now held him in the lowest regard, I still continued to believe most of the

material he disclosed in the wardroom political orientation discussions. These meetings, of course, continued
without interruption.

It was on this underwater voyage around Cuba, to Havana, that Raul Castro whetted my appetite for information on the progress of the Cuban submarine pens being
built for Soviet subs. Upon my questioning him, all he
would say was, "You will see, *Capitán,* you will see." And
on the subject of missile emplacements directed against
the United States, he would only grin and tell me that
upon our arrival, he would show me how everything was.
"Don't worry about it," Fidel Castro's small brother
whined, "soon enough you will see for yourself what progress has been made."

But the Air Force colonel, Ourusov, was more helpful in
allaying my apprehensions. "The sub pens are practically
completed on a makeshift basis in one location, on the
northeast coast, and I think they'll build a permanent pen
elsewhere later."

As a Soviet submarine skipper, this was most encourag-
ing news. It meant that the Iron Curtain, with its power
and influence, had extended from beyond the mantle of
the Old World and the Far East, and had now strongly
established itself in the New World. But, inexplicably, I
could not rejoice in this knowledge. I was able only to as-
similate it as a matter of course, in the performance of my
duties as a Soviet comander.

24

Introducing Castro's Zangarillejas

☐ It had not been our intention, despite Raul Castro's invitation, to remain in Havana more than a week or perhaps ten days at the most. Normally, seven days would be all the time required for upkeep work and routine repairs after a voyage of some thirty-odd days. But fate was to keep us in Havana for most of the month of March.

I realized immediately that we would have to resign ourselves to a rather indefinitely long stayover among Castro's revolutionaries the moment Rostopchin told me of the casualty. It was in the forenoon on March 8 that he gave me the alarmingly bad news. Bursting into my stateroom, he pardoned himself and then announced that we had used up all the main engine fuel injectors—that we had no more spares, and that we had had to put number 3 main engine out of commission.

This left but two engines for the patrol up the east coast of the U.S. and the return voyage to Russia. I could not risk such a long trip, knowing full well that undoubtedly other injectors would fail. If this happened in number 1 and 2 engines, then the *F-689* would be left without any means of propulsion—for engines are needed to recharge the batteries—and such a casualty occurring in U. S. coastal waters would be catastrophic! I had been most apprehensive all along about this possibility, for snorkeling is tough on engines—and during this cruise the *F-689* had done more than her share of this. I told Rostopchin to prepare an immediate message to Fleet Headquarters (to be sent upon our arival in Havana), urgently requesting that these engine parts plus additional spares be air-delivered to Havana, and advising that the return patrol would be delayed until the parts were delivered.

Our position at this time was some thirty to forty miles northeast of Cuba's Cape San Antonio, along the extreme northwestern coastline in waters marked by the Colorado Reefs. Havana was less than eighty nautical miles away.

Since we now would be approaching the coastal shipping routes, I ordered that we proceed with utmost caution. I did not want to take any chances on being discovered, and, of course, my orders stipulated that we time our arrival in Havana to coincide with darkness. Whereas I would have liked to get into port as soon as possible for liberty, it was mandatory that we shroud our arrival in secrecy.

Thus it was that we passed around old Morro Castle into the harbor waters where in 1898 the American battleship *Maine* was blown up, around the salient promontory, and then headed to the right to bring ourselves to the piers which Castro's Navy had reserved for us. Of interest is the fact that the entrance to the harbor from seaward was made in much the same manner as was my approach toward the quarry in Beirut back in 1958. I was up on the open bridge; the submarine had been surfaced about a half-mile off Morro Castle, and a Cuban patrol vessel had come out to intercept us. It had been sent after local Cuban authorities had been notified by the Soviet consulate of the expected time of our arrival. This information, of course, I had transmitted to the Soviet diplomatic office earlier in the day—when we were approaching Bahía Honda, forty-five miles westward of Havana.

As we had been previously apprised, there was indeed a huge, lighted sign across the front of several of the pier warehouses. It read, "Peace and Friendship" with the names "Fidel" and "Khrushchev" in smaller lettering directly underneath. The harbor was fairly full. Soviet merchant ships hugged almost every available pier berth, and several such ships were at anchor in midstream.

Without much difficulty, I brought the *F-689* into the slip designated and no sooner had the mooring lines been made secure than Cuban workers, massed on the pier, strove to rig large awnings around us for camouflage. I noticed that at the end of the pier, guarding the entrance between two long dockside transfer houses, there was a heavy iron gate around which at least a squad or two of Cuban soldiers were massed. A black Rolls-Royce automobile stood waiting just outside the gate. It was illuminated by the floodlights on the shore side of the pier entrance; I could see that it was a Rolls because the engine cover on no other automobile is so distinctively shaped. I presumed that this was Raul Castro's waiting limousine.

I was wrong. It was a car the consulate had provided for Post-Captain Lvovl And, as it developed, Raul Castro and Ché Guevara were met by a maroon-colored Cadillac which, chauffeured by a Cuban sergeant and guarded by a tommy gun-carrying corporal who sat in the right front seat, rolled up to the pier within a half hour of our tying up. Raul prevailed upon me and all but one officer, whom I had previously designated to remain on board as duty officer the first day in port, to go with him and Guevara to the Hotel Nacional. Prior to doing so, I gathered the crew together and, with senior Chief Petty Officer Igor Novikov at my elbow, delivered a word or two of caution to the sailors.

This, as the first and only "liberty" port which the men could enter for recreational purposes, was also one which was, I understood, fairly saturated with various kinds of venereal disease. I made this amply clear to all personnel, and warned them of the possible consequences if they failed to take every precautionary measure.

My Second Officer, Rostopchin, appointed several petty officers as naval policemen, issued them scarlet armbands for the benefit of the local constabulary (who could then identify them properly), and with my consent released all but a skeleton crew for the first night's liberty party. All hands were told to be back on board by nine o'clock the next morning. Colonel Ourusov had beforehand advised that it was planned to have a bus at the pier to take the crew to the Rex Hotel and to some houses of entertainment which, under police control, would not adversely affect the health or welfare of the men. I consented to the plan, and when the bus pulled up in front of the pier, felt satisfied that the crew would be under control in this type of organized liberty.

After the crew had departed in the big diesel-engined bus, I made a last-minute check with the duty officer, Baliuk, to insure that the submarine would be secure. This done, I permitted myself the luxury of departing with Castro, Guevara, Ourusov, and Rostopchin in the former's Cadillac. Makar and I sat in two pull-out seats, which opened from the back side of the front seat, occupied by the armed soldiery. The other officers were picked up by Lvov in his large Rolls-Royce, and they followed us down the streets and promenades, boulevards and alley-like thoroughfares. Although I had not the slightest idea where in Havana we were, or specifically where the Hotel Nacional was, I recall both Castro and Guevara from time to time saying something like, "Now, this is the old section . . ." or "This used to be called El Prado. Now we call it El Paseo de Martí . . ." and, "Do you know why we call it that? Because, señores, we want to honor the apostle of Cuban independence!"

Looking out of the windows as we rolled along, I could see that the "Paseo" was lined with big new buildings, some offices, and, apparently, some hotels or clubs. And there where all kinds of monuments to see as the car whisked us past several churches (two of them boarded over), up an incline, and then came to a stop in front of a pink and white building identified as the Hotel Nacional.

Porters and soldiery hustled up and escorted us inside. Throngs of grinning, milling Cubans greeted us. Interspersed in the crowds I could spot several Soviet uni-

forms, both Navy, Army, and merchant marine. Raul
Castro led us through the lobby and out to the other side,
by the swimming pool. Some guitarist were to one side,
playing Spanish melodies while several nighttime swimmers splashed in the lighted and sparkling pool water.
Upon Castro's intrusion on the scene, the guitarists automatically stopped until he waved, saying, *"Ustedes con-
tinuas."*

I was alert to see that by now Raul Castro had acquired
an aide. He seemed to have come from somewhere in the
crowd, but he was obviously Castro's own personal flunky.
Dressed up in a bright green nylon Army uniform, he literally exuded obsequiousness, not to mention a sickening
smell of heavy perfume. One of the first things this young
slick-haired aide did was offer Castro a king-size cigarette
and light it.

Winking his right eye at the aide, Raul chirped, *"Gracias,* José." Then, turning to me and taking me by the
arm, he said, *"¡Vamos!"*

The aide signaled two armed guards who quickly made
a path through the crowd, through which Raul now led us
all. Back inside and into the lobby, then up in elevators to
a high floor, where we alighted in a foyer arrangement
from which one could proceed into a large apartment.
But very much in evidence, and sitting to one side of the
foyer by the elevator doors, were two soldiers, heavily
armed. One of them had a light blue ribbon around his
neck, and two pineapple-type hand grenades were dangling from ringlets on his suspenders. Both soldiers had
Russian-made burp guns.

In a quick spurt of Spanish, which I could not fully
understand, Raul apparently ordered the two soldiers to
do something. Whatever he said to them, it must have had
something to do with where Rostopchin and I, as well as
the commissar and the other officers, would be staying. In
any event, after being led to small private rooms, all of
which led out into a large, oval, living room-like space

paneled in walnut and adorned with expensive-looking antiques, Castro bade us to get ready for a swim. This, he told us, was his own personal apartment. It had once been occupied by an American banana company executive, then later by his mistress. His *Cuban* mistress, Raul said with deliberate effect. And then he went on, intimating that if we were *"buenos muchachos"* he might let us meet this enticing *gorrona,* this *querida.*

It was Glinka who brought up the question of bathing suits. From a nearby bedroom in the apartment, I could hear him say loudly, *"Señor* Raul! *Señor* Castro! What are we to wear?"

But the aide had been on the job. Almost simultaneously, servants (all in Army uniforms) appeared, carrying assorted sizes of brand-new bathing suits. I picked a light blue one and watched Rostopchin choose a bright orange.

Somewhat later we were in the living room, drinking rum collins and Cuban planters punch, bath towels draped over our necks, waiting for Raul Castro to join us and take us down to the pool.

From one of the nearby rooms, I could hear the aide talking excitedly on the telephone, apparently giving orders and occasionally laughing uproariously. Once or twice I caught the word *"senoritas,"* and twice I heard him say he didn't want any *"zangarillejas"* and then he would burst out in loud laughter.

All but the commissar had come out of the luxuriously appointed bedrooms and gathered in the living room. Kulakov said he thought Lvov had never learned to swim, and hence wouldn't be joining us at all. But this latter point was promptly squelched when Lvov presently appeared with a Latin-American girl in a light orchid negligee. She was strikingly attractive, if not genuinely pretty, and her long eyelashes blinked seductively as she clung close to the big commissar.

"This is Eloisa, gentlemen," the commissar beamed.

Then, accepting a tall glass of rum punch from a tray offered him by one of the soldier-waiters, he said with a sigh, "I *wish* I could go down there with you for a swim in that pool . . . but I think I may stay up here and, er . . . get acquainted with . . . er . . . some of the indoor sports they play around here . . ."

He glanced leeringly down at the upturned, smiling face. Then, hoisting his glass for a final gulp and with a wave of triumphant farewell to his less fortunate shipmates, Georgy Milkhailovich Lvov, Post-Captain Commissar, Soviet Navy, guided his affectionate new friend out of the room and down the one hallway beyond which were several more rooms.

Guevara laughed pleasantly, and said, "That's the Special Treat here. Raul gives her to his honor guest." Then, realizing that Lvov, although he was a Soviet four-stripe captain, was not the captain of the submarine, Guevara added, "But of course we have even more pleasant things in store for you, *Señor Capitán*. Raul is seeing to it that you will all have a good time. Why don't we all just go right down now to the pool? I don't know what's taking him so long, but I'm sure he will be down pronto."

Thus the rest of us, led by Ché Guevara, went down to the ground floor and into the pool for a refreshing swim. The guitarists were still there; the armed guards were still there; the other swimmers had left the area; but also on hand and in the pool, waiting for us, were about a dozen scantily clad Cuban *queridas,* or *rameras*. All of them were pretty enough to be professional models. I could not help but think that Raul Castro was living higher than the harem keepers in the Near East.

Glinka took one look at the shapely bodies moving about the pool, and gave a shriek of uncontrolled delight. He was the first to enter the water, even before Guevara could tell us that these *bonitas señoritas* were for our own personal pleasure.

Professors Bogucharovo and Pozdeev had meanwhile

been taken to see Raul Roa, the Cuban Foreign Minister, who I understand had been expecting them for a late supper-dance at his confiscated villa, a huge, white marble palace not far away, which before the Castro revolution had been the Caribbean winter residence of an American sugar refining executive. In an undercurrent of conversation, I learned that Fidel Castro was also to be there and that the Soviet consul and also the ambassador were in attendance. My official call upon the Soviet diplomats would wait until morning. It apparently had been previously decided that on this, our first night in port, we were to just relax and have a good time.

For some that first night was a memorable one. When Lieutenant Glinka took his feminine selection back up to our lavish apartment (and he was the first to do so) he had already explored her adequately right there within the swimming pool. Perhaps that was why he had one of the attendants turn off the inside lights of the pool shortly after our arrival there for the swim.

By late on the afternoon of the ninth of March, I had managed to make my official calls on practically everyone of importance in Havana and, because the submarine was already being worked on with near feverish haste to make it ready for sea at the earliest, return calls had been dispensed with.

But at least one of my calls proved productive; the Soviet consul, an amiable gentleman under whose specific charge came the diplomatic arrangements for visiting Soviet officialdom, agreed to provide not only me but my officers with automobiles, together with chauffeurs, during the period of our stay.

The reason he had sent the Rolls-Royce to the pier as the vehicle for Post-Captain Lvov was that a special communication from Moscow had asked that Lvov be accorded the maximum in prestige items in order for him to properly represent Vice Admiral Grishanov in the various matters which he had been ordered to delve into once he landed in Havana. Upon my request, the consul placed a large green and black Daimler at my disposal, and ordered Chrysler Imperials to be made available to my other officers. These automobiles, he said with a chuckle, had been confiscated by Castro from the holdings of individual cane planters—that is, those who had proved difficult to handle after he had come to power. Since they had subsequently been sent to firing squads as obstructionists, the new State put the vehicles up for auction. That was when he, the Soviet consul, stepped in, and for certain considerations acquired them. They were, of course, now the property of the USSR, officially, at least.

During the course of my initial conversation with him, I asked how my injured officers and crewmen were. He told me that they had all been transferred to departing merchantmen bound for Soviet ports. The ships in which they were now sailing, said the consul, were well equipped with excellent medical facilities. He, the consul, after talking the matter over with the ambassador, had decided that in the interests of preserving the secrecy of the operations these wounded men had been involved in, it would be best to return them to Russia. As for the sailors now on liberty, the consul revealed that it was mandatory that they be kept under tight controls at all times, especially so that none of them might be seen and questioned by an international reporter. Hence, the Castro Government had turned the Rex Hotel into a Soviet sailor's haven, if not a heaven.

Raul Castro himself, as the Commander in Chief of the Armed Forces of Cuba, the consul confided, had underwritten all expenses for the sailors there. Everything from dancing girls to bedroom girls were being made available to them, and the rum and wine were "on the house." Also, for relaxation at the beach, the bus would take shore parties to a nearby restricted area of the shore where all personnel could enjoy the surf.

It was in company with the consul that I paid my calls on the ambassador and his attaché, and then went to pay my respects to the Premier. Before seeing him, however, I talked for nearly an hour and a half with both the consul and the ambassador about the several missions which my orders required me to fulfill in Cuba. Both of these officials promised to aid me in every way possible, to the end that I could take certain detailed information back to Russia.

My appointment with Fidel Castro was hurried and unpleasant. From the moment I met him in his palatial, well-guarded headquarters in Havana until I left him some twenty minutes later, all I received was a storm of abuse.

Castro was unhappy. Perhaps underlying his edginess was his own understanding of present Cuban economic chaos. He deplored the fact that Soviet Russia had not sponsored even more programs which he had devised for the complete changeover in Cuba. Though he appreciated the appearance on the scene of Professors Bogucharovo and Pozdeev, whom he had met the previous night, he felt that the USSR could ameliorate his economic problems by buying an even greater percentage of the sugar cane every year. He ranted about the recent United States embargo on Cuban trade, saying that the damned Yankee *gringos* ought to be horsewhipped; that he would show them what kind of man he was once the new big missiles came from the Soviet Union.

Then he screamed that I should go back and tell Khrushchev that he wanted more patrol boats, fast ones. And he wanted to get some guided missiles for some of his frigates. Then, he roared, he would be able to take on some of the Yankee destroyers which always snooped around from their base at Key West to the north. He was thinking about announcing a fifty-mile territorial limit. Why not, he wanted to know? And why didn't I sink some of those damned Yankee *gringo* aircraft carriers when I was down there off Guantánamo?

The ambassador tried to calm him down, first by saying that after all, I was only a mere submarine captain—and that he was the ambassador and as such the man for Castro to talk to about broad policy matters. This failing, the ambassador said that in regard to the embargo, perhaps it wouldn't be so bad after all. Castro chomped into his green-leafed Havana corona and wanted to know how come.

"Well, Señor Prime Minister," the Soviet diplomat said emphatically, "for one thing, I have just learned that even though the American president has called for an embargo on all goods originating in your country, the U. S. Treasury Department has made an unexpected ruling that Americans may nonetheless buy Cuban cigars just so long as they are first exported from Cuba to some other locality. For instance, if you send your cigar exports to the Canary Islands, they can then be reshipped to the United States."

Castro's dark face showed a slight measure of satisfaction. His mouth twitched, and he took a long puff on his cigar. "Do you mean that this way, we can still get American dollars?"

The ambassador nodded.

Fidel Castro smacked one of his huge clenched fists into the waiting palm of his other hand, and uttered an oath in what was to me quite unintelligible Spanish. Then he said, "We *do* have friends up there in the Yankee Treasury Department! Is the American press going to influence them to change their ruling?"

"No," replied the Soviet representative of Premier Khrushchev, "I don't think so. Already, there have been some congressmen who have made speeches about the situation, but the copies of the American Congressional Record which I have forwarded to me every day indicate that the U. S. State Department really isn't going to do anything about the matter."

Fidel Castro chewed his cigar passionately, and then asked an aide present to start subscribing to the Congressional Record. No damned reason, he said in unquotable Spanish, to have such a good information booklet, as this Congressional Record apparently was, go unread by his own staff. The subject of congressmen suddenly captivated him.

"Are any of those potbellied senators still yakking about me and what I'm doing?" he asked.

The ambassador thought for a moment, then said, "Well, Dr. Castro, you recall one of their senators has made a speech urging a pacific blockade of Cuba . . ."

"When did he make this speech?"

"Oh, some months ago. Back last summer, perhaps in August or September. He advocated a pacific blockade which he said would be recognized by international law and would not be considered a war measure. He apparently feels this blockade should be absolute. Complete."

Castro narrowed his eyes.

"And if they ever did try to pull something like that?"

"In that case, Mr. Prime Minister," I interjected, suddenly finding myself talking at a very high level of joint government, "our submarines would probably be deployed to assist you, *providing* we had a submarine base here in Cuba from which to operate.

Castro paced nervously back and forth across his marble-floored office. Taking a long puff on his cigar, he blew a series of deliberate smoke rings and, watching them diffuse into the atmosphere, said, "That, *Capitán*, is why I am allowing two submarine bases to be built for you."

My ears perked up. This was what I wanted most to know about. I started to enlarge on this conversation, but Castro suddenly looked at his large gold wrist watch and announced that the audience was at an end. *"Pues,"* he sighed, *"Buenas tardes, señores."*

During the following week, I met and had luncheon with Raul Roa and various other officials of the Cuban regime. I had the opportunity to tell them firsthand of the need for Soviet submarine bases in Cuba. My main theme was that since Russia today has over two hundred submarines which normally are not capable of making extended cruises across the Atlantic to prey on American shipping, what is needed in order to give the Communist world greater flexibility is at least one good, well-protected base in the Western Hemisphere. Since Russia has already supplied Cuba with a veritable arsenal in nearly every type of weapon, it is now Cuba's responsibility to favor the Soviet Union with a base for her underwater might, at the earliest possible time. The two hundred-odd submarines just referred to are of the "W" class, or similar. If two squadrons (about twenty) of "W" type were based in the western Atlantic or Caribbean, they would prove a most difficult problem for U. S. and Latin-American naval strategists.

Roa agreed that it was a good idea to build sub pens in Cuba. As a matter of fact, he said, the Cuban Government had already confiscated a good part of the land at a suitable location near Cienfuegos, on the southern coast of the island. There, he thought, would be an excellent spot for extensive submarine pens. These could be built out of massive steel-enforced concrete with giant lead doors and roofing for protection against nuclear attack. They would be practically impervious to any kind of assault save perhaps a nuclear direct hit. Anyway, they would be a lot stronger than the strong and massive old Nazi sub pens in Bordeaux. (There, the French are still embarassed by the presence of those gigantic installations, but [because of their size and solidarity] are powerless to remove them.) Moreover, Roa said, the Cuban Government had already begun constructing temporary facilities on the northern coast of Cuba. This was at the Bahía de Nipe in Oriente Province. This base could even now be used by submarines for limited upkeep and repair work. The news was good.

I asked if I might inspect these sites, as well as the missile-launching bases, and was granted the request. "Naturally," said the Foreign Minister, "we want you to go back to the Soviet Union with firsthand impressions of the progress which we have made in these projects."

The second night in Havana, senior Chief Petty Officer Igor Novikov got himself into trouble.

Not content with the planned program for enlisted men, Novikov decided to make a break for it. In this instance, "it" simply meant complete freedom and independence on liberty. As far as anyone could later determine, he had merely walked out the servants' entrance of the Rex at some time after 11 P.M., having already (so the story went) literally exhausted three of the *zangarillejas* who had been sent up to his room, and during that same period having emptied two full bottles of Ron Anejos, the premium dark rum of the Antilles. Hailing a taxi, he hopped in and demanded that the driver take him to an *"exhibición."* (The word comes from the French, was doubtless mangled in accent by Novikov, but nonetheless understood by the driver to mean just what it means to taxi drivers all over the world—a lewd, if not disgusting, demonstration of human sexual perversions and acts.)

Within a half hour, Novikov had been dumped at an indescribably dirty, ramshackle cluster of old adobe structures, some distance off the beaten paths of metropolitan civilization. Strewn over the soggy ground in front of the houses were literally hundreds of soft-drink and beer bottle caps. Novikov staggered into one of the dingy hallways to which the taxi driver pointed.

A black man suddenly confronted him and asked for ten pesos. *"Ten pesos? ?"* The response from Novikov was outraged.

The black man repeated, "Ten pesos."

Novikov stood there in the dimly lighted hallway, doubtless swaying under the influence of the huge quantities of rum which he had previously imbibed. "Where is it?" he asked, pressing about twenty centavos into the man's hand. The taxi driver, who had tarried to watch this performance, now witnessed the two men disappear through an open doorway.

On the other end of that doorway, a short hallway led to an already packed room, filled with dense cigarette and cigar smoke. About a dozen merchant sailors, several Cuban soldiers, and one or two civilians stood behind some manila ropes which had been rigged across the room, separating the interested observers from what turned out to be a nearly perpetual and continuing series of performances. These performances were enacted by a cast of a dozen men and women, some of whom were obviously Cuban with Spanish blood, some Indians from South or Central America, and others either mulatto or black.

There was one exception to this circus. She was a redheaded girl of about nineteen, shapely and wholly nude. As the parade of performers came in through a side curtain this redhead took up the slack by teasing the masculine audience with frequent body contortions and gyrations.

Her mistake—or perhaps her ultimate mistake—was made when she discovered big, powerful, drunken Igor Novikov in her audience. He had been there for perhaps thirty minutes, had watched as four separate pairs of performers had gone through their voluptuous acts, and then had begun to feel an uncontrollable urge for the inviting form of the redheaded tease. Novikov moved steadily closer and closer to her, until finally he was right against the rope and only a few feet from her. It was then that she reached playfully over to tease him . . .

Eyewitnesses later reported to police that she made her intended contact. And within literally seconds, so also did Novikov. Some witnesses said they merely thought it part of the act; others testified they were too surprised to do anything but watch in what they said was "horror."

As luck would have it, a Cuban policeman happened to

be passing the premises at the time that the redhead started screaming. Novikov was subdued forthwith and taken into custody.

The wheels of international justice sometimes turn slowly. Igor Novikov was still in jail when, late in March, we put to sea again in the *F-689*.

As for the other sailors and the Cuban "show girls," suffice it to say that the friendships formed were, however intimate, somewhat much less than durable.

25

The Favors of Eloisa

☐ One night in Havana, in the palatial former home of
the American sugar king, we were being entertained at a
Cuban "family affair" formal dinner. Fidel Castro sat at
the head table, with Commissar Post-Captain Lvov to his
immediate left; the Soviet ambassador was on his right,
and my officers and I were seated among Raul Roa, Ché
Guevará, Raul Castro, and other revolutionary officers of
the regime. Opposite each of us sat very lovely, if not
sometimes beautiful, *señoritas*. The Castro brothers liked
to look at their feminine companions during meals, I was
told; hence it was unlike the protocol in most countries,
wherein each gentleman is provided at dinner with a feminine conversational partner at his side.

Raul, who was sitting to my immediate left, wanted
to know something about Soviet hydrofoil development. I
told him of Russian progress in that field, emphasizing
that we had managed to get a good head start on the
United States by importing former Nazi marine architects
right after World War II. These men, most of them brilliant freethinkers in naval design, had just about persuaded Adolf Hitler to build a vast fleet of hydrofoil
transports to supply Rommel in Africa, when the Allies
bombed the major naval shipyards to pulp and hence
precluded this grand scheme from ever becoming a reality.

After the war, Russia had taken these men, made them
all personally rich, and had extracted from them the work
which had now made Soviet Russia the world leader in
hydrofoil ship-building. When Raul Castro asked about
the new United States Navy hydrofoils, which he had

267

heard were to be built for experimental use in antisubmarine warfare, I told him that it would still be many years before the Yankees could match Soviet progress along these lines.

Raul Castro then noted that the English were planning on sending the giant ocean liner *Queen Elizabeth* on New York-to-Nassau cruises for *turistas* next winter. His information was that the Cunard Line, failing miserably in transatlantic passenger and freight traffic in competition with airlines and other international shipping lines, would probably be consigned to bankruptcy if Russia could set up a faster travel means for such winter *turistas*.

He then asked bluntly whether our government might not investigate the possibility of introducing large hydrofoil passenger ships into the Caribbean runs—putting them under the flag of Brazil or some other Latin-American country not wholly opposed to the Soviet Union—and said that if this were done, the demise of the large Cunard Line would then be nearly assured. When that happened, it would be just one more defeat for capitalism. I then told him about the large passenger ship construction programs going on in Soviet Russia. I talked about the new 750-foot, thirty-thousand-ton liner now building in Leningrad, and told him that it would be able to carry over eleven hundred passengers on runs all over the world; then I brought up the impressive hovercraft programs and the expansion of Soviet ocean liner travel plans in other parts of the world, notably in the Far East. He was impressed with the USSR's concentration on building a new merchant fleet—especially at a time when the American Defense Secretary reportedly has vetoed the practice of giving federal funding assistance (subsidization) to American shipping companies who desire to build new and faster ocean liners.

Opposite me at this meal, looking very enticing indeed in a low-cut light blue evening gown, sat Raul Castro's Special Treat, the same Eloisa whom the commissar had become rather intimately associated with on our first night in Havana. I was aware of her studious, almost fascinated gaze in my direction throughout the dinner, and occasionally I would say something to her in the midst of my more important conversation with Raul Castro.

When at length I asked Raul when he would be arranging for my inspection of the missile sites as well as the submarine base sites, he looked over at Eloisa and asked her when it would be convenient for her to go on a little junket of about three days and nights. She seemed to blush a little at first, looking quickly down at her glass of 1959 *brut* champagne. This intrigued me. Perhaps I would be assigned her favors.

I turned to look at Raul Castro.

"The day after tomorrow," he said, "will be a good time to start out. Eloisa can make herself available to you, I am sure. Eh, Eloisa *querida?*"

Now I found myself blushing, and tried to avoid looking directly at this beautiful Cuban who had become a useful tool for the Castro Government. Leaning over and peering to my left, I saw Lvov talking animatedly with Raul's big brother Fidel. Suddenly there were some photographic light-bulb flashes and I realized that some of the Cuban guards were taking pictures of the assemblage. Fidel and the commissar were snapped as they sat smiling at each other. One such picture was later published in the local papers in Cuba.

The next day was another bright, sunny one. After the dinner the night before, I had left the Roa palace and, taking Eloisa with me, had gone in my Daimler back to the Nacional. Raul Castro had made arrangements for all of the *F-689* officers, including the commissar and myself, to be assigned individual suites in the hotel after the first few days of enjoying his own hospitality.

The quarters assigned me were nearly as sumptuous as those which he himself had taken over, although of course, mine were not as extensive. A large paneled drawing room, a sitting room, a study, a huge bedroom with a large double bed, a private bath with a sunken bathtub, and a balcony with comfortable chairs and swinging couches, made up my suite. There was also a small anteroom just off the entrance, where an Army servant waited to answer my every beck and call. He was also armed, interestingly enough.

On arrival back at the hotel, I was led into the casino by Eloisa. Reaching into her glittering rhinestone-ornamented handbag, she produced a packet of Cuban bills, which she stuffed into my pocket. Protesting was no use; she insisted that I use the money for the sport of just gambling to see how lucky I was. Since the casino was owned by the government, she said, and because I was a guest of that government, this was the only way they could let me play the roulette wheels. Raul Castro had given her the bills with specific instructions that I was to have a good time.

So, high atop the Nacional, in the glittering rooftop casino, I played the gambling tables. I don't know how many pesos I went through, but I do know that within a couple of hours the croupiers had collected every last peso in the bundle. One thing I was aware of as I stood placing money on the betting boards was the proximity of Eloisa. Before the gambling was over, I found she was clinging to me much as I had seen her hold Lvov some days earlier.

The sunshine of the next morning poured through the windows and woke me. Eloisa had already awakened, and was standing on the balcony, looking out at the sea. I arose, and walked out to join her.

"What were you looking at?"

"Oh, at the sea . . . out where you came from," she said softly.

"Out where I came from? That is many thousand miles away," I answered. "And within the next two months, certainly, I hope to be back there."

She turned and faced me. "Did you mean what you said last night?"

An uncomfortable concern swept through me. What did she mean by that? What could she be referring to? What had I said to her? I shuddered to think.

She walked over to me and, taking her light negligee and drawing it close over her bosom, looked up searchingly at me.

"Do you really think I am beautiful? Really?" She cocked her head to one side.

Inwardly, I sighed a breath of relief. Who could have known what nonsense I might have told her the night before!

"Why, yes, Eloisa, you are *muy bonita. ¿Por qué?*"

She smiled happily, and presently said, "Do you really like me?"

"Eloisa, of course I do, why?"

"Then would you do something special for me, *por favor?*"

I nodded acquiescence, and she continued.

"Today, after breakfast, would you take me for a little ride? I should like to take you somewhere."

It seemed apparent to me that she was not going to say anything further which might prove embarrassing to me, so I smiled and agreed to do whatever she wanted. After all, she would be coming with me on my three-day trip to see the various missile and sub installations in Cuba, and I most certainly did not want to alienate her. No, indeed. She was *much* too engaging and much too satisfactory for that.

But there were some questions which plagued me. Eloisa seemed intelligent. She had a ready wit, and gracious manners. She seemed to have been bred in comfortable surroundings, and most assuredly knew how to conduct herself in the most expensive circles. How had she become what she was? The question intrigued me. I had to find out the answer.

It was Sunday, March 18. I first realized it when the slow, ringing tones of seemingly far-off church bells echoed across the city. Eloisa had gone in to the bath and I could hear her splashing about in the tub, singing a bright and cheerful melody. I listened to both the church bells and the singing. Then I turned and walked in from the balcony, pausing near the bath.

"Eloisa, I hear church bells."

"Yes, they are from the Cathedral."

"The Cathedral?"

"*Sí amor mío. Es la catedral—la vieja iglesia de los jesuítas.*"

In my halting Spanish, I told her to please talk more slowly if she wanted me to understand her in her native tongue. Apparently she was saying something about the cathedral and an old Jesuit church.

Gay laughter pealed from within the bath, and Eloisa spoke again in English, which of course I understand quite well. Silly, she was saying, the bells I was hearing were coming from the Havana Cathedral, which at one time had been a Jesuit church. That was back when it was first built, she went on to tell me, and from what she knew, construction had started on the building back in the mid-seventeenth century. It was the only church now still open for regular devotional services in Havana, and even though the new Cuban Government had taken steps to discourage attendance there, many of the older generation still went to worship each Sunday.

I looked at my watch. It was nearly ten o'clock. The bells must be for the midmorning Mass, I was thinking, when suddenly Eloisa stepped out from behind the bathroom door, holding her towel around her wet, bath-perfumed figure.

"Did you know that *Cristóbal Colón's* tomb is in *la catedral?*" she asked airily, and then, seeing my transparent interest, said, "Well, anyway, one of his tombs. *Colón's* remains were moved from Santo Domingo back in the 1790s and interred here for many years. Finally during the Cuban War against Spain, the Spanish carried the bones back to Spain."

"Eloisa, how do you know so much about all this? And when you talk of the Cuban War against Spain, I presume you mean the Spanish-American War?"

Eloisa's dark brown eyes blazed. "No, *amor mío*," she said icily, "I mean the Cuban War against *España*. It was our war, our first *revolución, our fight! Los norte-americanos, los gringos,* have written their own history to suit themselves, and unfortunately, they have swayed the world with the deceit. Cubans did the suffering, Cubans did the fighting, and Cubans won the war. The United States helped us. They helped us the way the French helped *them* back in Washington's time, in their own fight for independence!"

She was indignant. She was furiously, charmingly, heat-edly, beautifully indignant! The Latin temper in her was overwhelming.

Here was the passion of a patriot! I grabbed her and, taking her damp, fresh body in a powerful embrace, crushed her to me with an irresistible force. Her initial wrenching to escape subsided into final acquiescence, and then, obviously electrified with an extraordinary transfer of passion, she dug her long nails into my back and sealed me to her in a vicelike clamp.

Then she drew back, and looking at me quizzically, asked if I had ever been to a *catedral*. It brought back memories of my boyhood in Aleksandrov. For a moment, I could repicture the promp and pageantry of the Russian Orthodox Church, with the candles, the incense, the chimes and bells, the mournful, sometimes overpowering rumble of the grand organs, the endless hundreds of prayerful communicants—and then I remembered my last visit to a cathedral, back in Washington, D.C., in 1959. Once more, if only for a moment, I could hear the choir singing that unforgettable hymn.

Eloisa was saying something. I cut her off gently.

"What did you say, my young Cuban *señorita*?"

"I was saying, *Dulcelitto novisimo,* would you like to see our *catedral*? ¡*Venga*! Get dressed. We can still get there in time for the late morning Mass."

She gave me a push backwards and brushed past me en route to the bedroom, turning her pretty head to call back, "I myself have not yet decided whether or not I should forsake the Mother Church. I have always been a good *Católico*. I find it comforting. It's only the priests and the bishops that I sometimes resent."

The big, high-roofed Daimler town car pulled to a stop in front of the one-time resting place of the bones of Christopher Columbus. The driver jumped out and opened the door, helping Eloisa out first and then offering his arm so that I could descend from the coach with maximum facility. I suppose the old car was a relic of the late 1920s, but it was certainly a well-kept, glisteningly polished chariot, rather suggestive of the royal automobiles used by the English Dowager Queen Mary before she died. Frankly, I was beginning to prefer it to any other private car in which I had ever ridden.

Telling the driver to wait, I took Eloisa by the elbow and let her lead me up the steps to the ancient great house of worship.

"Eloisa," I managed to say when halfway up the steps to the main entrance, "doesn't Castro mind your coming here?"

"Doesn't Khrushchev mind your coming here?" she shot back, turning her lovely face toward me and searching for my answer to this, the most controversial question she could have found to ask me.

My pace slackened. Khrushchev? He had been farthest from my thoughts.

"*Vamos,*" I heard Eloisa say encouragingly, "let's go in. Maybe you will feel better when we get inside."

That said, she reached up and, taking me by the hand, led me inside the high portals, into the olden-days monument to Christian worship, in under the towering archways, into a half-empty cathedral wherein three priests were busily officiating at the far altar, and where soft background music from a great organ provided a soothing curtain behind which the cares of the outside world could conveniently be forgotten.

We walked slowly down the center aisle of the ancient cathedral. Halfway to the altar Eloisa stopped, looked at me curiously, and then dropped to one knee, making the sign of the cross with her right hand as she did so. Quickly rising, she stared at me. What would I do?

I froze. The leading priest—perhaps he was the bishop—was now opening wide his arms to the faithful. His loose-fitting white upper gown was spread broadly above his cassock beneath, and I was sure he was delivering the invitation to the congregation to come near with faith and take the holy sacraments for our comfort. But it had been many, many years since I had genuinely participated in any kind of service—notwithstanding my actions in the Anglican Cathedral in Washington three years earlier. So I just shuffled in to sit down on one of the thatched cane chairs lined up on the floor. Eloisa seemed hurt. She gave me a look of concern and recrossed herself. Then she moved in beside me and knelt down. I continued to sit, but I was fascinated. The congregation was now chanting something I did not understand, and the three priests were all busily doing something way up there on the altar.

The chanting now ceased, and the organ notes swelled up. There was suddenly a silence, followed momentarily by three chimes sounding off in crystal clear and ringing tones. Eloisa crossed herself again and, nudging me, whispered that I was embarrassing her. Then she tugged on my cuff, dragging my arm down below the level of my knees, and causing me to capitulate. I squirmed off the seat and knelt down beside her. As I did, the organ increased again in strength, and with a flourish of majestic playing, sent a thrill through me. I looked straight ahead at the altar, at the spotlighted cross high above, and listened again as a chime rang out loud and clear three times.

The Lord's Prayer was now being said, in Latin, of course. I could understand parts of it, and the realization of what was being spoken sent my mind forcefully back in time to the days of my Christian youth. I closed my eyes.

Once again, I could imagine myself back in our small village church in Aleksandrov, when I was a young boy . . . my father and mother and brothers and sisters all there, faithfully on our knees in worship to the everlasting Lord . . . praying to that Great Power which Lvov and Sverdlov and Khrushchev and the others denounced as nonexistent! Lvov! That bounder! What did he know, anyway? Or Sverdlov, that idiot! . . .

And then the words came back to my mind, flashing before me with new importance . . .

> Once to every man and nation
> Comes the moment to decide
> In the strife of truth with falsehood
> For the good or evil side . . .

The organ music surged forth with triumphant power and majesty; I looked up at the high-arched overhead, and then returned my gaze to the altar. I was hypnotized. And then all I could think about were the words, later on, of that same hymn:

> Then it is the brave man chooses,
> While the coward stands aside
> Till the multitude make virtue
> Of the faith they had denied.

. . . And when the choir and the priests filed out down the aisle, as the crucifix flashed by, I found myself following Eloisa in her motions as she knelt reverently in the traditional motions of the genuflection.

My action did not go unnoticed by Eloisa. She glanced at me and smiled a strange smile.

26

Big Bananas

☐ During the next three days, I was whisked over the length and breadth of Cuba. Eloisa accompanied me, and during this junket I learned of her background. She told me of how Batista's henchmen had killed her brother, a liberal-thinking student who had come back from fashionable St. Matthews in the northeastern United States, to make speeches and engineer student protests in Havana, against the rigidities of the old dictator's regime.

She disclosed how her father, once a successful Cuban businessman, had been jailed by Batista, and how her mother had been thrown out of their large and rambling plantation home by the fascist, who confiscated her family's property after having jailed her father. His crime, it seemed, had been his active questioning of some of Batista's more inflexible policies. She herself had been educated in a convent and for a brief period had studied at a fashionable New York finishing school run by an elderly English spinster. However, the growing crises in Cuba during the high points of her father's difficulties with Batista had brought about her removal from the school, and she had been brought back to her family's plantation.

In the ensuing shuffle, she had been channeled to her near relatives in Oriente Province, where Fidel Castro was then in hiding, preparing for his take-over of the country. In a series of moves, she had finally, as a fervently idealistic reform enthusiast, managed to find Castro and his band of rebels. And there, in the remote mountain fastnesses of Oriente, far from the gentility and cultivation of the life she had known, she had been accepted by the Castros. To her, both Raul and Fidel seemed to be the saviors of the good life she had known and dreamed of having reinstituted. It was not a large step at all, then, for her to ease into the position of intimate companion with Raul Castro. Finally, she became his constant shadow . . . until she suddenly realized, quite by accident one night, that Raul Castro's affection was shared with others, many others. From that time onward she had cared little for her own status and, although still idealistically looking forward to the day when the revolutionaries would storm the Presidential Palace in Havana and make Cuba a Shangri-la, she had permitted herself to degenerate into a near nightly bedtime consort for every one of Raul Castro's friends.

Finally, she had been persuaded to return to Havana where the Cuban underground had made her available to an executive of a large North American banana company. She became his Cuban mistress, and lived with him in the large apartment now occupied by Raul Castro. As part of the bargain, she was to listen to the conversations this big businessman had with his aides and associates, for doubtless such conversation would reveal some of Batista's plans for dealing with the guerrilla forces of the Castros. She was then to pass this information on to her revolutionary contacts in the underground.

Eloisa had done a good job. And when the Castros entered Havana in triumph, Raul had taken over the banana company executive's apartment and, of course, had retained Eloisa as the added attraction for his most favored guests. She had become known, indeed, as the Special Treat.

Hence, it had been no mere accident that she had been offered to Commissar Post-Captain Lvov the first night of our stay in Havana. And Eloisa had not flinched from her duty. She had been prepared—as always she was, these days.

But her subjugation of herself to such a role as she now starred in did not in any measure detract from her almost blind acceptance of Communism, now, as the best method of establishing world order. She would, she told me several times, do anything necessary in order to advance it. And thinking back now on these statements of hers, I suppose I should have taken her at her word.

The first site we visited was the intermediate-range rocket base at nearby Matanzas. With Colonel Ourusov and Raul Castro, together with a train of his aides (including his favorite, José), we traveled by motor caravan to this particular site some fifty to sixty miles east of Havana. There, I saw the cement launching areas, camouflaged against possible detection by American U-2 aircraft or other spying means. I asked Raul Castro how soon the site would be provided with some of our new seventy-foot missiles. He replied that within the next few months they would be ready for them. Meanwhile, Cuba was depending on the older, sixty-foot rockets. Several of these types had been received only a few months ago, he said, and a large number of these missiles were expected soon. We joked, I remember, about the lack of American determination regarding Cuba's getting the armaments with which she might pulverize most of the eastern and central United States.

The following day, we motored to a remote missile-launching base in the interior of western Cuba, at Pinar del Río. There, the Castro Government had succeeded in establishing a veritable storehouse of intermediate range ballistic missiles which could be launched from cement pads against almost any place in the United States east of the Rockies and south of Kansas City. Should larger, longer-range missiles be forthcoming, as Fidel and Raul Castro desire, then Cuba will be truly in a position to annihilate all of the continental U.S.

The last trip we made was via airplane, and it was a circuitous bit of travel first to Cienfuegos, a good-sized and pleasant city on the mid-southern coast of Cuba. There, I was shown the proposed construction site for the huge

Soviet submarine pens which the Castros had agreed to build. Preliminary work was already going on there. Then we flew to Camagüey, in the central Cuban wilderness. Here, as at Pinar del Río and Matanzas, the Cubans had built extensive missile launching sites, and had stored at least five squadrons of ready rockets.

Finally, we inspected the missile-launching areas at the Oriente Province base at Holguín. The sight of those missiles on their launching pads and in storage was somehow disturbing. Could these mercurial Latins be trusted? I planned to persuade my superiors in the Soviet Union that they could not be.

Less than fifty miles from the Holguín base I saw the submarine repair station at the Bahía de Nipe. Granted that it is but a temporary facility, it nonetheless will serve the Soviet Union until the huge concrete emplacements eventually go into operation near Cienfuegos.

Raul Castro was thus far delighted with the support which the Soviet Union had given his Armed Forces. According to him, Cuba presently has thousands of troops, many of them armed with better individual weapons than the United States Army provides it soldiers. For instance, the Russian automatic rifle is standard equipment now for Cuba's soldiery; these rifles can fire faster and are lighter than the comparable American weapon. Russia many months ago delivered nearly a hundred MIG jet fighters to Cuba, about 250 medium and heavy tanks, one hundred assault guns, over two thousand pieces of field and antiaircraft artillery, five hundred mortars, over two hundred thousand small arms, and about a dozen patrol vessels and motor torpedo boats.

Talking about the military weaponry which he had been successful in getting from Russia, Raul Castro flipped a burned-out cigarette stub from his fingers and told me, "That trip I took to Moscow last year certainly paid off. But I'm not finished. You boys are going to have a return call from me—and soon. I need more weapons and more of everything to beat the Americans."

With a shake of his fist, he spat at an imaginary Yankee *gringo* and then laughed inanely.

Raul Castro, Raul Roa, and Ché Guevara are Big Bananas in Communist Cuba. Fidel is the biggest. But tomorrow or next month they may not be such Big Bananas. It all depends on how much of their military skins the Kremlin decides to peel off.

PART III

PERIL FROM THE SEA

27

"Back in Our Natural Habitat"

☐ In 1710, Peter the Great commenced smashing his way to control of the Baltic, which until then had been no more than a Swedish lake. His brilliant naval commander, Admiral Fedor Apraksin, directed not only the capture of Viborg, but also commanded operations along the Finnish coast in 1713, defeated the Swedes at Gangoot in 1714 and, through his assaults on the Swedish fleet and coast in the ensuing years, hastened the capitulation of Sweden in 1721. Peter, aware of his own inferiority to Apraksin as a sea commander, participated in most of the naval actions of the period as a subordinate flag officer to this admiral. It is noteworthy that after the Russian naval victory at Hango-Udd, where the Swedish fleet had been almost annihilated, Peter allowed himself the privilege of self-promotion from rear admiral to vice admiral. Apraksin himself handed his Czar the new personal flag denoting Peter's more senior rank in the Russian Navy!

Such was the illustrious hereditary background of Soviet Navy Lieutenant Commander Ivan Fedorovich Apraksin, descendant of Russia's "first Admiral." On the twenty-seventh of March, 1962, Apraksin reported to the *F-689* for duty. With him was another officer, Lieutenant Josef Ozerovich Marsk. Both had been flown to Havana as replacements for two of the three officers I had lost in the operations to date. Apraksin, a mild-mannered, urbane officer of pleasant personality whose finely chiseled facial bone structure set himself immediately apart from most of the other officers (whose features tended to reflect the more common coarseness of tough peasant stock), came on board with specific orders as relief for Volkonski. The Soviet Navy High Command had apparently chosen to override, if not ignore, my earlier-placed situation report, in which I had indicated that engineer officer Rostopchin had been performing most satisfactorily as Second Officer, and in which I had asked for his retention in that capacity.

Tactful and wholly unpresumptive, Apraksin was able with seemingly no effort to introduce himself with widespread favor not only to the other wardroom officers, but also to the crew. Taking over the duties as Second Officer from Makar Rostopchin was thus accomplished with ease and with notable absence of any antagonism, active or passive. However much I regretted Rostopchin's personal deprivation of responsibility as second-in-command, I nonetheless felt refortified by Apraksin's addition to my submarine. The fact that he had already commanded a small coastal-type sub operating in the Black Sea gave to him priceless experience quite lacking in Rostopchin's professional qualifications. Additionally, I learned that immediately prior to his being sent to the *F-689,* he had been undergoing extensive training in undersea mining operations. Hence, he would be of value, I was sure, in our projected activities off the North American continental shelf. There we would shortly be engaged in the strategic placing of electronics devices and underwater navigational beacons. These would be for the subsequent assistance of Soviet missile-firing subs if called upon to move up to predetermined firing lines off the American Atlantic seaboard. Apraksin was indeed a welcome newcomer.

Lieutenant Marsk, ruddy-faced and young, was reporting fresh from a Kotlin-class destroyer. A three-week basic orientation course in submarine navigation and tactics were all that qualified him for subsurface duty. However, his orders stipulated that his tour on board was to be one of learning fundamentals, and that on return to Russia he would revert to the Soviet destroyer force. Thus, his cruise on the *F-689* would prove mutually beneficial to both him and to the submarine. I was to use him as I saw fit, and teach him what I could of submarine operations. With a firm foundation in underseas craft thus established, he would then ostensibly be of value to the destroyer forces, for he could bring to a surface-navy staff the impressions of an officer who has actually served in the destroyer's traditional antagonist—the submarine.

Marsk, for such a purpose, was an outstanding selection. Already officially qualified as professionally competent to command Soviet destroyer types by the Commander of Destroyer Forces, Northern Fleet Headquarters as well as by the Central Navy Administrative Commander, Marsk's resolute determination to acquire as much knowledge as possible about antisubmarine warfare would ultimately result in his inestimable value to the Soviet Navy. For despite the current accent on submarine operations, and the heavy emphasis on training officers for submarine billets, Soviet Russia has few officers experienced in surface-ship antisubmarine tactics appropriate to meet the challenge of modern nuclear-powered subs built and building for the U. S. Navy.

I assigned Marsk to the navigator for integration into the watch routine, and concurrently gave to him such administrative duties as both Dedusko and the commissary officer (Rodzianko) had been charged with prior to their transfers.

It was also on the twenty-seventh of March that our Havana-based intelligence conveyed word to us that the Soviet research ship *Vglo,* which since mid-February had been conducting a covert intelligence mission off the U. S. east coast, was now precisely in the middle of a U. S. Atlantic Fleet antisubmarine (ASW) group. This American fleet group, consisting of an aircraft carrier, seven destroyers, and two submarines, was presently located approximately 250 miles southeast of Cape Hatteras. *Vglo,* operating in the vicinity of the American units for about a week, had been amassing important electronics information. I checked the chart of the Atlantic seaboard and the areas in which the U. S. ships were operating. I had no desire to make contact with such an antisubmarine hunter-killer group as this! Fortunately, further intelligence revealed that the enemy would not be in continuous operation for more than another week.

Other than that, the Communist intelligence apparatus in Havana was able to provide me with the information that a major amphibious exercise involving the U. S. Marines would commence during the second week or so of April, probably on about the ninth. More than forty thousand Navy men and Marines, embarked in eighty-three ships, would be participating in a full-scale amphibious assault at Vieques Island, off Puerto Rico. This exercise, to be a three-week maneuver, was ostensibly for the purpose of maintaing combat efficiency of the American Atlantic Fleet amphibious strike forces. But in Havana, the Castros viewed this intelligence with alarm. They believed the *yanquis* would doubtless conduct a trial landing at Vieques, but that they would then jump off for a landing somewhere on the Cuban shore. Consequently, Raul Castro ordered a general alert for his armed forces.

As we left Havana, Communist Cuba was writhing in a massive mobilization of all reserve units and police. Special orders were being disseminated to the populace to remain calm, but to stand ready to help evict the fierce invader from the Fatherland's beaches when the attack came. The word arriving in Havana was that the newly converted antisubmarine carrier *Intrepid*, (once an attack-carrier in the Mediterranean Sea), a helicopter assault ship, two command ships, a guided missile cruiser, and a missile-carrying destroyer, would all be involved in the operation.

Additionally, there was a rumor that the large carrier *Forrestal* might be involved. This infuriated Raul Castro, who, just prior to *F-689* departing Cuba, personally chided me for not having sunk that huge floating aerodrome when I had had the opportunity several times in the past.

The only other bit of intelligence we received from Intelligence Headquarters in Havana, prior to our getting underway, was that the American fleet was planning a large-scale fleet review off Virginia, to take place the second week in April. The President of the U.S., it was reported, would be present.

On the morning of March 28, Sergei Mikhailoff, Ivan Baliuk, Ivan Apraksin, and Commissar Lvov joined me in looking over the navigational charts of the American Atlantic seaboard—for the last time preparatory to our getting underway. Baliuk, from his voluminous intelligence material, laid out his hydrographic charts alongside those which the navigator had put down for us on the wardroom table.

Baliuk's special charts showed precisely the locations of the Mid-Atlantic Ridge, the Caloosahatchee Sea Mounts, and the other underwater island peaks such as the Poconos, the Nashville, New England, Muir, San Pablo, Rehoboth, and Kelvin Sea Mounts, all of which, accurately plotted by painstakingly conscientious Soviet oceanographers, now provide such positive navigational information to Soviet sumarines operating in these waters.

My eyes moved slowly up the oceanic areas along the continental shelf—that region of the ocean bottom extending out from forty to a couple of hundred miles from the shoreline, and beyond which there is a steep drop, as in a canyon, to the ocean floor. Norfolk Canyon interested me, as did the Hudson, Atlantis, and Hydrographer Canyons which extended northward. These were the points where the continental slope drops precipitiously to great depths. And it was along this boundary of the continental shelf, at depths of about six hundred feet, that we would place the special electronics navigational beacons.

From our detailed information about where the trawler fleets had anchored their many underwater navigational landmarks (for subsequent use by our submarines), we were able to start our own operations in such a way as to complement their work. I assure you it was not difficult to determine where our own submarine-launched special aids could best serve to augment the larger trawler-planted devices. The latter are, in some cases, atomic generators, powering navigational beacons resting across the expanse of the Atlantic, from sea mount to sea mount west of the Mid-Atlantic Ridge. In particular, they indicate precise launch spots for Soviet missile submarines. These subs are thus able, now, to home in on the beacons. Having done this, they can use the positions of the beacons as settings for their rockets' inertial guidance systems. With this sort of check, our underwater craft can cruise indefinitely underneath the surface of the sea without ever having to surface for a position correction.

Of course, Soviet intelligence is aware of the fact that the mammoth American Navy has possibly discovered some of the Soviet radioactive navigational beacons on the ocean bottom. But the naval forces of Soviet Russia will continue frequently to check, monitor, and replace these devices as necessary.

Thus, the interesting possibility may arise whereby an increasingly grotesque game of hide-and-seek will develop off the American coastline.

Based on the latest intelligence report received the day of our departure, it was determined that we could be in a position to encounter the American fleet's presidential review off Virginia—assuming that it was carried out anywhere from the tenth to the fifteenth of April. I decided I would attempt to rendezvous with this parade of U. S. ships. It would be perhaps one of the greatest thrills of our lives, to be secretly planted, unseen but seeing, close aboard the otherwise so powerful American Navy. And for their Commander in Chief to be on hand would be like frosting on the cake.

Shortly after four o'clock in the afternoon, as I was inspecting the outer hull of the submarine from the pier, Colonel Ourusov paid us a farewell visit. The previous day, I had brought all the officers back on board the submarine from the plushy accommodations in the Nacional, and we had been striving mightily to insure complete readiness for sea. Rostopchin had reported successful dock trials and the electronics equipment had been thoroughly calibrated and checked.

Ourusov confided to me that upon completion of our current mission, we should not be surprised to find ourselves being ordered to the Far East. There might be trouble brewing over there, he said, and it had something to do with a request of Mao Tse-tung that the Soviet Union provide more submarine support in the event that Chiang Kai-shek launch an American Navy-protected amphibious invasion of the Chinese mainland.

Were we to be moved from here to those far Pacific waters, we might possibly find it necessary to put into Conakry, the capital of Guinea, to take on supplies or make voyage repairs prior to going on with the long voyage around the world. Of course, there are other ports like Conakry where the USSR now has submarine facilities established, and any of these might be utilized in such a deployment. For instance, at Surabaja, Indonesia, the Soviet Union now has the exclusive use of the former Dutch submarine pens at that port.

However, I informed Ourusov that I could not help but doubt our ever receiving such orders to deploy to the Pacific. After all, Mao has already been given about thirty submarines, most of which are snorkel-equipped medium-range types like the *W-7*, and all of them quite capable of thwarting amphibious landings. Then too, the Soviet fleet based at Vladivostok would be the likely reservoir for any additional submarine strength detailed for Mao's protection or support. It therefore seemed most improbable, to my mind, that Supreme Naval Headquarters would resort to ordering the *F-689* to the Pacific. These I enunciated to Ourusov, who shrugged and sighed that, well, he wasn't a naval tactician or strategist, all he was doing was telling me about a new possibility for international fireworks.

How had Ourusov arrived at his conclusions? Questioning him revealed that the worldwide Communist espionage network had intercepted some correspondence between certain high-ranking U. S. military officers. This correspondence pointed to the fact that a significant element of American officers experienced in Far Eastern affairs were pressing the Washington government to endorse a Chiang invasion of Red China. It would be an invasion logistically supported by U. S. naval forces—and, naturally enough, Mao was alarmed about the prospects.

Our departure time had been set for 10 P.M.; at nine-thirty, a black Cadillac limousine pulled up to the pier and Raul Roa, accompanied by the Soviet ambassador and a well-armed bodyguard, alighted. Making their way to the side of the submarine, they asked one of the topside watch to go below and call me up. This was done, and within a minute or so I was shaking hands with them in a farewell gesture. Commissar Lvov was at my side, also accepting their best wishes for a pleasant voyage. Missing from the groups of well-wishers who had intermittently come down to say *"Hasta la vista,"* or *"Adios,"* was the pretty young Cuban girl with whom I had spent so much time during my stayover in Havana.

It was 10:10 P.M., March 28, 1962. That was when all lines were cast off and I commenced maneuvering the *F-689* out into the harbor, leaving the docks and the sleeping masses of Cuban citizenry well in our background as we headed toward the open sea and the final phase of our extended deployment in the Western Hemisphere. By 11 P.M. we were splashing northeastward outside Havana, moving along on the surface, bow pointed toward the Straits of Florida and the Gulf Stream. And fifteen minutes later, we were pushing along under the surface of the sea, snorkeling. Our speed was six knots; I had confidence in our ability to dodge contact with American naval forces from the Key West station to the north, and was sure of our successful transit up the east coast of Florida.

I went over the navigator's chart and pinpointed our position. We were at sea again. In fact, we were under the sea, back in our natural habitat.

28

To the Presidential Review: Naval Power Assessed

☐ Except for my new, personally engaging Second Officer, Lieutenant Commander Apraksin, and our temporarily assigned destroyer officer, Lieutenant Marsk, the officers and men of the *F-689* had all by now experienced the tension and stress of submerged operations in the immediate proximity of United States Navy men-of-war. It is a curiously intertwined mixture of apprehension, nervous excitement, and thrill, overridden by confidence in our own professional capability to acquit ourselves creditably against any hostile forces arrayed against us.

Save perhaps for active combat operations, I know of no stimulus more yearned for by professional naval officers than the adventurous probing into the heart of territory under the national control or influence of one's established foes. In the present East-West conflict, there are two very good reasons why goose-pimples involuntarily break out on men, however brave, who enter oceanic waters considered vital to the defenses of the enemy. The first is that Premier Khrushchev as early as the summer of 1961 vowed to sink upon detection any unidentified submarine sneaking close to Soviet-controlled shores. The second is that the American Joint Chiefs of Staff have "leaked" to the press the word that they are "studying" the wisdom of similar action in the case of unidentified submarines found cruising near the United States.

I am certain that every officer and crewman on board the *F-689* felt near-climactic tension as we moved into the Straits of Florida during the forenoon of Thursday, March 29, 1962. As was my custom many times during every day of every cruise, I studied our navigational position with frequent regularity. At 9 A.M. on this day, we were moving through an area marked on the chart as an "explosives dumping area." Presumably, this was where the American Navy's Key West forces sank their unwanted projectile warheads. In any event, I knew of no reason not to traverse this twenty-mile-diameter area; since it lay halfway between the Cuban coast and the Florida Keys, I decided that our movement up the Straits would best be accomplished by cruising dead-center through that passage.

I had no desire to encounter any of the Key West antisubmarine forces—especially the submarines based there. And, too, I knew that for years, the American Navy had kept ASW blimps in the Florida Keys. Despite our information that blimps had recently been retired by the American Navy, I wanted to take no chances on possibly meeting one of these craft.

Thus, we cruised submerged as always during the daylight hours, and proceeded along at six knots. I knew, of course, that the Gulf Stream, into which we now moved, would carry us along at an additional two to three knots. In fact, because of the Stream, we were able to make exceptionally good time most of the way up the Atlantic coast.

Excerpts from my personal patrol log read as follows:
March 29, 1962

7 P.M.—Indiscriminate merchant shipping detected plying coastal routes throughout preceding hours of day. Now passing Alligator Reef roughly 30 miles to the west-northwest. Should be abreast of Miami after midnight.

March 30, 1962

1 A.M.—At periscope depth, snorkeling. Miami 30 miles to the west. Huge bright orange and pink glare in sky accurately pinpoints city. What a target—even for a primitive rocket aimed by eyesight! Should be

east of Fort Lauderdale by daybreak, if not before. Electronics intercepts indicate we have been passing at a distance several ships.

5 A.M.—Heading west-northwest, closing shore.

5:30 A.M.—Heading north-northwestward; intention is to pass close aboard Palm Beach. Desire to inspect area from seaward.Possibly Baliuk can identify the Kennedy *dacha*.

11:30 A.M—Passed close ashore Palm Beach, avoiding several sailboats and small coastal vessels. Also photographed one large merchant tanker. Baliuk, Lvov, and I searched for Kennedy house but so many similar cannot identify without additional intelligence. One thing certain: whole area vulnerable. Even small coastal-type sub, if based in Cuba, could obliterate entire area. Miami, too.

12:30 P.M.—Heading north-northeast to get back into Gulf Stream and pass clear of Canaveral. U.S. may have antisub devices in area. Last Soviet sub here reported suspecting he was under surveillance by aircraft. Don't want to repeat his experience.

3 P.M—Passing Cape Canaveral, leaving it 60 miles to the west. Increasing speed, which with help of Gulf Stream will give us up to 12 knots. Intercepted wireless messages from several American ships indicate considerable naval activity over a wide area in nearly all directions. Assume must be assembling of ships for the amphibious exercise, or perhaps for the presidential review, or both. Desire to arrive off Cape Charles as soon as possible to be able to select good position for observing U. S. fleet review. Electronics emissions coming from area near Jacksonville appear to emanate from American radar picket destroyers or possibly aircraft carriers. Confirmation and positive identification of sources not possible.

It was not long after we had passed Jacksonville, Florida, abeam to port at a range of nearly 120 miles, that Rostopchin and Lvov had another altercation. Now that he had been relieved as Second Officer by Apraksin, Makar Rostopchin was no longer able to conduct himself with such outward indifference to what Lvov had to say. Now, as just another officer of the submarine, he fell more sharply under the continuous "guidance" of the commissar. This meant that when the commissar recommenced scheduling his orientation courses in the wardroom each day, Rostopchin could no longer claim that other pressing business prevented his being present. Hence, he was compelled to sit through Lvov's every session nowadays, and at this particular time, the commissar chose to discuss the intellectual superiority of the Communist theories over all other doctrines of human society, but with particular emphasis on the fallacy of religion in the scheme of life.

This might not have been so bad, in itself, because Makar Rostopchin had long since understood the intention of the Communist State to discourage, if not openly suppress, organized worship in the Soviet Union. But Lvov decided, this day, to bring up some recent Party propaganda which he had received by broadcast-wireless the previous night. It had to do with the freshly revamped attacks on Jews for the siphoning off of Soviet resources. Lvov began his tirade with the statement that it was becoming necessary for the government to destroy Jewish communal links, in the frank hope that Jewish communities, as such, would be eliminated in the Soviet Union. The reason he gave was that the Jewish population was politically suspect because of its ties with the West and with Israel.

While he was thus talking, Makar Rostopchin, with an obviously forced clearing of his throat, settled back in his chair and, contempt clearly written across his features, opened his silver snuff packet and took an excessive whiff. An explosive sneeze not only interrupted the commissar's talk, but produced spontaneous laughter and chuckles from the other officers. Then, slumping low in his seat, Makar closed his eyes in pointed insolence.

Post-Captain Commissar Lvov chose to ignore this performance, and went on to announce that on March 17, a typical Jewish embezzler of state property, one A. F. Kleimanov, had been executed for his role in crimes against the People. Furthermore, he declared, an even worse scoundrel, a Jew named Mordekh Abramovich Kakiashvili, had just been found guilty in a court in Tiflis, capital of the Georgian SSR, of extensive illegal currency speculation. He also had been executed for the good of the Soviet Union. Lvov thus made his point that there was a Jewish conspiracy with international connections, that it was known, and that something was being done about it. But to clinch it, the commissar went on to reveal that Kleimanov and Kakiashvili were only two of several Jews who had recently been executed on economic charges. At least twenty-two Jews, he said, were known to be among forty Soviet citizens who had received death sentences. Prison terms had been given to between one hundred and 150 Soviet nationals, of whom a majority were known to be Jews.

"The tinkle of gold and the rustle of bank notes have died down, the luster of diamonds grown dim," intoned Lvov with a heaviness in his voice, "but the way of these Jews has been logically ended, commencing with their having been brought forth to the harsh bench of justice in the courtroom!"

Makar Rostopchin managed to endure it until Lvov pricked him with the words, "And of course, the sooner we rid ourselves of Jews in the Navy, the better it will be for the People." When he heard these words, obviously directed at himself, he rose and turned to leave the wardroom. Lvov called him back.

"Makar Rostopchin," barked the commissar, "you need not go. You are only *half Jewish.*"

There was a half-empty glass of vodka on the wardroom table near Rostopchin. With a flash, his arm shot out and his hand grabbed the convenient object. He pitched its contents across the table, splattering the surprised face of Post-Captain Commissar Lvov. And then, smashing the glass to the deck, Rostopchin told Lvov to make the most of the incident.

For the next ten days, except for periods when his presence was required in the engine room, Makar Rostopchin was confined to his berth. There, his meals were brought to him by the commissary-porter. The real punishment was not to come, however, until later.

Of course, the present situation in Russia goes far beyond a mere anti-Semitic wave of terror reminiscent of the *pogrom* conditions of the prerevolutionary era. The criminal code there now authorizes the prosecution of those engaged in *any* religious activities, or even those who simply profess belief in God.

Highlights from the patrol account further reveal the following as having occurred during the next several days:

April 1, 1962
Commissar Lvov completed drafting his personal report about Rostopchin's insubordination, and sent it out over wireless from the whip-antenna while snorkeling during the early morning hours. Message was encoded and addressed to Vice Admiral Grishanov. I informed Rostopchin about it and advised him it would probably mean a court-martial on our return, but that I would do all in my power to defend him.

Checked the chart and noted our passing Charleston Harbor, some 275 miles to the westward, at the same time wondering what nuclear submarines are now operating out of that city. After checking with Baliuk and the navigator, unloaded three underwater radioactive navigational beacons just inside the continental shelf across the approaches to Charleston. Positions logged for reference and use of other Soviet submarines. A good triangulation made of them. Changed course to northeast. Idea here to be well seaward of amphibious and task fleet sortie areas during this known period of U. S. naval operations in the vicinity.

April 2, 1962

Off the North Carolina coast, moving northeastward from latitude near Wilmington, N.C., to area off Cape Hatteras. 9:05 P.M., while snorkeling, conning watch officer suddenly sighted aircraft running lights circling to westward. Aircraft turned in toward us, flying low, and when 2000 yards away, turned on powerful searchlights in our direction. Watch officer ordered fast emergency descent; aircraft known to have passed overhead within five seconds of our dive. Best estimate is that aircraft was a U. S. Navy antisubmarine patrol plane from one of the antisubmarine aircraft carriers. At 9:41 P.M., tremendous, powerful vibration coupled with a roar of sudden rumbling heard close aboard, as though colossal impact of a heavy mass into the sea had occurred. Soon, underwater sound reported fading echoes. Commenced using creep motor. Continued listening. Nothing. Waited some more. Then returned to periscope depth for a quick 360-degree look. Nothing seen. Descended again, this time to 150 feet, and turned westward at 3 knots. Believe loud crash was possible bomb concentration intended for us from the aircraft, or possibly *the aircraft itself*—assuming the latter had unexpected and sudden flight trouble while homing in on us so extremely close to the surface of the water. The conning watch officer reported to me that the aircraft he had seen through the periscope initially was a twin-engined, propeller-driven plane. Since we were then about 150 miles southeast of Norfolk, Virginia, I as-

sume that this aircraft was probably one of the American
Navy's carrier-based submarine-tracker planes. Perhaps
an S-2-F, so famous in antisubmarine circles . . .

April 3, 1962
Wireless revealed that the huge American nuclear carrier
ENTERPRISE was just starting the final phase of her
shakedown cruise in the Caribbean.

April 4, 1962
Placed three more radioactive navigational beacons on the
bottom, plotted their locations with precision, and moved
twenty miles farther north.

April 5-7, 1962
Sneaked in close to shore off Virginia Beach. Sighted
through periscope and saw nothing of unusual significance.
Not too many people on beach area. Had to exercise extreme caution due to large amount of shipping, both naval
and merchant, in general vicinity. Was reminded of the
performance of Soviet submarine skipper, Captain Boris
K. Mischenko. Later, activity in and around the port appeared to accelerate—due, probably, to the forthcoming
fleet review scheduled for a few days hence. Therefore,
decided to head seaward again, cruising at about 2 knots.

[Captain Mischenko, referred to above, was the competent officer who perhaps somewhat brashly took his Z-
class long-range submarine into the chanel between Capes
Charles and Henry, back in 1959, I believe it was—and
cruised right into Hampton Roads, opposite the huge U. S.
Naval Operating Base at Norfolk. Unfortunately, he was
detected. But he outfoxed his hunters, and slid back out to
sea without the American Navy regaining contact for three
days. Then, not far from the beach off Fort Monroe, track-
ers picked him up while snorkeling. Again, he managed to
escape.]

April 8, 1962

Electronics intercept equipment picked up radar emissions from a nearby Soviet trawler during the night. Trawler then operating some two hundred miles east of Cape Hatteras. *F-689* still heading eastward from Cape Charles. Other electronics intercepts indicated various U. S. naval ships in waters to the east.

April 9, 1962

About 250 miles east of Norfolk, Virginia, while snorkeling at near-daybreak, watch officer noted aircraft in vicinity. Went down deep quickly to avoid detection. Stayed deep for next several hours.

By midafternoon, about 300 miles east of Norfolk. At 3 P.M., came to periscope depth to take look around. Saw American destroyers and a carrier in distance. Then suddenly saw another American S-2-F-type aircraft circling to the northeast several thousand yards away. Quickly changed depth to 400 feet, turning away from aircraft. Rigged for silent running. At 3:30 P.M., turned hard left and came up to depth of 150 feet. Suddenly, as boat turned, underwater sound picked up loud screw noises close aboard, obviously reaching us now as a result of our having passed into a more favorable temperature layer. Noises readily identified as steam-propelled screws also heard, some distance further away to the east. Quickly turned submarine around to head toward closest echoes. Gave orders to come up to periscope deapth for visual investigation of strangers in area. Periscope trained in direction of screw noises. To astonishment, found self peering at submarine periscope, moving away and to eastward, toward several destroyer types visible through haze. Suddenly, noted that a destroyer was veering and bearing down on the unidentified periscope . . . submarine periscope faded under bow wave of onrushing destroyer . . . looking very much like a collision. American destroyer suddenly emitted large clouds of white smoke and came to standstill dead in the water. Just beyond, a few seconds later, shooting to surface in explosion of white water was a submarine—the largest I have ever seen.

Quick reference to *Jane's Fighting Ships* silhouette patterns revealed submarine to be nuclear-powered Polaris missile-launching type. Went deep quickly, this time to 450 feet, where sound wasn't penetrating too well. Ordered *F-689* to clear the area to the westward at 16.5 knots. This speed maintained for twenty minutes, at the end of which period, slowed to 2 knots and remained deep for several hours.

The next five days were spent cruising on an east-west axis in the Gulf Stream, at best determined depths to avoid being discovered, save for snorkeling times under cover of darkness. We were biding our time until the U. S. Navy's presidential review. This we knew would shortly take place, and we now turned south to intercept the fleet off the Carolina coast.

On the morning of April 13, the *F-689* arrived some thirty-five to forty miles off the Carolina shores, and on the morning of April 14, was in an almost perfect position from which to review the presidential parade. I was able, at periscope depth, and in a mild but choppy sea (excellent for our purposes) to cruise close enough to the two passing columns of warships—giant aircraft carriers, cruisers, frigates, and destroyers—so that I could do a fairly thorough job of spying.

Of especial interest to me was that the two ships leading the columns of assorted warships were aircraft carriers I had only recently observed in Cuban waters. The *Enterprise* and the *Forrestal* were certainly magnificent goliaths of the seas.

Naturally, I was impressed with the seemingly endless caravan of ships—two long columns stretching as far as the eye could see. I counted a total of forty-eight American ships—all combatant types, and all proudly manned along their maindeck rails by thousands (or so it seemed) of sailors dressed in blues with white hats. Nothing can detract from the sheer magnificence of such a sight. It was, indeed, a demonstration of tremendous mobile naval power.

It seems doubtful that President Kennedy would have looked as confident as his news pictures showed him to be, on the occasion of this review, had he known at the time that we had been watching, firsthand, all developments in that long parade of his many-ship task force.

When the rockets, depth charges, and other devices were fired by the participating units in the review, the F-689 was hastily pulled away. Our course was northeastward, and at a depth of 450 feet we slipped away—confident that we could have acquitted ourselves with glory and in honor, had a shooting war suddenly been triggered.

29

The Penetration of New York Harbor

□ It was at a depth of 450 feet, and at six knots, that we left the North Carolina coast and headed seaward. By one o'clock on the morning of April 15, the *F-689* was some sixty miles due east of Cape Lookout, and about equally distant to the south of Cape Hatteras. Northeastward from here until nearly abreast of Hatteras, and then northward for roughly the next 180 miles was my plan. We followed it with but minor variation. Hence, by 7 A.M on April 16, the U. S. naval authorities at Norfolk, Virginia (where the American Atlantic Fleet Commander in Chief is headquartered) would have been more than mildly interested, I feel sure, to know that we were not much more than 115 miles to seaward from Cape Henry. Our course now took us on a heading which, if continued, would place us at the entrance to New York Harbor!

But there was business to be done. We had several strings of underwater navigational beacons to plant, and positioning them would take a combination of good judgment and precise navigation on our part. The first series of devices for this general area were placed on the floor of the American continental shelf not more than seventy miles east of Winterquarter Shoals, about a hundred miles south-southeast of Atlantic City, New Jersey. Others were planted along a track heading roughly northeast from this point, for the next 120 miles. Their placement just inside the one hundred-fathom curve would be invaluable for possible later use by missile submarines required to position themselves accurately. Needless to say, such extremely eastern cities as New York, Philadelphia, Baltimore, Norfolk, and of course Washington, would all become probable targets for our Soviet missile-launching submarines. But so also would many of America's inland cities—such communities as Detroit, Cleveland, Pittsburgh, and any others of importance within about a seven-hundred-mile radius from any seaward launch point.

By late afternoon on April 17, we had completed our work off the mid-Atlantic seaboard, and were ready to proceed northward for the placement of our remaining devices off the Georges Bank. But it was now that I made a daring decision.

I knew, of course, that the commissar had sent at least one unfavorable report concerning me back to Moscow. Thus far, my mission had been accomplished, however —and consequently, nothing the commissar could say would detract from my professional performance and integrity. My Mediterranean cruise in the submarine *W-7* had spotlighted me as a future contender for Soviet Navy glory, and this cruise would doubtless have a telling effect on my life henceforth. At this point, my love for my country was strong enough to insure my voluntary continuation in the Soviet Navy—despite the Communist ideology which by then I had increasingly felt was intrinsically wrong. But what I needed was a smashingly daring professional success, an exploit to go recorded in Soviet naval annals as one of the most daring of all time!

Calling Baliuk into my stateroom, I inquired what the coastal shipping off New Jersey and just south of New York might be like in midweek. Baliuk, of course, with his personal experiences aboard trawlers in the area, was invaluable to me. His opinion was that we could move in close to the Jersey beaches, and right on up to outer New York Harbor. It wouldn't even be necessary to invade America's three-mile limit in order to observe activity on the shore. As a matter of fact, he confided, if the weather was sufficiently warm, we could observe bathers on the

beaches from Atlantic City north to Sandy Hook. His remarks reminded me of the Nazi U-boat sinkings of coastal
tankers right off those same beaches during World War II,
when (according to the American historian Professor Mor-
ison) it was not at all unusual for German subs to sink
U. S. merchant ships within full view of the beach-loving
salt water bathers from Virginia Beach north to Coney
Island!

I had almost made up my mind. Now all that remained
was to assemble all officers in the wardroom and ascertain
whether there were any on board who might object to my
taking the submarine on an operation beyond the scope
of our orders. In particular, I was concerned about the
commissar's attitude. Were he to oppose any bold devia-
tion from our basic orders, I was not sure that I would
want to execute such a fantastic plan.

"Gentlemen," I began, "a wonderful opportunity now
presents itself."

All eyes were focused now upon me. If any of the officers suspected the extent of my thinking, none showed it.
Rostopchin reached into his shirt pocket and produced his
silver snuff packet, which he promptly put to its intended use.

His sneeze punctuated my asking whether any officer
present felt he might want to decline a chance to enter
New York Harbor—*submerged*.

Even Lvov's face registered not only approval but a
keen delight at the prospects. As a matter of fact, his only
comment served to cement my until then most tentative
plan. Said the commissar, "When do we make the penetration?"

Notwithstanding Lvov's obvious enthusiasm about
entering New York Harbor in a submerged submarine, I
went on to remind all officers that according to the orders
under which we operated, I was to keep us outside the
three-mile limit. In the eventuality that we were discov-

ered by the Americans, we would have to surface fully or subject ourselves to a possible depth-charge attack. In any case, we would not have the support of the Soviet Government. Nonetheless, the experience, if successful, would prove to be unforgettable—and for many years to come, would be the topic of discussions in many Soviet warship wardrooms.

The decision was made to enter the world's most famous harbor. Sergei Mikhailoff produced his sailing schedules, and pointed out to us that on the next day (Wednesday, April 18) the *Queen Mary* would be departing New York for Southampton; the American Export Line's ship *Exeter* would be leaving for Piraeus, and the steamer *Israel* would be departing for Haifa. Thursday, according to the navigator, would be a better day to attempt the harbor penetration. I looked at his shipping lists and agreed. The next day, so far as I was concerned, could be spent moving up the New Jersey coast—as Baliuk had mentioned—and we could spy on the surf bathers.

The Soviet intelligence-gathering apparatus which provided the navigator with the merchant ship schedules also revealed that on Thursday no American naval activity could reasonably be expected from any units at the New York Naval Shipyard in Brooklyn, nor anywhere in the vicinity. Ships slated to arrive Thursday morning off Ambrose Lightship, at the entrance to New York Harbor, included the *United States,* due in from Bremerhaven; the Grace Line's *Santa Monica* from Cartagena, the *Santa Paula* from Port-au-Prince; and the military transport *Upshur*. All these ships were due to arrive at their piers by 8 A.M.; this meant they would be approaching Ambrose Lightship any time after five o'clock in the morning. Consequently, that would have to be the time for the *F-689* to appear there.

As finally decided, we would move into New York on the morning of the nineteenth in the wake of one of these large vessels and take our departure some few hours later in the wake of either the North German Lloyd liner *Berlin*, scheduled to leave New York at 11 A.M., or the French Line's *Flandre*, set to sail at 11:30 A.M. Although the *Vulcania*, *Buckner*, and *America* were all listed for departures from New York later in the day, I decided that they were all leaving too late for us. It would have to be either the *Berlin* or *Flandre* which would serve as our camouflage on departure, if we could tarry *that* long in the harbor.

The operations officer was detailed to make ready the camera, for we would want a complete panoramic view of New York as seen through the periscope from our world of inner space.

Going with Sergei Mikhailoff and Ivan Baliuk to the navigator's desk at the conning station, I indicated where I wanted the submarine taken. Proceeding on a course due west-northwest, we would arrive off the New Jersey coast on the eighteenth at a point just southeast of Asbury Park. It was here, I seemed to recall, that an ill-fated American excursion steamer, the *SS Morro Castle*, had burned and beached back in 1934.

My orders to the navigator recommended a speed and course suitable for our arriving off this area of beaches in the late afternoon. I was anxious to compare the American beaches this far north with the Russian seaside resort areas on the Black Sea. Highlights taken from my personal copy of the patrol account for Wednesday and Thursday (April 18 and 19) follow:

April 18, 1962
At 3:30 P.M., passed inside three-mile limit off Ocean Grove, Asbury Park, New Jersey. Numerous bathers on beaches, despite variable cloudiness. Commissar Lvov remarked that beaches did not compare favorably with Soviet resort areas by the Black Sea. Too many billboards

and advertising signs along the shoreline. At 5:30 P.M., set course for Ambrose Lightship. Intend to night snorkel and recharge batteries en route Ambrose.

April 19, 1962
4:10 A.M, batteries recharged. 4:20 A.M., finished snorkeling before morning twilight. 5:13 A.M., watched sunrise and commenced approach on huge American luxury liner *United States*. 6:05 A.M., en route New York Harbor, approximately 250 yards astern of *SS United States.* Channel shipping ahead reduced American liner's speed sufficiently for *F-689* to maintain station astern.

Upon entering New York Harbor, referred to Esso road map of New York City (obtained in Havana), and was thus provided excellent references to landmarks—supplementing our navigational charts of the area.

I noted with mixed amusement and sentimentality the Ferris wheels and high roller coasters at Coney Island. So as to allow each officer the maximum opportunity to benefit from this expedition, I permitted all to take turns looking through the periscope at various times while proceeding up Ambrose Channel, and later, in New York's Upper Bay. There were no problems encountered from other shipping until after we transited the Narrows and entered the Bay, bounded on the west by Staten Island and Bayonne, and on the east by Brooklyn. Along this stretch of our track, I observed that the myriad numbers of harbor craft, ferry boats, small ships, and larger liners—all of which were moving swiftly and often on converging courses —might make our submerged entry more than ordinarily dangerous. I checked the chart, noticing the depth of water to be variable between forty-four feet and sixty feet. The tide, I felt sure, was peaking during our entry. But even so, there were not more than a few feet to spare between the bottom of the bay and the bottom of the submarine. If we were to strike a submerged cable, or in any way become tangled in debris, or collide with a ship, we would be in trouble. And there was another worry. If a fire were suddenly to break out on board, we might be compelled by the fumes to surface. Besides collision, a fire on board a submarine is one of ths casualties most feared.

At one point, a large red ferry boat came up along our port quarter and then passed (miraculously) astern of us. It was an indescribable moment of anxiety. True enough, most ferry boats have a small draft, but the idea that this one could have rammed our conning tower, or smashed our periscope, was quite unnerving. As a matter of fact, this near-collision occurred only minutes before another nearly catastrophic convergence in the Bay. Between Greenville and Red Hook Channels, or at least in the vicinity, a fast-moving, green-colored ferry boat suddenly came up off our starboard side and passed painfully close aboard (over us, I was sure, in the final nerve-wracking moments) on its way from Brooklyn to the Jersey side. Fortunately, we were hugging the stern of the *United States* so close that there was no trouble from the scores of tugs and tows which dotted the harbor view. Passing the Bayonne terminals, we could see the massed but moth balled U. S. warships of an earlier day, tied up like great cocoons awaiting their final day of glory. I could not help but wonder what that day would be: another, or a series, of future naval engagements—or dismantling day at a junk heap?

I could make out the hull configurations of at least one large World War II-type battleship, several cruisers, and I believe some small carriers. Of course, there were also some destroyer types there. My new Second Officer, Lieutenant Commander Apraksin, upon his own sighting through the periscope at the mothballed fleet, voiced a thought which had momentarily occurred to me. "What use, do you suppose, Captain," he asked, "will they ever make of those big battleships in the present age?"

I chuckled. After all, the Soviet Navy has recently been scrapping the remainder of its own cruisers. The trend for the USSR has been to diminish the strength of the larger surface ships, in favor of an expanded submarine force. The Soviet Navy's role is mostly to provide a flank for the Army and to deny the use of the seas, in event of war, to such a country as the U.S., which does depend on ocean transport for her very survival—in peace or war.

"Well," I answered Apraksin, "one possible use of those large old battleships might be as big headquarters ships for the American fleet commanders. After all, they're still among the fastest ships in the world; they have enough armor to ward off most projectiles and, with modifications, they could house intercontinental or intermediate-range missiles. If those huge and potentially powerful ships were ever converted for that purpose, and were able to enjoy protection from subs, it certainly wouldn't be anything for the Soviet Navy or other military to take lightly."

Apraksin grinned.

"I'm sure you're right, Captain," he said, "but I don't think it'll ever happen. Know why?"

"Why?"

"A simple matter of American public opinion, Captain."

I only nodded agreement, for I had no time to further discuss the issue during this critical period of maneuvering the *F-689.*

As we passed abeam to starboard of the entrance to Buttermilk Channel, a waterway passing between Brooklyn and Governor's Island, I decided to change course to the left and move over closer to Liberty Island, where the Statue of Liberty stands so majestically and so dominatingly over the entire harbor scene. Conveniently, a tug and tow passing downstream from the Battery was sighted making a turn toward the somewhat narrow channel just to the south of the Statue of Liberty (leading to the Lehigh Valley Railroad piers), and I maneuvered the submarine close aboard the tow, following it over to the Jersey side of the bay. The whole series of maneuvers within this incredibly busy and beautiful harbor was actually a tribute to the navigational advice of Sergei Mikhailoff as well as to the professional skill and competence of Apraksin, who doubled with me in conning the sub. I say doubled, because whenever I was looking at the navigational layout on the chart, he was at the periscope and actually responsible for maneuvering the craft.

By now, a host of tugs had descended upon the *United States* and had escorted her upstream, where she now was maneuvering to make her berth and disembark the approximately fifteen hundred passengers on board. Doubtless the passengers were too engrossed in looking ahead at the New York skyline to catch sight of the tailing *F-689*.

Kulakov succeeded in taking several photographs of the Statue of Liberty and the New York skyline.

Briefly, I entertained the idea of going upstream in the North (Hudson) River. I had once before had the occasion to ride over the famous George Washington Bridge (at the time of the Soviet Premier's visit), and the urge to look at the span from periscope level was indeed a strong one. However, I realized that with all the big ships twisting and maneuvering to ease into their berths at the downtown piers, it would be unnecessarily risky to attempt moving any further upstream than generally where we were right then. A check of our position indicated that we were almost on a parallel with the old American roundhouse fort on Governor's Island. Furthermore, the water upstream was bound to be less briny, and the consequent loss in buoyancy would be considerable, I felt sure. We just could not risk an underwater penetration any further northward.

This decided, I maneuvered the submarine around and cautiously started our departure from this magnificent but nervewracking American seaport. Another of those fast-moving ferry boats came careening by close aboard (nearly inducing a heart attack in me), but this time I took full advantage of it and pursued it as closely as I could. This wasn't too close, because we couldn't maintain his speed in such shallow water. But at least I was able to utilize the ferry's foamy wake for hiding our splashing periscope. The state of the water in the bay was good from our point of view, too. There were small wavelets and occasional small whitecaps. Spotting the periscope would be difficult except to a trained observer.

Twice, passing close aboard large liners, I gave the order to lower the periscope. I counted on a few moments of dead reckoning and previous visual observation of the area to insure against our colliding with anything. It worked; apparently no one ever saw us.

Once again, I was given some concern by the movements of a green ferry which appeared to zigzag between some other vessels and buoys and then cut across the main channel at a reckless speed. But within another hour and a half, we had successfully transited the Narrows and passed by Coney Island. Even as we crept down Ambrose Channel, heading for the open sea, Kulakov was busy developing the film we had taken.

In the vicinity of the Ambrose Lightship, I spotted a white-colored customs, or Coast Guard ship. The satisfaction I felt at having passed her by, earlier, and now again slipping past her as she lay to, "guarding" the entrance to New York Harbor, was sweet indeed. With the lightship as a base for departure, I accepted a course of 080 degrees true from Mikhailoff, and proceeded now generally eastward along the southern side of Long Island. There was still so much shipping in the area that I was fairly sure that any American antisubmarine detection systems would find it hard to detect us. Regardless, we now cruised along just outside the three-mile limit.

Passing the conning station duty to Lieutenant Baliuk, I left instructions to cruise at periscope depth with frequent periscope observations to be made of the entire area. Thus we would be able to see, firsthand, what the Long Island beaches looked like in late April. The weather seemed warm enough; the passengers on the ferries and steamers all appeared clad in lightweight spring or summer garments. Perhaps we would see more people using the beaches. I was primarily interested in this because the Communist lectures in Russia always point to the USSR beaches as paradises for the average Soviet worker —not just havens for the wealthy or privileged. I wanted to see more of the American attitude, as perhaps would be reflected by the number of people actually on the beaches themselves. My reasoning was that if there were many, it might indicate a widespread economic stability of the capitalist class; if there were few, then perhaps Americans, in working so hard for their now famous "Yankee dollar," might not have the time to spend in living "the good life."

I now retired to the wardroom and allowed the commissary-porter to break out a bottle of French champagne —one of the last remaining vestiges of the epicurean reign of former Second Officer Volkonski.

Lvov, joining me at the wardroom table where Usoupoff now placed some cool, fresh, gray-colored caviar down on a silver-plated tureen, was effervescent. "A splendid feat of seamanship, Captain," roared the commissar. Then, pouring himself a glass of champagne, he offered a toast:

"Having just looked at the navigator's chart and noted where our track will now take us, let us drink to the supremacy of the ultimate socialist state—quite a shocker for some of those capitalist manipulators whose estates we will shortly be passing off Southampton."

Raising our glasses, we drank the toast.

"Yes, Commissar," I smiled, "it would be an even greater shock if some of the people just a little further to the east of Southampton knew we would be cruising within swimming distance of their beaches—representing, as we do, a far-flung but powerful probe into the recesses of a capitalist stronghold . . ."

"What do you mean, to the *east* of Southampton?"

"Well, when I was in Washington a couple of years or so ago, I attended a garden party. That was when Nikita

Khrushchev was touring the United States. Anyway, at this garden party—and as I recall, it was held at the British Embassy—I was told that on Long Island, there are three points of interest. The first is Oyster Bay, which they used to call the 'Gold Coast,' and where that great capitalist warmonger of yesteryear, Theodore Roosevelt, made his summer home; the second is Southampton, where some of the older rich have long gone to pass away their summers; and then, there is *East* Hampton, where the new and filthy rich now go each summer to golf and drink."

"*East* Hampton?"

"Yes, Commissar. But they don't pronounce it that way. The accent isn't on the *East*. Besides, they pronounce it East *Homp*-ton."

"East HOMP-ton?"

I nodded, and together, with an uproarious belch of laughter not at all routine for Lvov and me to join in spontaneously, we poured and drank another round of bubbling, sparkling, golden French champagne.

30

Consummate Satisfaction and Pleasure

☐ The sun, setting at 6:39 P.M., gave way to a moonrise which lit up the seascape nearly as well as the sun had earlier. Under the illumination of a giant full moon, many ships became excellent objects of visual attention by all the conning officers of *F-689* as well as myself. Even if the brilliance of their lights had not pointed to them as most inviting targets for a possible enemy submarine (were it wartime), the light from the moon alone would have been sufficient for torpedo aiming purposes.

During the night of April 19, as our submarine crept slowly along the southern coast of Long Island just outside the three-mile limit, heading eastward while snorkeling, our visual and electronic eyes detected a host of surface contacts. Significant ones which I was able to identify with little difficulty included the Europe-bound *America*, which of course we had encountered on the other side of the Atlantic very early in the cruise. The Italian passenger liner *Christoforo Colombo* was another ship positively identified during this night. She was detected racing westward, bound for New York, while passing through well-traveled shipping lanes to the south of us. Other liners departing New York on the nineteenth, and which overtook us either by late afternoon or early evening, included the *Berlin*, *Flandre*, *Vulcania*, and *Buckner*.

Lvov, at one point peering through the periscope at the caravan of shipping, added the interesting postscript that after Soviet Russia has placed the first scientific-military community on the moon itself, the tactics of war will change so vastly that enemy shipping might well be pre-

317

targeted through satellites controlled by Soviet space sailors temporarily quartered on the moon!

The thought, farfetched as it seemed, was at least equaled by an exclamation made by Lieutenant Baliuk, to the effect that the USSR may some day discover how to manipulate or otherwise control—perhaps from the moon —earth's oceanic tides in specific areas of the world. Better still, Baliuk continued, would be for the Soviet Union to find a way to alter the paths of some of the world's great ocean currents. Needless to say, were the Gulf Stream ever deflected or diverted away from the coast of the United States on the Atlantic seaboard, there would be no more wintertime sunbathing in Florida. And maybe even there, people would have to change to heavy woolen underwear and fur coats in the wintertime. The thought was a chilling one—even for the cold war.

The ensuing week was one of transit from the southern coast of Long Island to the Georges Bank, where we planted the last of our electronics devices on the North American continental shelf, and then proceeded on to an Atlantic Ocean point about 180 miles southeast of Cape Race, Newfoundland—which put us squarely in the center of the Grand Banks. That our course took us squarely into the middle of a large Soviet "fishing" fleet in those waters was not, of course, a mere coincidence. You will recall that my orders directed me to arrive at latitude 45° north, longitude 50° west, en route to the USSR from our operations off the American coast.

But getting to this rendezvous point was not without incident. Witness an extract from my notes and commentary for the day:

April 20, 1962

Moonset at 5:22 A.M., observed by conning watch officer through periscope while making routine area surveillance. Sunrise evident a few minutes earlier. Crew shifted to day routine in view of probability of possible contact with American naval forces in area east of Long Island. Coded bulletins received during night by wireless indicate that U. S. destroyer and submarine forces from New London and Newport are operating during daylight hours in area south of Block Island and Martha's Vineyard. (Intelligence received from Soviet trawler mother-ship off Cape Cod.) . . . Approached beaches off Southampton and East Hampton shortly after 1P.M. Not much activity noted. Baliuk states that summer residents usually migrate from the city to this locale after the middle of June. Probably explains why we didn't see more than a few bathers on the beaches along the Hamptons.

. . . Turned due east and commenced exercising extreme caution in view of our imminent approach to deep-water operating areas of United States submarines stationed near New London. Speed of advance 2 knots until arrival south of Martha's Vineyard, after which time intend to increase speed to 5 knots.

. . . Television reception (using the whip-antenna) was poor. Video image and audio reception night of April 19 was excellent; perhaps most interesting were the American news analysts late at night. Their interpretations of foreign news and international events vied with those of the commissar, who during the TV commentaries punctuated the remarks of the news analysts with some of his own views on the particular subjects under discussion.

We contented ourselves the night of the twentieth by looking at one of the American movies provided us by the Havana naval authorities. Their film library, consisting of old and outdated Hollywood movies confiscated by the Cuban Government (from the hitherto privately owned and operated cinema houses in Cuba) was nonetheless a treat for us. Twice previously, while cruising up the Atlantic coast of North America, I had authorized the showing of some of these films. Now again, I allowed the projectionist to show one to the crew—the better to keep them alert and imaginative during this period of transit in unfriendly operational waters. It was Commissar Lvov who picked the cinema for this evening: It was *Mr. Smith Goes to Washington,* a story he seemed to relish watching. Previous movies shown on board had been one with Clark Gable, entitled *It Happened One Night,* and another called *The Plainsman,* starring Gary Cooper. I might say here that all these movies taken on board in Havana had been selected in deference to the popularity of the particular actors playing in the individual films. James Stewart, Clark Gable, and Gary Cooper have always been popular with the average cinema-watching Russian.

At 2 A.M. on April 21, sonar alerted me to the sounds of many warship propellers, seemingly coming from the east to east-southeast. Our investigation by periscope revealed nothing, and my course of action was to go down well below the thermal layer and slow down, using creep motor speeds to insure maximum safety from detection by what must have been American naval forces. Glinka and Kulakov voiced the opinion that our passive sound information could very probably be reverberations from the propellers of one of the United States carrier hunter-killer groups known to be operational off the U. S. east coast. Fortunately, the sounds diminished as the hours passed. Hence, we were able to come up to periscope surveillance depth by 3:30 A.M., and for the ensuing hours until just before daybreak, snorkeled and recharged our batteries.

In the early morning haze, prior to the sun burning off the mists from the surface of the sea, sonar suddenly picked up light, fast propeller noises fairly close to our position. The conning watch officer, who had just brought the submarine up to periscope depth after getting a bathythemograph reading to 350 feet, immediately trained his periscope in the direction of the sonar contact. Out of the mist, he could faintly make out the configuration of an American destroyer type. She was coming along at about ten knots off our port bow, at a range of approximately eleven hundred yards.

With expert precision, the alert quartermaster secured the camera properly to the periscope faceplate and stood by as the ship passed us close-aboard. Meanwhile, I was notified and was on the way to the conning station on the run. By the time I arrived there, Kulakov, who had been the officer on watch, had taken a picture of the American ship and had, besides immediately lowering the periscope, given the order to take us down to 275 feet—a depth which both he and I agreed was well below any thermal layer.

The gratifying sounds of the American ship's propellers becoming steadily more faint indicated that once again, we had been undetected—right under the nose of a fairly new United States Navy antisubmarine vessel. Alert lookouts on the destroyer could possibly have spotted our periscope, however. Reports which we have received of recent efforts to improve American submarine defense capabilities come as a most curious bit of news. For the Soviet submariner, it is comforting to know that no matter how much attention America now suddenly devotes to antisubmarine improvements, her failure to concentrate on this field of naval warfare sooner (that is, during the past decade) will allow Soviet submariners a good initial advantage in combat operations—should open war at sea break out between the United States and the USSR.

Upon the development of the film taken of the U. S. warship, it was readily determined that the destroyer type which Lieutenant Kulakov had come upon and photographed was a ship of the post-World War II era, a destroyer escort of the Dealey class. Unfortunately for the U.S., but certainly gratifying to Soviet submariners, is the fact that statistics mentioned in *Jane's Fighting Ships* portray the Dealey class as too slow to keep up with carrier task forces, too slow to run down nuclear submarines, undergunned for antisubmarine work (ahead-thrown rockets, depth charges, and a limited-range directionally trainable rocket called "Alpha," in addition to carrying a truly ineffective antisubmarine homing torpedo). They are also equipped with sonar of questionable characteristics.

April 23, 1962

In the late morning hours, at a point approximately 150 miles south of Cape Sable, Nova Scotia, I maneuvered the submarine into a position for releasing our last underwater navigational beacons.

At 12 noon, I ordered course changed to a heading of 060 degrees true, for our rendezvous with the trawlers off Newfoundland.

Around midnight, and while snorkeling, we received a coded wireless message from one of the trawlers which not only indicated the present location but also the intended positions of the trawler fleet for the next few days. Additionally, we received word relayed from Supreme Soviet Naval Headquarters advising that we should have a "clear shot" of it in returning homeward between Iceland and Great Britain. Apparently, the American antisubmarine group working in that area would be off-station during our transit. I found this rather amusing, in light of what we had already accomplished.

April 24, 1962

Glinka, assigned as games officer, initiated The Great Chess Tournament drive. Before midafternoon, twenty-seven men had signed up for the competition. To instill greater interest, I announced to the crew that the two crewmen who came off with the highest number of wins from the tournament would then be pitted against the Second Officer. Whichever of the two crewmen most decisively beat *him* (if he were beaten at all) would then have an opportunity to play the Commanding Officer. However, whether he won or lost against me, he would be the Crew's Chess Champion; playing against me would be only for "prestige" purposes. I made certain everyone understood this.

By midafternoon, six different chess games were in progress—the forerunners of a long series.

April 25, 1962

At 3 P.M. Lieutenant Marsk, complaining of an impacted wisdom tooth which had infected his gum area, sought relief at the hands of the medical corpsman. Given ten quick and sizable shots of 90 proof vodka, and with a half hour allowed for its optimum diffus onary effect within his system, Marsk was then subjected to the probes and twistings of an ordinary pair of wire pliers wielded by the corpsman. It is said that the patient never knew what was happening, and the ensuing operation was held to be successful.

In the evening, wardroom officers met for a political lecture by the commissar. His subject dealt upon the increasingly weak, apparently ever more unstable, American economic system. Lvov quoted Lenin as having said at one time, "The U.S.A. will spend itself into bankruptcy and then will fall into our laps like a ripe apple."

Via the whip-antenna, we received relayed wireless reports from one of the Soviet trawlers far to the south, about 140 miles north of Puerto Rico, that she was continuing to shadow the American aircraft carrier *Forrestal* and a U. S. task force which had for the past few days been steaming in that area. I wondered what secret orders the other two Soviet submarines, the *Z-521* and the *F-700*, were now operating under. We had never made actual contact, even when we were operating in the same general geographical area at the time of the Glenn orbital flight recovery. Perhaps both these submarines were now back in Russia . . . or perhaps they were, like the *F-689, still* engaged in covert operations of a highly sensitive nature. I wondered.

And of course, the matter came up for discussion at the wardroom table. Lvov initiated the conversation about the other subs when Baliuk read us the decoded trawler message about the surveillance of the *Forrestal* and her task force.

Another subject which came up for general commentary was the Soviet advance in measures to combat the American Polaris submarine. According to up-to-the-minute intelligence available to us through the coded Navy Headquarters messages, the USSR had recently proof-tested an underwater H-bomb in the Arctic. These messages indicated that this bomb has the capability to kill any submarine within a one hundred square mile area. The resultant damage sustained by a submarine within this area would be inflicted as a result of a terrific underwater hammer effect, set up by successive shock waves.

Of course, I reasoned, the cost of detonating thousands of underwater H-bombs in an effort to cover the millions of square miles of ocean hiding areas would be prohibitive, unless in the meanwhile we can develop better submarine localization devices.

The next few days were quiet ones; the distance from U. S. shores had opened to more than five hundred miles and was steadily increasing. We could afford to relax at last . . . not completely, but sufficiently so that I could reflect now, for the first time, on the over-all operation which we had been conducting, and which now was drawing to a close. As the range to American shores grew greater, I took to surfacing the submarine for brief intervals at night. The hatches were thrown open and fresh air was allowed to enter the craft; I took full advantage of these occasions to go up on the open bridge and benefit most completely from the refreshing salt air, the invigorating white spray, and the expansiveness of the surface environment.

For the American reader who has never been on board a submarine, I would recommend that for a vicarious moment of standing on the plunging, rolling weather deck of a surfaced submarine, he might do well to look carefully at an oil painting I saw in the Pentagon during my 1959 visit to Washington. This canvas, the work of a World War II artist, was an on-the-scene impression of a submarine splashing along at nighttime in the bleak North Atlantic. This paint'ng was exhibited with scores of other wartime canvases. It may still be there. In any event, it compared very favorably with some submarine-scene oils by leading Russian marine artists, which I have seen in Moscow, but which of course are not easily viewable by most Americans.

April 29, 1962

At midafternoon, a single sweep of our surface-search radar disclosed the massed Soviet fishing fleet for which we were heading. They were strung out over an area of about a hundred square miles just to the east of us, and apparently moving northward. This conclusion I derived from prior receipt of their intended position projected over the next twenty-four-hour period.

It was during evening twilight that we finally broke surface some few hundred yards from the large mother-ship, a trawler-tender whose cavernous compartments contain vast electronics storerooms as well as on-the-spot canning facilities for the fishing hauls daily taken on board from the smaller craft of the fishing fleet.

The commanding officer, Commodore A. V. Rudzogdin, in addition to having spent some thirty-three years in the Soviet Navy surface fleet (where he last commanded, in 1960, the heavy cruiser *Aleksandr Nevskii*), is presently one of the Soviet Union's most knowledgeable oceanographers. He has been highly decorated by the Soviet Navy and also by the Supreme Soviet for his recent outstanding achievements in hydrographic work along the Grand Banks southward to the approaches of New York.

After maneuvering the submarine alongside the tender's leeward side, Lvov and I, followed by five crewmen visitors, boarded the big ship by climbing adroitly up a Jacob's ladder to the main deck. There, to our astonishment, we were met with ceremony and fanfare.

After dabbling in some delicious appetizers in the commodore's stateroom, we were taken into the wardroom, where about twenty-five officers of the Soviet Navy—all dressed in mess jackets—awaited our arrival. Not having expected such formality, and particularly surprised to find the wardroom so full of naval officers (there were less than a dozen merchant marine officers there), I found myself somewhat embarrassed. Neither Lvov nor I had bothered to dress properly for the occasion; we were attired in old salt-sprayed, oil-spotted blues. The gold braid on our uniforms was tarnished and in marked contrast to the flashing brilliance of the French lace adorning the commodore's and other officers' uniforms.

A trio of musicians stroked out chamber music and popular Russian songs on fiddle, bass violin, and cello, as we sat down to enjoy a delightfully sophisticated meal afloat —champagne, caviar, sardines, haddock, lobster, borsch, steamed rice, fresh salad (a real treat), sliced oranges (another treat), and Armenian cognac.

Midway through the meal, the commodore arose to say a few words and to toast our continued submarine successes. It was obvious that he knew some of the activities in which we had been engaged. Just before he sat down, he announced with obvious pleasure that the Soviet Navy Commander in Chief, Admiral Gorshkov, had just been elevated to the rank of Fleet Admiral. "And do you know why?" the commodore inquired rhetorically of his attentive audience.

"I'll tell you why!" he exclaimed with enthusiasm.

Both Lvov and I glanced from him to peer quickly at the faces of the other officers. All were turned toward the speaker; each expression registered respectful interest.

"The Kremlin has made him our first Fleet Admiral— the first in all the history of Russia—as a direct result of two ambitious programs initiated by Admiral Gorshkov.

Both programs have been hugely successful. Both programs are vital to the interests of the Soviet Union. Combined, these two programs will give us ultimate victory over the Western world."

I was entranced. Commodore Rudzogdin was not just *speaking*. He was *orating*. With polished articulateness and a velvety toned voice, he elucidated.

"Gentlemen," he said, "for his brilliant foresight and planning in developing our current oceanographic effort, as well as for his correctly assessing the Soviet Union's naval requirements, which in turn has led us to producing such a mighty underseas fleet, our nation has today promoted Sergey Gorshkov to the highest rank to which a naval officer can aspire. We, here aboard this great ship, as Soviet oceanographers, represent one of Admiral Gorshkov's magnificent, brilliant programs. And our guests this evening, from the submarine now in company with us, represent the blossoming supremacy of our Navy over the navigable waters of the globe. Let us drink a toast now to our great Fleet Admiral!!"

The chairs shuffled and squeaked as more than seventy shoes moved in a responsive demonstration, Rudzogdin bringing the assemblage to its feet for a champagne toast to the number one Soviet sailor, Sergey Gorshkov.

After dinner, I circulated briefly with the wardroom officers, answering their many questions about our operations in these waters, but confin ng my statements to the unclassified aspects of our activities. Lvov took keen delight, however, in announcing that we had just come from New York, where we had sighted in on the Statue of Liberty—through periscope cross hairs. I was quick to tell the other Soviet officers that actually, were we ever to receive orders to destroy New York—and were we equipped with missiles, as a large number of Soviet submarines now are—we would fire the rockets from distances as far from the target as seven hundred miles.

Furthermore, I informed them, present Soviet research

and development will shortly provide us with the means to fire Polaris-type missiles from distances up to and in fact exceeding fifteen hundred miles! Most of the tender's officers, although ranging in grade from lieutenant to captain, were surface-type officers with oceanography degrees. Few of them, I found, were knowledgeable in submarine weaponry, although most of them appeared well versed in the biological and hydrographical aspects of oceanography and the underwater environment in which submarines operate.

Before leaving the ship, Lvov and I were conducted on a tour of the huge floating command ship. It was an ingenious combination of trawler repair ship, communications command vessel, repository for thousands upon thousands of fish netted by the smaller ships, floating cannery, oceanographic research platform with extensive laboratories set up in several massive compartments on the second deck aft, electronics spare parts ship, and mine-laying ship in the event of war. The crew's quarters were astonishingly luxurious. To use a lesser adjective would be to describe improperly the living conditions for the rank and file. Thick, soft carpets, plushy furniture, comfortable bunk rooms, large reading rooms and a theater, as well as a crew's dining room (as differentiated from a mess hall) made up the living compartments for the men. Ample showers and privately compartmented toilet facilities added to the comforts of the crew.

The ship's Second Officer, Captain Peter Onglorovo, a meteorologist, was quick to compare his ship with the best of the American fishing vessels he had observed in the area.

"It is nearly incredible," he remarked, "that right here off the Grand Banks, where American fishermen from New England once reigned as the dominant force in taking riches from the seas, we Soviets now put the Yankees to shame. Their fishing vessels are hopelessly ancient, they are small, they are almost unseaworthy, and they must be more than a hardship to live aboard. Compared to our modern fishing ships, the American boats are nothing more than a jest in this kind of work."

I was intrigued by the comparison.

"Why don't they modernize their fishing fleet?"

Captain Onglorovo shrugged his shoulders and, throwing back his weather-beaten head with a laugh, suggested that perhaps America couldn't afford the expense. The thought did indeed seem amusing.

By 10 P.M. the tender had off-loaded onto the *F-689* considerable fresh provisions, plenty of fresh fish and, on my request, a case of champagne for the wardroom and ten cases of red wine for the crew. The large cargo booms of the tender eased the loaded nets down into the open maindeck hatch of the submarine while I was being conducted on a tour of the mother-ship. Thus, when Lvov and I were brought back into the wardroom for a parting glass of brandy, all was ready for our departure.

Commodore Rudzogdin, in parting, said he would send a direct message to Supreme Naval Headquarters, indicating our rendezvous had been effected.

By midnight, only the lights of the fishing fleet far away in the distance could be seen from the open bridge of the *F-689*. I had elected to take advantage of the proximity of the fishing fleet for a couple of hours of surface cruising, and I knew it would be one of the last times, so far away from Russia, that I would be able to cruise the craft in other than a submerged condition. Just before going below from the bridge, I turned to take one last look at the many lights to the westward, denoting the many ships of the fishing fleet. How smart and shipshape they all looked, I recall thinking. And us! We looked slovenly and unkempt in comparison. I felt my lion's mane of hair, and involuntarily stroked the masterfully groomed beard which I had been cultivating for the past three months. We were on our last lap of the cruise; I would want to ease the crew into proper shape for re-entry into our home port . . . they must look smart and well disciplined, I remember telling myself . . . after all, perhaps *Fleet* Admiral Gorshkov himself will be there at Kola Inlet to greet us . . .

I told the conning watch officer to stand by for diving, indicating that we would snorkel for the remaining hours of the night, and then dropped down the hatch to the conning station. There I found the navigator and Second Officer bent over the charts showing our track homeward.

"Gentlemen," I began, noting Mikhailoff's full-grown beard, the result of nearly ninety days of painstaking growth and care, as opposed to the stubbly beginnings of Apraksin's whiskers, "tomorrow morning we shall start the earliest preparations for entering port. I am quite tired of looking at Castro-like faces all about me. At breakfast, let us have a clean-shaven wardroom. And upon our rounding the northern tip of Norway, let us have the crew following our example."

Apraksin grinned and responded with a cheery, "Aye, aye, Captain!" But Sergei Mikhailoff's reaction was instantly to reach up and hold his well-groomed whiskers in a defensive move. He had obviously taken great pains to amass a genuinely attractive beard, and may have been contemplating keeping it.

"Relax, Sergei," I told him, "after all, you'll be seeing your favorite girl in a few weeks, I'm sure. And I'll bet she would rather have you bare."

"At least, bare-*faced*," Apraksin said quickly with a twinkle.

Despite his beard, I sensed Sergei Mikhailoff was blushing. And possibly to offset his embarrassment, he now attempted to divert attention from himself.

"I suppose it probably is better, in dealing with the ladies, to be clean-shaven. Certainly, the commissar's beardless face seemed to open up countless opportunities for *him* down there in Havana!"

Sergei's thin lips parted in a wide grin. Apraksin, after a mild frown, joined quickly in a grin which in a twinkling changed to a snicker. Curious, I inquired what was so amusing. To my surprise, Mikhailoff's flashing grin now cascaded into an explosion of laughter, not, however, wholly mirthful in its ring.

It was the Second Officer who answered my question. Deftly glancing about him in an apparent seeking of some small measure of privacy, Apraksin leaned over and whispered into my ear. And the message he delivered stiffened me immediately in astonishment. I was incredulous, and my automatic response was a surprised exclamation.

"No!" I said.

Lieutenant Commander Apraksin's wide smile narrowed, and he repeated his announcement. "It's true, Captain, the commissar really *was* a little too bare down there in Cuba. Now his little indiscretions have caught up with him, and the medical corpsman is giving him sulfa twice a day!"

Perhaps not unsurprisingly, my resultant humanitarian concern was not for the welfare or condition of the commissar, nor did I express, then or later, any hope that his distress would be alleviated. Rather, my instantaneous thoughts centered on the other officers and men, for my hope was that Lvov's affliction would not be contagiously transmitted to any other man on board.

As for the commissar and his condition, I found myself viewing it all with a secret sense of consummate satisfaction and pleasure. Whatever he had acquired I was more than willing to concede he deserved!

31

Death Holds No Charms

☐ Navigator Mikhailoff's intended navigational track from Newfoundland to the Norwegian Sea would bring us between Iceland and the Faeroe Islands, and was aimed at the old geographical point "B" through which we had passed on our way south from the Barents Sea back in February. As the submarine was brought around, then, to a more northeasterly heading on April 30, nearly thirty-five hundred miles of ocean stretched ahead until we would turn to starboard and proceed more nearly eastward toward Soviet waters. My estimate was that if would take us nearly two more weeks to complete the cruise. Our tentative arrival date at Kola Inlet was slated to be about the twelfth or thirteenth of May. This word was transmitted to the trawlers for relay by Commodore Rudzogdin's command ship direct to Soviet Naval Headquarters.

Recognizing that even in the last phases of a cruise, an otherwise well-trained and experienced crew can become careless and thus endanger the lives of all hands, I insisted that we still continue general drills. The accent was placed on casualty exercises. I was unwilling that slovenly performance in the event of a real casualty, at this late date, might override our significant accomplishments on this patrol. Hence, the crew was ordered to maintain a general training alert until the day we tied up at the submarine piers at Saida Guba.

But the verve and enthusiasm were becoming increasingly more difficult to maintain. The chess tournament, the nightly folk-singing presently initiated by Apraksin for the crew, and the showing of more old-time American movies all contributed somewhat to keeping the minds of the men from wandering into boredom or daydreaming of our homecoming. Inadvertently, about four days after we had left the trawlers, it became widespread knowledge within the ranks of the crew that Commissar Lvov was suffering from a venereal infection. However, as might be expected, the gossip in the galley expanded the basic fact into almost unbelievable proportions. It appeared, in fact, as though the crew derived greater enjoyment, entertainment, and satisfaction out of listening to and telling the "inside story" of the commissar's plight, than they did from any other single, or even combination of, sources. And, of course, the "inside story" grew more elaborate each day. To the reader himself will be left the imaginative extent of the constantly more descriptive accounts of Lvov's condition.

Thereafter, Makar Rostopchin sought me out several times in my stateroom. He was perplexed and worried. Moreover, he evidenced a growing concern over philosophical values and morals of our people. What appeared to worry him most was the fact that although he was a Russian, with patriotic roots dug deep into the soil of the Motherland, his unyielding determination to adhere to his religioius beliefs would probably render him *persona non grata* not only in the Navy, but also in the Soviet Union, in the not too distant future. As proof, he offered the commissar's many harangues, and the personal insults which had been hurled at him by Lvov on this cruise.

There was little I could do to console him. If anything, his words had the peculair effect of causing me to consider, as I never had before, the fullest implications of the Communist State dominance over the minds of men. I found myself perturbed and uneasy following his visits to my room. There is no doubt that the principal effect of Makar's unafraid discussions of his own intense thinking was to induce a considerable degree of reflection on my own part.

I found myself bothered by the age-old question concerning Reason, and the cause of man's existence. The more I thought about it, lying on my bunk in the homeward-bound submarine, the more doubts I had of the validity of an ideology barren of the recognition that there must be a Higher Power than man himself. I considered that man of himself is, alas, a most miserable and insecure, ephemeral type of being. I assessed the Communist doctrine, finally, as incompatible with the realities of man's own quest for intellectual growth and personal betterment. On the other hand, I considered that since men are not, in reality, equal, it behooves a just and paternal governing authority to insure that the lesser endowed of the citizenry are not subjected to the tyrannical abuses of an unchecked mercenary system.

And finally, one night in mid-Atlantic, as we snorkeled along on our course for home, Makar Rostopchin left me in particularly troubled spirits. He had decided, he said, that overriding his devotion to service of the Russian State, he must remain at peace with himself. The only way he could do that, he declared, was to divorce himself from all association and attachment to those reins of governmental authority which led to the hands of men who rejected an Almighty and everlasting Force in the individual lives of men. He would, he confided to me, submit his resignation from the Soviet Navy upon our arrival in port. For him to do this was certainly understandable, but it was dejecting to consider that the Soviet system had brought a faithful servant of the Russian people to this realization that he could no longer serve their government. His severance from the Soviet Navy would be a substantial loss in professional capability at the operating force level of the service. The more I thought about it, the more I decided I needed fresh air . . .

For this underlying reason alone, then, I had the submarine surfaced this night, and went aloft to the open bridge where I could refresh myself. It was a mildly thrashing and confused sea which confronted me. Spray struck out across the bows and was flung back like a whip across the face of the submarine sail area. Within moments, my face was dripping with brine. But the taste of the salt water was not unpleasant; and the cool breeze was a magical tonic. I took deep, full breaths and clung, white-knuckled, to the bridge combing.

Overhead the stars sparkled like tiny diamonds and only the scattered cumulus clouds gave any feeling of foreboding to my already depressed outlook. The sea itself was black; only the wave crests, as they rose and fell, produced a whiteness and gleam. This was my habitat; this was my home. I loved it. The tangy salt air, the cool breezes, the skies above unending. And Life itself? Was it, too, unending? My eyes scanned the far and bleak horizon, then turned upward toward the stars. I preferred to think I would live forever, perhaps away out there in the expansive universe, but anyway, live! And this, of course, Communist leaders reject. As Khrushchev has said, "What heaven there is, man must find for himself while living, here on earth." He might be right—but, I could not help thinking, Death holds no charms for *me!* Better, indeed, to believe in the possibility of life eternal, life after death— at least in some form or other. Better, perhaps, to keep the faith of my fathers . . .

> Once to every man and nation
> Comes the moment to decide—

The words resounded in my mind like ricocheting bullets beating about inside a steel drum.

And now, my thoughts turned to the international affairs of our day. Was this era in which we lived truly what Marx and Lenin had sa'd it was—a predestined time for world upheaval and revolution, at the conclusion of which all men would live in the ideal socialist state? Or, to the contrary, was this present strife between East and West what the leaders of the Church have been saying it is—a struggle between good and evil? The decision was mine to make. I thought of Eloisa in Havana, a strong-willed Communist, perhaps, but then, wasn't she also a Christian? Hadn't it been she who had introduced me to that ancient cathedral, and she who had crossed herself so intently on entering into the worship services there? Perhaps there could be a justification for Communism while at the same time not abandoning one's religious principles and beliefs.

But this notion was readily dispelled when I thought again about Makar Rostopchin's case. Surely, the Soviet Government's assault on the Jews could be interpreted as the forerunner to undermining *all* religious groups!

As I saw the international game of power politics going on, the Communist world would never be satisfied until all countries and all peoples fell to the subjugation of the working class, where that class is ruled by professional Communist politicians who for their own peers and social acquaintances, elect to take scientists, doctors, professional men, and industry managers, rather than the multitudes of workers they govern. And as far as I could fathom the Western world's intentions to be, the so-called democracies are determined to forestall if not block any wholesale governmental ownership and control of national economies.

Within both camps, there are radicals who would move for an aggressive strategy to defeat the other side at once. Presently, I believe moderates are in command of both contending fact ons in this world of ours. But I also believe that a show of force may easily come at any time. If it does, the Soviet Union is better prepared than America probably realizes. Even her cold war position is good compared to that of the United States.

For example, although the Soviet Union is essentially a landmass nation mostly independent of other countries for her reliance upon raw materials for sustenance, Russia today has a merchant marine numbering 895 ships. This compares more than favorably with the United States merchant ship listings, which place the total American merchant vessels at 938. Furthermore, the Soviet Union plans on doubling its merchant ships by 1966. This is of interest because the United States does depend on her merchant marine for the transport of all but about a tenth of the raw materials which she needs for her very existence. Unlike the Soviet Union, America is a maritime nation through geographical circumstances.

Every day, more than twenty-five hundred merchant ships plow the Atlantic Ocean, pursuing their mission in either supplying or exporting goods to foreign ports. Soviet Russia's disadvantage as a sea power lies in the limited numbers of ports available to her for trade as a relatively landlocked country with few egress points to the sea. Yet the Soviet Navy is capable, today, of denying to America the free use of the seas which the United States relies on for her very survival. Russia can achieve this through employment of her vast submarine fleet.

The Soviet Union's efforts in the investigation and exploitation of the seas themselves are far beyond any corresponding efforts in this field made by the Unites States. Russia, for instance, has over three times the numbers of oceanographic survey and research ships possessed by the United States, and is ahead, now, in the international race for the control of inner and outer space. Over a thousand Soviet oceanographers are at sea working at any given time of the year; there probably aren't more than eight hundred oceanographers in the entire free world!

And, of course, in sea power as in all else, America helps to defeat herself by making too readily available all her military and naval secrets. Not always openly available, but at least fairly easy for Soviet espionage agents to pick up data here and there—through personal contacts, cocktail parties, magazines, newspapers, and the like—which in the aggregate adds up to worthwhile information.

Upon such facts did my mind dwell that night early in May, when I stood upon the open bridge of my submarine,

knifing its way northeastward, bound for the Soviet homeland—mission almost completed. Nothing lay between us
and our home port except some Soviet trawlers to the south
of Iceland. A pertinent coded message received the night
of May 3, as a matter of interest, told us that the customary U. S. Navy antisubmarine force, normally stationed
between Iceland and the British Isles, had been steaming
along the waters of the English Channel and in the Baltic
during the past few days. One trawler, following the carrier *Wasp* in the Baltic, reported that the ship had turned
in toward the West German coast and could therefore be
discounted insofar as our particular worries were concerned. This was gratifying news, of course.

Nothing of any particular interest occurred during the
remaining few days of our voyage.

32

The Final Accounting

☐ SUNDAY MORNING, MAY 13, 1962

History tells us that a Dutch admiral, several hundred years ago, established an enduring naval tradition now recognized by all modern navies. The story goes that upon returning home from a singularly successful and brilliant operation against his country's enemies, he had a broom lashed to the top of his flagship's mainmast. This was a flamboyant advertisement of his having "made a clean sweep" on the cruise just ending.

Neither unknowledgeable nor unmindful of such international naval custom, and the value of having re-enactments of such demonstrations when appropriate, I insured that the conning officer of the watch, Lieutenant Baliuk, had a galley cook come up topside and lash one of the mess deck brooms, at a forty-five-degree angle atop the raised periscope, several hours prior to our arrival at Kola Inlet. We had been fully surfaced since cruising generally to the north of Vardo, Norway, the last foreign territory we passed before entering Russian homeland waters.

The chipping away of significantly rusted portions of the topside hull and conning tower, and the application of red lead to these areas on the previous day, had been a prelude to the actual repainting of such sea-corroded parts early on this Sunday morning. The object was to so titivate the craft that on our arrival home we would present an image of outstanding smartness and enduring maintenance of the highest order. The weather helped. The sun was warm and bright; the near absence of a sea breeze precluded the whipping up of an undesirable sea spray.

Overhead, the sky was patched with slow-moving, billowing cumulus clouds whose whiteness contrasted refreshingly with the pure and deep blue expanses beyond.

This was the day we had all been looking forward to with such increasing impatience. This was the day of our triumphal return! The white, chalky-looking sand shores of northern Russia on the Barents Sea, with the barren landscape beyond, excited a curious fascination probably undeserving of its actual physical enticements. The sight of these otherwise desolate shores stirred the roots of sentimentality and emotion in all who peered out across the smooth blue waters at this, the Motherland. That seemingly unpeopled coastline seemed to beckon with a warmth, a welcoming embrace known but to men returning to the soil of their origin after a long absence. Fond memories were rekindled of friends, family, and home.

The crew were in excellent spirits. All faces were clean-shaven and everyone looked spankingly clean and seamanlike.

A torpedoman named Turusov was riding the crest of newly won fame. He had achieved the distinction of winning the chess tournament. He had matched the Second Officer, and on playing me, I had let him win on general principle after hours of painstaking play. Now, as a celebrity, he was allowed to stand on the open bridge with the conning watch officer for our entry into port.

Maneuvering into the submarine harbor at Kola Inlet, we were greeted by two fireboat tugs which came up off our bows and then preceded us to our berth, the while shooting streams of gushing white water into the air from pressure hoses. Signal flags spotted on the halyards of the shore installations headquarters building, not far from the submarine piers, spelled out a welcome for the *F-689*. On the pier, a brass band broke into a medley of favorite Russian songs as we turned hard left to ease into the slip. The men standing in two lines, fore and aft on the maindeck, presented a gratifying picture of well-disciplined and smart-looking seamen; in the throngs crowded onto the open pier were many of the families and friends of the officers and men of the homecoming submarine. It was a happy occasion, I thought.

Then, over near the band, I spotted a military police vehicle, with the giant letters MVD emblazoned on one of its license plates. Behind this vehicle was a large black sedan, and my initial most fleeting glances at it revealed that there were two officers of fairly senior rank standing nearby.

No sooner had the submarine's mooring lines been made fast and doubled up than two military policemen jumped onto the maindeck from the pier and climbed to the top of the open bridge, where they confronted me personally.

Whipping out a court subpoena, one of the men thrust it in my face and, first making sure I was Aleksandr Ivanovich Zhdanov, declared that I must consider myself under investigation as a result of several irregularities occurring within the past three months. I was then informed that to insure my availability for questioning, without detriment to the continued proper functioning of the crew of the F-689, I was to consider myself relieved as Commanding Officer, effective at once. The shock was instantaneous. I felt wilted immediately. Hence I was unprepared to argue when the senior of the two military policemen next asked for Makar Rostopchin.

"Rostopchin?" I repeated his name numbly. Great day! What did they want with him? As a matter of fact, what precisely did they want with me? Was it just the animosity of the commissar? Was it something he had written in one of his reports?

My mind swirled with indignation mixed with anger.

"Lieutenant Commander Rostopchin! What do you want of him?" I asked.

"This officer is charged with direct insolence to a superior officer, assault upon a superior officer, disobedience, and profession of a religious faith denied to genuinely patriotic citizens of the Soviet Union," I was told.

There was little I could do. Meanwhile, Makar Rostopchin must have sensed what reception would be awaiting him upon our arrival. For when sent for by messenger below, he reported within a few seconds to the bridge. He was attired in full-dress uniform, complete with the round-the-neck ribbon of the Order of Voroshilov, Second Class, which he had won in better days. At once understanding the situation, Makar merely turned to me and, taking my hand in a farewell gesture, expressed his sorrow at having to leave under such stress.

"I shan't forget your kindnesses and sympathetic attitude," he said slowly. "Despite the way things have turned out, I want you to know I have enjoyed my long cruising association with you, Captain, and I hope that some day, the system which sustains such organized terror as this, will be supplanted by a more just and intelligent one."

The conning watch officer, Baliuk, together with Sergei Mikhailoff, held out their hands and shook Rostopchin's in a goodbye gesture.

And then, Makar Rostopchin was led off the submarine, onto the pier—and into the vehicle with the MVD license plates. I watched as the vehicle started up and moved out of sight. It was the last time I was to see my bright and resourceful young engineer officer; I have not even heard reports as to what his fate was.

Only one military policeman went with Makar. The other stayed behind with me.

Within a few minutes, the workers on the pier had thrown a brow over from the wooden planking onto the topside of the sub, and the two senior officers I had spotted earlier came walking over. I climbed down and met them, at once recognizing Captain Anatole Chichagov, Soviet Navy Operations Officer for the Northern Fleet, and Captain Georgy Novgorod, Chief of Staff for Political Admin-

istration, Northern Fleet. Saluting them smartly, I managed
to force a wide smile and then, turning to nod in the direction of the waiting military policeman, asked what was
wrong.

Chichagov's Mongolian features were devoid of emotion, his eyes remaining an apathetic study in stare. But his
thin lips parted enough to say, "Commander Zhdanov, let
us first welcome you back. I'm sure your patrol reports will
tell us that our confidence in you for this job was indeed
well placed . . ."

Novgorod interrupted.

"But," he said imperiously, "before we do anything, we
have to establish whether the Government can count on
you to clearly and strongly support the truths under which
the Party operates . . ."

"What Captain Novgorod means," cut in Captain Chichagov, "is whether your personal convictions may possibly be, well, less than firm on certain Party matters—"

"Purposeful resistance to Party doctrine or teachings is
something the Government can't put up with, you understand," interposed Novgorod. Then, frowning, he said,
"To be quite frank with you, there are charges which have
been filed against you. They allege that you have violated
certain aspects of the law. They also allege that you aren't
amenable to acceptance of Party doctrine, so necessary
for our higher commanders to accept . . ."

The rest of his words were now interrupted by the shrill
blast of a boatswain's pipe as heard over the public address
system. Lieutenant Commander Apraksin had apparently
authorized general liberty for officers and crew, for in a
moment the boatswain's mate was announcing the good
word, and not long after that the beginnings of an exodus
took place. More than half the *F-689* crew began to
crowd the gangway waiting to disembark. I waved them
by us, and thus started the crew on their first joyous re-
union with home, family, and friends. It was my last look
at them.

Issuing orders to the watch personnel to send my compliments to the Second Officer, I asked that he report to me immediately. The military policeman had directed me to turn over command without delay, and I intended to do so with no commotion. It was essential, I felt, to preserve my dignity at all costs.

Apraksin showed up within a minute at most, saluting smartly. I looked at him searchingly, and then at Novgorod and finally Chichagov. The latter cast his eyes downward, avoiding my gaze.

"Lieutenant Commander Apraksin," I said, "I am under orders to devolve this command upon you. That I now do. May I tell you now that I have enjoyed my cruise with you, and I wish you every possible success. I'll thank you to tell the crew I shall always remember them."

The words were becoming choked. Above and beyond Apraksin floated the naval ensign of my country. It was a standard I would not look upon again with quite the same attitude. Flapping gently in a mild zephyr, it seemed to wave farewell to me, for a life I had known so long that all other pursuits seemed alien and strange.

Apraksin saluted smartly, then shook hands firmly. "To carry out your orders, sir, will be a pleasure. I shall not forget your coolness and decisiveness which took us so successfully into the lair of the enemy," he said. Then, with a frown, came the words, "I relieve you, sir."

Leaving my personal effects to be gathered and delivered to me at a later date, I followed the two captains, Chichagov and Novgorod, onto the pier and into the waiting black sedan. Following hallowed naval custom, I, being the junior, entered the sedan first—moving in well over to the far left-hand side of the rear seat. Novgorod sat next to me, and Chichagov climbed in last, taking the seat of honor on the extreme right. The chauffeur slammed the door and, walking briskly around to the driver's seat, turned to ask directions.

"Headquarters, oaf!!" bellowed Novgorod, with an impatience I would have thought quite unbecoming a senior naval commissar had I not been well conditioned to the previous antics of both Sverdlov and Lvov.

The car pulled up in front of Northern Fleet Headquarters, and an attendant opened the right rear door for us to disembark. Two armed guards came to a rifle salute as we passed into the main doorway and entered Admiral Chabanenko's headquarters reception lobby. Colorful oil paintings of Russian sea fights, dating back to the time of Peter the Great, and now hanging majestically in this large anteroom, all served to instill a bursting pride within the breasts of most Soviet seamen. Yet for me at this time, I could feel only foreboding and depression.

We moved down the long corridor at the far end of the reception room and presently entered the Northern Fleet main conference room. A long walnut table was planted in the middle of the space, and large blue and white colored leather chairs were neatly placed around it. Several easy chairs and some odd small tables and lamps were grouped around the room and in front of the fireplace. On the wood-paneled walls hung more oil paintings of Russian sea history, including a portrait of the great Admiral Apraksin. I could not fail to note how my former Second Officer, the now present Commanding Officer of the *F-689*, resembled so favorably the likeness of his ancestor!

"Be seated, my dear Zhdanov," Novgorod said with a condescension comparable to that of a haughty master about to rebuke an errant servant.

Chichagov seated himself at the table and I followed suit, at the far end.

Captain Novgorod walked over to the fireplace and, standing in front of it, stood with arms akimbo as he started his questioning.

"Commander Zhdanov," he began, "Post-Captain Commissar Lvov has submitted several reports which reflect adversely on your capability for dealing with situations involving a high degree of loyalty to Party doctrine. One of his reports, discussing your actions in scheduling a swim call wherein you lost two men and had others injured, was not very complimentary. Your good judgment was questioned."

Novgorod looked at me with raised eyebrows, as though anticipating an answer. Not getting one, he continued.

"However, there are two other incidents that occurred on your recent cruise which demand more severe consideration . . ."

I swallowed hard. Doubtless Novgorod was about to discuss Lvov's insistence that I take overt action against the American Colonel Glenn. Or was he going to raise the issue of my having supported or befriended poor Makar Rostopchin? I had but a few seconds to wonder. Novgorod went right to the point.

"Commander Zhdanov," he intoned, "on two separate occasions, you have publicly drawn attention to yourself as a supporter of a superstitious and moribund religion. Charges have been filed against you by Commissar Lvov to the effect that you on more than one occasion, while Commanding Officer of the *F-689*, called loudly and openly for help from 'God.' As I recall, the times that this occurred were laden with tenseness and tragedy was near."

Chichagov broke in.

"When your submarine got fouled up in seaweed and you didn't think the blowing of ballast would correct the dive in time," said the Staff Operations Officer, "Commissar Lvov has charged that you vocally besought supernatural guidance or protection or somehow expressed a faith in a God when this incident happened. He has also said that one night when he went to your stateroom, he found you moaning and blabbing incoherently about why 'God' had allowed your men to be attacked by sharks! Foolishness, I'd have to say, personally. But mind you, Zhdanov, these two incidents of themselves wouldn't be enough in my own m nd to warrant calling you to task. After all, we have to consider that you were brought up as a Christian, believing, as we all did at one time, in a supernatural Force . . . and perhaps naturally, when an emotional strain overcomes you, the natural instinct might be to revert psychologically . . . to regress, you know, to childhood's early and in your case wrongful beliefs and superstitions."

Captain Novgorod walked around now to another door on the rich-looking sidings of the room. Here he stopped momentarily while listening to Chichagov continue.

"Well, Zhdanov," went on the latter, "there remains one inexplicable and damning incident which I personally prefer to believe just didn't happen. All you have to say is that it's a lie, and by the Blood of the October Revolution, both Admiral Chabanenko and I will stand by you."

Captain Chichagov eyed me closely. His Mongol countenance was devoid of emotion. It was obvious that he reflected Admiral Chabanenko's appreciation of superior professional competence and downgraded the political aspects of my case insofar as he hopefully could.

Novgorod now reached into his breast pocket and drew forth a gold humidor, from which he took a small brown-paper-wrapped cigarette. This he lighted with a small flint lighter and, after one or two good puffs, threw his head back at a rakish angle sufficient to channel well-configured smoke rings skyward from between delicately pursed lips.

Chichagov made my mind hum. What could he be referring to? I had not long to wait. He continued.

"While you were away, laws have been dredged up which dictate that all persons found guilty of patronage to the several church groups, or persons found to have publicly proclaimed their allegiance to religious tenets at the expense of Party beliefs, are subject to punishment as in the case of perpetrators of crimes against the Government."

"It is," spoke up Novgorod, "a criminal offense to profess belief in God publicly."

"Aside from your inadvertent exclamations on board your submarine, during times of unusual stress," interjected Chichagov, "I hope, sincerely, that you will deny any such unworthy a manifestation . . ."

Novgorod's hand slipped down to the brass doorknob, which he turned. Then, before opening the door, he said, "Commander Zhdanov, I am not so sure of your innocence as is Captain Chichagov."

With that, he flung open the door and shouted, "Come in, you who would talk. We are ready!"

My heart pounded rapidly. Who was to talk against me? What witness or witnesses were aligned against me? I craned my neck to see into the next room. The open door led out into a room from which, directly opposite me and at the far end of the space, shone the brilliant and blinding glare of sunlight from a large open window, I blinked.

I could hear a slight murmur and shuffle in the adjacent room. Then suddenly, a man's shape was silhouetted against the bright glass window across the threshold. I was so blinded by the light that I could not identify the form at first. In a moment it had crossed the portal and had passed in front of Novgorod and stood facing me at the far end of the table.

My hands clenched the table in front of me. I stared at the man looking down at me. My mind was confused. What could *Sverdlov* have to do with this little inquisition?

Unbelievingly, I arose. Slowly, my hands came to rest on my hips. The color returned to my hands and, I am sure, to my face. This was galling, and I was indignant.

"Sverdlov!" I gasped.

He was still pale and flabby; his thick lips now curled into an expression of amusement and triumph. "Welcome home, my dear former *Captain* Zhdanov," he said with intense sarcasm. "Unfortunately," said the man who had tried to ruin me in 1958, "the High Command failed to believe me four years ago, when I warned them of your failings. But I have never forgotten the mental anguish you caused me when I was on board your old submarine, the *W-7*. How could I? You and that boor, Rurik, nearly finished me. Luckily, your request for my court-martial wasn't acted on. And Vice Admiral Grishanov has been a source of great strength to me, great strength!"

I turned savagely to Chichagov.

"Captain, by what right does this man have to confront me at this time? I resent this! Four years ago, this contemptible, officious political hack was my Third Officer, and he damned well nearly brought failure to my mission. What is this all about?"

Chichagov raised his hands defensively. "Commander," he said, "I have nothing to do with this. But for your own sake, take hold of yourself."

Sverdlov's sneering lips convulsed into a quiver, and he snickered, "It's taken me a little time to nail you to the bulkhead, my dear *Captain,* but nail you I have. I dare you to deny the testimony of my most credible witness!"

Then, walking briskly a few steps over to the open doorway, he sounded off, "Now! we are ready! Come in here!"

The words were barked out with an apathy of tone, and a demand for instant compliance was inherent in the manner of his command. My eyes blinked again as I focused upon the light-flooded doorway. Quickly, silently, a shape, a form, moved across the doorframe. For an instant it was silhouetted against the bright sunlight. And then I saw clearly. I saw all too clearly, and slowly, I sat down.

It had been more than a month since I had bade fond farewell, in Havana, to lovely, curvaceous, stimulating Eloisa! And here she was, responding with alacrity to the call of Commissar Igor Vladimirovich Sverdlov!

The details of this confrontation will be spared the

reader. That I was unnerved one must imagine. Suffice it to say that Lvov, in direct communication with Sverdlov as well as Vice Admiral Grishanov, had communicated to Moscow the possibilities of my falling into a trap. And a trap was designed. Eloisa, blind Communist adherent that she was, had readily agreed to lead me "astray," and for the record.

Coldly, with an accurate insight into my proclivity toward a faith in a Divinity (through word of mouth from Lvov), Eloisa had steered me into a position where I had publicly professed such a faith. When she had taken me to the cathedral in Havana, she had known exactly what she would exact of me. She knew precisely what she wanted to extract from me. She led, and I followed. She suggested, and I executed. She gestured, and I followed suit. And she had observed my physical acceptance of Christian worship. She had, in fact, reported the matter as soon as she had found it convenient to do so. And, to insure my conviction in a Party hearing, or worse, in a court-martial, Sverdlov had arranged to transport Eloisa to the Soviet Union. As the star witness for the Communist Party, she would, indeed, perform!

At the confrontation, there was little I could say, so I chose to say nothing. My best defense, I thought, would be to register complete ignorance of her testimony; this I attempted to do. Although ultimately I would never have been successful in persuading a court of my innocence, I was at least able to defer an immediate judgment at the time. Chichagov, against the advice of both Sverdlov and Novgorod, granted me the privilege of limited freedom of movement without bond until the projected trial date. This, for Captain Chichagov, was disastrous: I seized the opportunity as a windfall from Providence and, with but two weeks to go until my scheduled arraignment before the bar of "justice," sought refuge in an underground escape apparatus fostered by a combination of Church and other groups.

My precise escape route I shall not, of course, divulge. I hope that others may continue to use it, in defecting from a Godless, unethical, tyrannical State.

I have since heard the disquieting news that because of his decision to defer trial and release me at the time, Captain Chichagov was arraigned before a special Party tribunal and sentenced to oblivion in a work camp for "liberated" laborers from Latvia. Whether he is now in command of such a camp, or whether he is, alas, one of the inmates, I know not. But I do know that his decision to release me pending trial was, for him, a personal tragedy.

And now I am in exile. Far enough away from the reins and power of a despotic, autocratic State, yet still within the grasp of its tentacles. For though today I live in a non-Communist country, I realize that the probing apparatus of international Communism may yet find me and mete out a fate not unlike that which Trotsky received at the hands of Stalin almost a generation ago. This manuscript I have written in a central European country, where I have found relief and asylum. Where, I cannot divulge. But no matter how long God grants me life, no matter how long I can manage to elude my most certain pursuers, I shall always retain in my heart the hope and the prayer that my countrymen will reawaken to the truths of this life; I shall always press for a greater understanding among peoples, to the end that the world might live at peace. For it was as the Prince of Peace that Christ sought men's souls. The choice, indeed, is between darkness and light.

I believe the ravages of Communism must be averted. I believe the tide of the Red offensive must be contained and thrown back. The free world will never win unless it faces up to the realities of Soviet power, and nowhere is that power so strong, nowhere is that power so mobile, nowhere is that power so potentially effective, as at sea!